Asian PEN Anthology

Asian PEN Anthology

Edited by F. Sionil Jose
and with an Introduction
by Norman Cousins

TAPLINGER PUBLISHING COMPANY
NEW YORK

First published in the United States by
Taplinger Publishing Co., Inc.
29 East Tenth Street
New York, New York 10003

Library of Congress Catalog Card Number 67-10849

Printed in the United States of America

To the memory of
Patrick Judge

Foreword

This book is the first regional anthology sponsored by PEN. It was first conceived in Manila in December, 1962 during the Asian Writers PEN Conference. As such, it is the result not only of a common undertaking by those who believe that in literature there can, perhaps, be a better way by which Asians may draw from one another deeper insights and understanding. This anthology does not pretend to be exclusive or inclusive; the problems of collation and communication are often difficult, but the assistance of the board of editors surmounted most of these difficulties. To them I am greatly indebted, particularly to Madam Sophia Wadia, founder of the Indian PEN Center and editor of the *Indian PEN,* Mrs. Bonnie R. Crown, director of the Asian Literature Program of The Asia Society, Miss Nilawan Pintong, secretary of the Thailand PEN Center and Miss Yoko Matsuoko, secretary of the Japan PEN Center. *The Asia Magazine* in Hongkong also gave an award for fiction, and *Quest,* the Indian quarterly, gave another for poetry.

This, certainly, will not be the last Asian PEN Anthology; the next is already in the press, and barring the usual problems of publishing, it should be out very soon.

F. Sionil Jose

ACKNOWLEDGMENTS

We are grateful to the following publications for granting us permission to reprint the following stories and poems:

Quadrant *of Australia for "A Place I Knew Once" by John Hetherington, "Four Impromptus" by Gwen Harwood, "Fever" by Rosemary Dobson, "The Kaleidoscopic Dark" by Lola Jackson, and "Swan" by Rodney Hall.*

The Encounter *of London for "Pietà" by James McAuley, and "Philosophy" by Nissim Ezekiel.*

The Arizona Quarterly *for "Prelude to Glory" by U Win Pe.*

The Antioch Review *for "Death of a Sawbwa" by Daw Mi Mi Khaing.*

The Illustrated Weekly *of India for the English translation of "Flight and Pursuit" by Annada Sankar Ray.*

The Writer's Workshop *publication of Calcutta for "Enterprise" by Nissim Ezekiel.*

The Quest *of India for "The Sirens" by Kamala Das, and for "Poet, Lover, Birdwatcher" by Nissim Ezekiel.*

The Indian PEN *for "Summer in Calcutta" and "I Shall Someday" by Kamala Das.*

An Anthology of Modern Indonesian Poetry *edited by Burton Raffel, published by the University of California Press (USA), 1964, with the permission of the Asia Society, Inc. 112 East 64th Street, New York, New York (with c. 1962, 1963, 1964 by The Asia Society, Inc.) for "Meeting" by S. T. Alisjahbana, translated by Burton Raffel and Nurdin Salam; "Traveler First Class" by J. E. Tatengkeng, translated by James S Holmes; "In Praise of You" by Amir Hamzah, translated by Burton Raffel and Nurdin Salam; "Ballad of the Men of the Limestone Soil" by W. S. Rendra, translated by Derwent May; "To A Friend," "Twilight at Little Harbor," and "A Tale for Dien Tamaela" by Chairil Anwar, translated by Burton Raffel and Nurdin Salam.*

The Japan Quarterly *for "Brief Encounter" by Nagai Tatsuo, "Three Million Yen" by Mishima Yukio, and "I Mean To Live" by Hirabayashi Taiko.*

xi

The Japan PEN News *for the translation of "Clay Doll" by Sata Ineko.*

The Beloit Poetry Journal *which was dedicated to contemporary Asian poetry, for, "Poem" by Shuntaro Tanikawa, "Bird" by Ishikawa Itsuko, and, "The Afternoon of a Solar Eclipse" by Shinjiro Kurahara.*

The Philippine PEN Anthology of Short Stories *for "May Day Eve" by Nick Joaquin.*

The Sunday Times Magazine *of the* Manila Times *for "The Enchanted Plant" by Bienvenido N. Santos.*

The Comment *Magazine for "Dusk" by Carlos A. Angeles.*

The Thai Center of International PEN *for "Champoon" by Theb Mahapaorya, "Rising Flood" and "Nang Phanthurat's Gold Mine" by Riem Eng and "The Grandmother" by K. Surangkhanang.*

The Chatra Press, Ltd., *for "The Tropic Night," "The Canal of a Hundred Thousand Sores," "The Flute," and "An Early Morning Thought" by Prem Chaya.*

Traces *of Los Angeles for "Chasms and Gold Harvest Crumble" from "Descending," a collection of poems by Wai Lim Yip.*

The Oxford University Press *of Kuala Lumpur for the volume on Modern Malay Verse, for "My Lion City" by Masuri S. N., "Gift" by Usman Awang, "Direction" by A. Samad Said, and "The Child in a Red Shirt" by A. S. Amin.*

BOARD OF EDITORS

Introduction

Is there anything that genuinely ties the writers in this volume together? The backdrop of Asia is much too general to serve as common ground; any designation that takes in such contrasting states as Australia and Burma, or Japan and Ceylon, or the Philippines and Pakistan, could just as easily be enlarged into a world category. Geography is too often an unreliable denominator in literary matters, especially when the geography is Asia. One country alone—India—has at least fourteen linguistic and cultural groupings. The problem of introducing talented Indian writers to a considerable number of their countrymen is no less difficult and is certainly more poignant than the problem of bringing writers with national reputations to the attention of a world audience.

What then, is the connective tissue that holds the contributors in this book together? It is the simple fact that they have a specific and significant common sponsorship. This volume grew out of the Asian P.E.N. Writers Conference in Manila in 1962. Writers from fourteen Asian countries met and quickly discovered they knew far less about one another than their individual national prominence might warrant. Much of their time at the Conference, in fact, was spent in exchanging notes on national literary inventories. To be sure, they talked about the things writers like most to talk about—philosophical questions; the moods of their national societies; how to bring characters to life; techniques in plot development; trends in literature and poetry; themes and principles of literary criticism; dealings with publishers and the literary marketplace in general. But the most popular and most consequential discussion was related to their lack of access to one another and their own comparative ignorance of the literary output of their countries.

The primary purpose of this volume, therefore, was to introduce Asian writers to Asians. The Asian P.E.N. sought not to foster a regional cultural jingoism but to eliminate an unnatural condition in the Asian literary situation. The board of editors assigned by the Manila P.E.N. Conference to plan this volume was headed by F. Sionil Jose, of the Philippines, and included Jack Wong, of Hong Kong; Sardar Khushwant Singh, of India; S. Takdir Alishahbana, of Indonesia; Jun Takami, Japan; Ko Won, Korea; Syed Ali Ahsan, Pakistan; Leonidas V. Benesa, Philippines;

Chia Luen Lo, Taiwan; Prem Purachatra, Thailand; and Nghiem Xuan Vict, of Vietnam. The book was three years in the making and was first issued in Manila by the Solidaridad Publishing House.

Most of the material in this book appeared originally in Asian languages. That the language selected for this volume should be English is attributable not so much to a desire to appeal to a Western audience but to the fact that English is the foreign language most understood by the educated communities throughout Asia. This may seem ironical in light of the powerful reaction against Western imperialism that has dominated most of the history of Asia during the past half-century, but many Asians have made a distinction between English history and English literature. In any event, the English language is a functional and literary asset for a large part of the world. It has converted some of history's most treasured creative and philosophical possessions into a human heritage. And it is the medium through which many of Asia's leading poets, novelists, and essayists may now be known to an American audience. For too many years Americans have concentrated on developing a Voice of America rather than an Ear. This volume promises a pleasant opportunity to approach a balance in our literary relationship with Asia.

Norman Cousins

Contents

Asian PEN Anthology

The Sounds of Sunday

Kerima Polotan Tuvera

IT WAS HER DAY for meeting old friends. Emma Gorrez had ventured out twice before this, to school and to Martinez Kiosk, but she had met no one she knew. Even the woman behind the books at the Kiosk did not remember her. Emma had lingered than she should, five, ten minutes longer, although there had been nothing of interest to hold her to this spot where she had bumped into Domingo several years ago. That time, he had stood at the rack, thumbing through a book; when their looks had met, he had bowed slightly.

He had bowed too in their room two weeks ago, one night after a wearying fight. He would hear no more from her and he had cut short their argument with one vicious swing of his fist against the bedroom wall. No tears, none, except the audible panting of their selves, like two runners come to the end of a race. He had bowed, holding his head in his hands. This was how married people fought, she had thought — like complete strangers, with anger pulsing in the air between them.

That day in the Kiosk, wondering where he was and what he did while she stood three hundred kilometers away, she thought then that *if* he returned, *if* she should see him suddenly looming in the doorway, *if* he strode in, scowling or not, loving her or not, she would run to him, and it would not matter that they hurt each other terribly. But only the rain fell outside the Kiosk entrance. Doming had not appeared; no one she knew had appeared, and the girl tending the book store tapped her fingers impatiently. Emma threw the book down and hurried home.

She had also gone to Mr. Rividad to see about her old job. She had written to say she was coming but the first thing she saw when she pushed the familiar batwing doors was her letter resting casually above his glass top, unopened. It had seemed like a rebuff. Even the information that he was out of town did not help.

But on this day, she ran into them all. She had not taken the first turn on Tañedo Street when Mrs. Pintoy sprang from behind the corner. She made an expansive gesture, opening and closing her mouth, unable to speak, until Emma dragged her to a table at De Luxe. Then Mrs. Pintoy's torrent of words came and Emma stopped her ears, pretending to be displeased but actually happier than she had been since she left Domingo Gorrez in Sampaloc.

She met Rene Rividad outside Plaridel High School.

"Three years," he said, taking her hand.

"Will you take me back?" she asked.

He stood, shifting his weight from one foot to the other, trying to veil his thoughts.

"In all ways," he smiled.

"You have learned to make beautiful speeches," she said.

"And you — what did the city teach you?"

Emma Gorrez ignored the question. She would not do her remembering this way, outside in the street, beneath a hot sun, before the searching eyes of this thin, greying man who had once said he loved her. He did not ask her about Doming and she volunteered no news except that he was well.

She met Norma Rividad, too, swinging her potent hips up the street. Mr. Rividad's wife made her way, unseeing, to the bus stop, there to wait for the next Pantranco bus to Dagupan. That hadn't changed, Emma thought, passing her by.

But many other things in Tayug had. The snakes in the plaza were dead and their wired cages had been taken over by a pair of deer, captured in the hills nearby. They limped about, dragging themselves around the enclosure, looking up with accusing eyes when Emma approached to throw them bits of grass.

The shanties on Tañedo had been torn down to give way to sturdier buildings and now they lifted their falsely modern facades to the sun. Towards the railroad station, two moviehouses had been erected and their faulty sound system pierced the air of noon. Together, with the twelve o'clock whistle, sonorous declarations of love and anger straddled the town.

I LOVE YOU! I hate you! came the screams and the echoes would carry to the periphery of the town. It lasted for hours. Emma Gorrez, the first day she heard it, shut the windows of the old house. It did not keep the voices away. Some of the stridency did not reach her, with the windows shut and her ears plugged with cotton, but the echoes persisted. Emma would gather the children in the room farthest from the noise, reading stories from books salvaged from the wreck of the Gorrez marriage.

Emma Gorrez had been strong for both of them, and yet the marriage had come apart. It was difficult to understand. They had loved each other through the various crises of their married life — the times when he chucked jobs and walked out of agreements and turned his back on decisions. Even that terrible time with the Cosios had drawn them together. The business blowing up in their faces like that — they had left Tayug, lured by the Cosio's promises of friendship, and set up the press, and gone through the harrowing months when both the business and the friendship wavered, and finally the nearly fatal end. Emma had wrecked the Glockner and turned upon Nora's slim, well-tended hand beneath the blade of the huge cutter. But someone, Isabelo or Paco or Doming himself — she has never afterwards asked who — kicked the plug away and slapped Emma and Nora down. That was all.

Emma did not go back to the press again. She left Doming Gorrez to pick up the pieces, and this, he did admirably. This man whose dark moods she could not completely grasp, charmed them out of the frightful mess her foolish rage had plunged them both into, and the Cosios had been amenable to letting them go since they were themselves not too eager for a scandal.

Perhaps, it was from that moment the marriage began to go. Emma Gorrez wanted to return to Tayug. Doming would not hear of it. To her pleas that they would feel safer in the old town, Doming snorted. No one was safe anywhere, Doming said. Life waited for a man's unguarded moments, and there were plenty, he said. "We're staying, Em," he said. "I'll get a job. Then we'll show this place a thing or two," he said.

After that, Doming simply walked into Quality Products, bluffing his way to a desk in the Public Relations department. It meant doing all the things that Emma despised. He slid into it smoothly, effortlessly, wearing the inevitable shirt sleeves and thin tie. When he left the house, Emma would watch him go — it was not like those mornings in Tayug when she had stepped back while he drove the jalopy out of the yard. There had been the assurance of things familiar; the hills looked down benignly upon them and benevolence unwrapped them all surely, Doming, Emma, and the life in her womb.

But in the city, she watched him go into a world that repelled her. He returned each night speaking the jargon of the trade and donning the jesting attitudes fashionable among his friends. It was a life worth living and she tried to reach him. In the high, airless room of the Sampaloc apartment house, she spoke from the depths of her blanket at night. "This is not what we want," she said.

The passing cars cast strange, grotesque shadows on the wall, lighting up with criss-crossing forms the peeling blue paint of the bedroom. He replied with a groan. He did not like arguing over an unrealized peril. But when she was insistent, when she talked yearningly of returning to Tayug, to all that she felt was meaningful to both of them, then he replied, in monosyllables at first, hoping to discourage her, but finally in long, passionate statements full of his desire to conquer this city which had humiliated him twice.

"We want the things that will last," she said.

"The money lasts. You like the money, don't you?" he asked.

"I don't deserve that," she said.

"Em, Em," he said, in a voice approximating the old tenderness. "You are the child, not I. You see ghosts where there are none."

"You can't go on plotting and tricking forever, buying respectability for Big Man in Quality."

He knew what she was talking of. "It was a test of skill," he recalled. "I liked pitting myself against a real foe," he laughed.

"That old man," she flung at him. "He was seventy. If nothing else, he had earned the right to die with his illusions: honor, courage, honesty . . ."

Mr. Navarro had come knocking at their door, one evening, an old man in threadbare, baggy pants. His daughter had worked at Quality, a silly girl, of whom perhaps it was true what they had said later, that she deserved what she had gotten in the suffocating office elevator, tragically stalling between floors one twilight. Stumbling, panic-stricken, out of the cold, steel box, bubbling hysterically of an attack perpetrated by Number 2, the executive who loved pastel-colored shirts and who gobbled fruit pies greedily at the office canteen. Mr. Navarro had stormed the offices of Quality, demanding a form of redress that took everyone aback because it did not include the consideration of money. He wanted to send Number 2 to jail. Nothing that they could say or offer could deter him. It was a most fundamental sort of outrage and he demanded a most fundamental sort of satisfaction: the sight of Lopez behind bars. The legal force would not touch it. There were all kinds of predictions, oh, the various fateful ramifications of that single, senseless act. Stocks plummeting, faces lost, an entire business built upon the goodwill of a people (who had been led to believe that Quality employed only God-fearing men) going up in smoke because this chit of a girl disdained payment.

Until Doming had stepped into the fray, bringing the inimitable charm of his father's son to bear upon the old man. Gorrez had invited Navarro to the house where, willingly and gladly, Navarro

4

had gone because Gorrez had spoken his dialect and had used its native diphthongs well.

"Yes, Grandfather," Gorrez had cajoled. "A little talk about your problem? Supper, and the sight of my children, and my wife, a fine woman, and my guarantee that nothing I might propose to you will mean disgrace. Yes, Grandfather?"

Navarro had wobbled from the bus stop to the house of the Gorrezes, trapped by his own bewilderment and the shame. When Doming was through with him, you could see them: in the heart that must have bled quietly to death because, fed and warmed and made much of, Navarro had allowed himself to leave the Gorrez house with a check. He had killed himself later. A week after the funeral, the check had returned by mail, torn into filmy tiny bits.

For a long time afterwards, Emma Gorrez would not allow Doming to touch her. Quality had given him a good bonus, a raise, a larger desk, and his own name in black, glossy letters upon an opaque door. Emma would not spend the new sum but Doming brought it all to her, again and again and again, until she finally took it. She went to the most expensive store in town and spent it on things that in her sober moments she would not have dreamt buying. When she stepped out of the store onto the sidewalk, a pile of packages beside her, she looked up at the sun, but the sun was not there, only a vague, diffused terror, peculiar because it frightened her no longer. The memory of that trembling old man did not hurt her anymore, and she said to herself, flagging a cab, this was corruption.

In their room, she spelled the word for him and Doming Gorrez laughed. Emma lay back in her bed, watching the headlights momentarily illuminating the darkness upon the wall. The feelings that God vouchsafed a man — pain and joy, love and lust — they were like the lights upon the wall. You knew an instant of pain or joy or love or desire and you would never be the same again because the darkness inside yourself had known so much brief illumination. And at the end of it all, what? A gentle discernment, a manner of soft speech and belief, belief.

"We're all in fragments," she said to Doming another time. "And I want us both whole. Complete." He had pulled desk drawers open, searching heatedly for something she did not guess until he threw it at her — the dark-green, compact bankbook filled with deposits. It was as if he had said something obscene and she knew then that she would have to leave him.

"I am all here!" Doming announced, thumping himself on the chest. "All here!"

She shook her head. "No, you're not — you were easier to love before. Do you remember yourself then, Doming?" she asked. "You were a good man," she said simply.

The money, the ease, the new status, had come to them and they had ceased being themselves. That was the core of their dilemma: to go through the streets of the city and not lose their innocence, not to be warped and twisted into the ugly form of city folk.

"We could live in Tayug quietly and modestly," she said. "You would not have to arrange people's lives for them."

"You and your airs!" he snarled. "Everyone's doing it but you're better than anyone. There's never any doubt in your mind about yourself, is there, Emma? You say a thing is so, and it is so, because Emma says it is so. How can you bear to live with someone like me, Em? I don't want to go to heaven . . ."

At the bus station where they had gone three mornings afterwards, they stood uncomfortably until the familiar 812 pulled in and began to load up.

"Will you write?" he asked.

She nodded.

"You don't have to go, Em. None of this has to happen," he said. But the children were scrambling up the vehicle and they waited for their mother who turned now swiftly on her heels and climbed up. She had touched Doming quickly on the cheek and said something that the bus, starting all at once, had drowned. When they pulled away, she held her grief-washed face above her sons' heads. She had said, "Love. Love."

DOMING, SHE WROTE *from Tayug, what does a man work for? Is it not for a corner and a moment to be tender in? Outside the door, beyond the gate, there, it is always a rush to get to somewhere where there is finally nothing. We spin like tops, straining for what will maim and sear us. We think we know what we want and we chase it, but when its hood falls off, it is the macabre face of death . . . I have left you because I cannot live without you. That is a statement that should do your department at Quality proud. You turn out platitudes like that at assembly-line speed but do you honor them? You buy and sell beliefs, you buy and sell sensibilities, and of course, in the final analysis, you buy and sell people . . .*

His answer was full of newsy bits: the neighbors had asked for her but were not overly curious. He might trade in the car for a two-toned mauve. Big Man had bought a two-toned mauve; mauve was the latest hue of success. They were panelling the conference

6

room at last. There was a sale of pin-striped Van Heusens at his favorite store . . .

He can get along without me, she thought bitterly.

Nobody asked why she had returned to Tayug. Everyone presumed that Domingo Gorrez would follow in a short while. Even after she had begun to teach again at Plaridel High, she heard nothing to indicate that people were wondering why she and her two sons lived by themselves. It was the quiet and modest life that she had wanted. Each day, she walked the boys to the primary school building atop Manresa Knoll and then turned downhill again towards the high school. At a certain point, she could see the depot where Doming had worked before. The derricks were still there, stark against the sky.

On her way home in the afternoon, she looked in on the deer. The Rizal statue near the patio, religiously white-washed by town officials, lifted unwearied arms still unburdened with ageless overcoat and books.

"You would think," Mr. Rividad said, catching up with her one afternoon, "that he had seen nothing at all."

Forty years before, his father had led an abortive insurrection — two hundred people had perished, strewn all over the plaza. His own mother, three months pregnant, had died at the foot of the statue, one bullet through her heart, her rough hands grasping the folds of a flag she had fashioned in the ravines of the Mangatarem mountains where they had gone to organize. "They had sent me away before that," Mr. Rividad had told Emma the story that first year she had come out to this town. "And when I saw them again, it was here, among the hedges." They were dead, and he, the fifteen-year-old son of Amang, was not. At the sound of gunfire earlier that day, he had run to the plaza where the people had said the Colorums were and found his parents sprawled like that. They would not let him bury them. The officer who had shot his mother had approached and said, "Go home, kid."

I am their son, he wished to answer but no one had paid him any attention. He had lived with that guilt. He had left town for years, studied in the city, returning to set up the high school. And then he had lived with another kind of guilt, he was living with it still, in fact — his wife, Norma Rividad, sick with a greed he could not satisfy, meeting strange men in strange rooms in strange towns.

"He has seen everything," Mr. Rividad went on, falling in step with Emma Gorrez.

The wind from the hills was sweeping out to sea. "Everything," Rividad repeated. They looked at each other. Her own sons would

7

be at home, waiting for her, but here she lingered, glancing at this old friend's face. Did he mean *everything?* That twilight they had both stood in the plaza five years ago, watching the school girls playing on the grass, two weeks before her impulsive marriage to Domingo Gorrez. Mr. Rividad had blurted out a few words that had brought down upon both of them a delicate, enveloping silence.

". . . only the brief timid pleasure," he had said, speaking slowly, painfully, ". . . letting you know . . . what harm can it do now? . . . you're marrying Gorrez. I cannot stop that . . . and soon another complete, self-contained bubble on the face of the earth . . . the sounds of Sunday joy: baby in crib, pot upon the stove, rain on the roof, and large warm bed beckoning in the corner . . ."

THE PUBLIC RELATIONS department of Quality Products, Incorporated occupied a whole suite on the seventh floor of the Zenith Building in Plaza Tanduay. The Zenith was one of those modern, spare designs, seemingly fragile, rising on stilts. Row on row of cobweb-windows dazzled the passerby. Three cobweb windows belonged to Domingo Gorrez who now drew a monthly pay in four digits, not including allowances.

When Ernesto Bello, chief plotter, was out of town, Gorrez called the shots: it was his voice, coming over the intercom set, that set them all skittering over the well-sanded floor of the PR suite. Heads were constantly being chopped off, in a manner of speaking, but Bello and Gorrez held on to theirs, although grapevine had it that more than once in the past, conflicting ambitions had nearly precipitated an open break. But both knew better than to court disaster. They were favorites of Big Man who played the game so dexterously that neither knew who was favored more. It was one way of ensuring loyalty. They were loyal to the boss, to-the-death loyal, Gorrez particularly.

Before their estrangement, Doming gleefully brought Emma the latest news of Big Man's current playmate. Each night, as soon as he had loosened his tie and kicked off his shoes, Doming would give her the latest communique: "Emma, it's Ruby Trias of Accounting, this time." Or Fely Barba of Files. Or Mercedes Sulit of Copy. They were all the same to Emma Gorrez — hungry, eager young girls, fresh from college, their foolish little heads filled with sleek magazine stuff. Whoever it was Big Man fancied slipped each noon into Doming Gorrez's room "to nap" — while in the office adjoining, the boss sat, licking his chops, his limbs trembling with ague and desire. Fifteen minutes later, after a sufficiently refreshing nap, the connecting door between Gorrez' and the boss' rooms would open. It was a door anyone well knew was there but no one mentioned. At Cafe Luxaire, Gorrez asked for a second cup of coffee, sometimes a third, stood to make a phone call to his desk, noted the busy signal, and took his time.

You could always tell, said Domingo to his wife, who had done pretty well by herself. Three or four weeks afterwards, someone was certain to be sporting a diamond ring. One girl had built a summer house for a sick father, in addition to the sparkler on her finger. Mina, the knowing minx, had demanded to be sent to Hong Kong several times, from where she had returned loaded to the ears with several luxury goods which she peddled at tremendous profit to the other girls in the lunchroom — bags, cashmere sweaters, and silks. Squealing excitedly, the girls fought for the privilege of being listed in Mina's ledger, a brown, hardbound book she carried all over PR twice a month, into whose pages she wrote the names and debts.

There were the office parties.

Big Man honored all office parties with his presence. Executives 1 to 10 came, bourbon under their arms. Skull caps were passed around. Music was loud, laughter raucous. At the party celebrating the defeat of the strikers against Quality, the boss danced with all the wives, including Emma Gorrez. Including Mrs. Testa, whose husband had led the strike. Mrs. Testa had not been invited to the party on the Zenith roof garden but she had come just the same to plead for her husband's job back. Big Man had not known who she was. He was whirling her around in a fast rhumba and was probably toying with the idea of asking her to nap in Gorrez' room when a man's angry hand cut his pleasure short. There was Testa, in a sweat-stained polo shirt, three days' beard on his chin. He had led the strike and lost, and here, gathered for a victorious evening, were the enemy, Bello, Gorrez, Reyes, Paez, and the whole necktied bunch, who had pledged support, and then sold him out. Testa took his wife by the elbow, smiling crazily, and walked to his friends and shook their hands solemnly, ceremoniously, saying something that froze the joy in their faces.

"What did he say?" Emma asked Doming on their way home that night. "Doming?"

The bastard, Doming had muttered under his breath. The gaddam son of a b — ing bastard. Doming had cursed, shifting gears.

"What did he say?"

Something Latin, replied Gorrez.

"Latin?"

"Yah," Gorrez said drunkenly, stepping on the gas, swinging the car around a curve. *Morituri te Salutamus.*

Gorrez' role in the ill-starred strike had not been as villainous as Bello's but it had been wicked enough.

Bello had done the dirty job, worming his way into the strikers' confidence, listing a few personal grievances himself, leading his name to the manifesto. But Bello had not marched with them into Big Man's office. When Testa and the rest of the boys had walked in, Bello was already there, behind the boss' bar, mixing himself a drink.

But Doming could have swung it for Testa, had he been so minded. "Well, Gorrez?" Big Man asked. "What do you think?"

Doming had picked up the demands. Quality stocks were up a hundred per cent, provincial outlets were never better, public relations was going great guns, a few raises would have not hurt. Why, the old goat spent more for those brief contraband moments in Gorrez's office. But Big Man's steely gaze did not leave Domingo Gorrez's face, which blanched and burned by turns. Hell, Gorrez had thought, life was rough all around.

"I shrugged my shoulders," he told Emma later.

Emma pushed him away.

"But don't you see?" he had asked.

"I should ask you that," she said. "Everything led to that one moment, Doming. You could have redeemed yourself. You could have done the right thing. But a shrug is a smart reflex, it comes with half a dozen others in a handy kit they distribute among today's bright boys . . . Are you sure," she asked aloud, "are you sure pimping is all you do for him?"

Emma felt Doming's blow even before it landed on her cheek.

SHE FELT it again, sitting with Rene Rividad one Saturday at a table in De Luxe.

In Tayug, on Saturdays, there was nothing to do but walk around town. After you had seen the deer and the patio, you invariably dropped in at the restaurant and took one of its battered tables and ordered coffee. The beverage came, strong and steaming, in a thick wet cup, and when she remembered food, she asked for a roll and spread it with a fork. She was doing just that one afternoon when Rene Rividad walked in and took the chair across her.

She did not ask but she knew, instinctively, what he was there for. The last bus from Dagupan came at 7 past. He would wait for that and go through the farce of welcoming Norma Rividad from one of her trips. He would then take her home — it was an act of kindness.

Emma and Mr. Rividad were comfortable together, making small talk.

He asked her how she found the students these days?

She asked him if he went often to Mrs. Pintoy?

He told her that Plaridel was beginning to attract people from Balungao, they had twenty students from that town this year.

She told him that the Gorrez tenants from Anonas had descended on her one morning, bringing chickens, fruits, and eggs, asking about Apo Laureano's son, Doming. They had wanted to know when he was arriving. With the drought, it was not easy to grow a pig.

"What did you tell them?" Mr. Rividad asked her. He spooned some sugar into his coffee and held the milk can over it until the liquid turned white.

"Didn't you get enough milk as a baby?" she teased.

He laughed with her. She noticed his fingers. They were long, nicotine-stained, square-tipped fingers. They shook perceptively. "A nervous illness," he explained, spreading his hands over the table. "Happiness just barely misses my grasp, you know."

Emma Gorrez said, "Who has taught you to make pretty speeches?"

"And who has taught you to ignore questions?" he asked.

"What questions?"

"When is Doming coming home?"

"I don't know," she said frankly. Doming had stopped writing. The money came regularly, twice a month. In the beginning, there had been notes. Three or four times saying hello and asking if the kids were well. But they had stopped. The money orders were reaching her now with nothing more than a clerk's letter, typed neatly and sparingly: *Dear Mrs. Gorrez, Please acknowledge sum.*

"We're living apart, Rene," she said. "For a little while, I hope. We had some — differences," she ended lamely. She looked at Mr. Rividad's hands once more and remembered Doming's palm against her face.

Mr. Rividad glanced at his watch and said, "Norma will be here soon." They stood up and together waited on the sidewalk outside of De Luxe. There was the red Pantran, easing itself into the parking lot across the street. "She always comes home," he said.

It was two Sundays later when they met again and Emma could not tell if it was by design or not. Like that earlier Saturday, Rividad walked in and Emma's heart lifted at sight of him. They saw each other in school but there was no time to talk and there were always too many people. At De Luxe it was different. A public eating place, in the heart of town, five minutes away from the church pulpit. Father Tomas weekly exhorted them to shy at sin.

There was nothing wrong in sitting and talking, several tables away from Mrs. Puray's cashbox. Lean one's head against the hard wood of Mrs. Puray's grimy restaurant wall, and talk. Bring the cof-

11

fee to one's mouth, sip and swallow and talk. Tell of the business that went ph-ff-t. Tell of city lights and city loneliness. Tell of Big Man, Bello, Mina the minx. Tell of the strike, tell of Testa, tell of the boss' "naps." Tell of Navarro, beyond whom no treachery more terrible was possible — so that when the time came to tell of her parting from Doming, Emma spoke in a measured, reminiscent tone, as if she was telling the story, not of herself, but of some old friends she had wished well a long time ago.

"They had everything when they started, Rene. Youth, good looks, courage. Where did all that go?"

Mr. Rividad smoked quietly across her.

"You remember saying once, 'The sounds of Sunday joy' . . .?"

He nodded, smiling suddenly. "Yes, but there are other days in the week. And other sounds."

"Oh, no!" she said, in mock pleasure. "You are not wooing me, are you?" she asked lightly.

"And if I am?" he asked, matching her mood.

"Norma will be here soon," she said.

"I am not waiting for Norma this time," Mr. Rividad said quietly.

It was not Norma he waited for on all the other days that he and Emma Gorrez met in the restaurant. The last bus from Dagupan would drive in; still Rene Rividad sat glued to his chair, smoking interminably, waiting for Emma to be done with her stories, or telling some of his own. Did she hope to escape unscathed? Back of her mind, a knell sounded, foreshadowing anguish. Some affection was bound to spill over, sitting with Mr. Rividad like that, talking intimately with him, but Emma was summoned to that table every Saturday at sunset by a voice stronger than wisdom.

Her sons would be in the yard, playing, when she passed them. Hair pulled back, face clean of powder and lipstick, she wore the simplest clothes to these meetings. She took a long, circuitous route, looking in on every store on Tañedo, crossing over to Luna Street for a leisurely-spaced walk beneath the trees. But as soon as the sun was gone, her feet took her to De Luxe. With a will all their own, they bore her, despite herself, to where Mr. Rividad was waiting. Sometimes, she fought the wish to see him. Deliberately, she sat on a bench in the plaza, telling herself it was not important if he was there or not.

One day, she sat longer than she had intended. When she stood up, it was evening. A desire to weep possessed her. He had probably not waited, and it was an eternity to the next Saturday. She began to hurry. At the second corner, she ran, forgetting everything else.

12

When she reached the lighted door of the restaurant, she saw him at the table, a sad, hurt, puzzled look in his face. She stepped in quickly and said, "You are here."

"Would you have wanted me to go?"

"No," she said. It was a bold thing to say; it was a perilous thing to say. She felt her defenses go: such a brief word yet it stripped her completely.

He looked at her. "May I wait for you here on Saturday?"

She did not meet his gaze.

"Dear Emma," he said suddenly.

"Don't." Why had she let this man become important to her?

"Em . ." he had never called her that before. "I would like to wait for you," he continued softly, "here, and in all the places you can possibly think of, for all the hours life will allow me."

"Don't do this to me, Rene," she begged.

"Are you afraid?"

"This is catastrophe," she said.

"Are you afraid?" he insisted.

She nodded dumbly.

"Let me give you strength," he said.

She looked at him now. Five years ago, as earnestly as now Rividad leaned across the table. Domingo Gorrez had leaned across another table, and pleaded as Rividad pleaded today. What had happened to that earlier love? She had wanted that more than anything else; she had wanted that to last but it had gone because—she tried too hard, and Doming, too little? Could you kill love with a surfeit of loving? In the happier days, discovering each other for the first time, Doming had spoken as gently as this man: "Em," he had said once, "your hands within my hands —" Some poetry he had learned in college: *Your hands within my hands are deeds; my tongue upon your throat; singing arms close; eyes wide; undoubtful, dark, drink the dawn — a forest shudders in your hair!*

Emma Gorrez let her head fall back against the wall. She closed her eyes. A tremor shock her.

I wish I could cross over to the safer side of today, she thought. I wish I could go back to the plaza, to half an hour ago, beneath the trees, in the thickening dark, where I mused, lonely, and afraid, but not this afraid. This man asked me would I have wanted him to go and I said No, and it was like a dam breaking, like a wall giving way, and here I bob in the flotsam, not wanting to save myself. I am being swept awash, the shore is near, one step, and I am on safe ground, but I do not wish to go ashore.

13

"And Norma?" she said aloud. "Am I to be like Norma after all?" she asked unhappily.

"You are not Norma," he said, "there is a difference."

"Difference?" she asked.

"A big difference," he said. "You are Emma. And I love you."

They sat in silence, the cups between them. Perhaps, I could love him, she thought. The jukebox in the corner began to sing softly. Perhaps, I love him already, she thought. *Over the edge, ah! down the precipice, and sweet disaster.*

She had run away from violence to meet it here in this quiet, empty restaurant, with the electric fan whirling overhead, and Mrs. Puray dozing near her cashbox.

The joys of Sunday seemed far away now. The licit sounds of happiness had slid past her. She had loved Doming with everything that she had been but they had been careless, and one paid for carelessness like this—sipping coffee in exile, vulnerable and tremulous because, in this wayward inn, someone had said a warm and tender thing.

Kamala Das
India

Summer in Calcutta

What is this drink but
The April sun, squeezed
Like an orange in
My glass? I sip the
Fire, I drink and drink
Again, I am drunk,
Yes, but on the gold
Of suns. What noble
Venom now flows through
My veins and fills my
Mind with unhurried
Laughter? My worries
Doze. Wee bubbles ring
My glass, like a bride's
Nervous smile, and meet
My lips. Dear, forgive
This moment's lull in
Wanting you, the blur
In memory. How
Brief the term of my
Devotion, how brief
Your reign when I with
Glass in hand, drink, drink,
And drink again this
Juice of April suns.

The Sirens

The night, dark-cloaked like a procuress, brought
him to me, willing, light like a shadow,
speaking words of love
in some tender language I do not know.
Aniruddha, dream-lover, hide from him
this kind night's deceit, for I know too well
that he loves me not.

With the crows came the morning, and my limbs,
warm from love, were once again so lonely.
At my door-step I saw a pockmarked face
a friendly smile and
a rolleiflex. We will go for a drive,
he said. Or, go to see the lakes. I have
washed my face with soap and water, brushed
my hair a dozen
times, draped myself in six yards of printed
voile. Ah . . . . . does it still show, my night of love?
You look pale, he said. Not pale, not really
pale. It's the lipstick's
anaemia. Out, in the street, we heard
the sirens go, and I paused in talk to
weave its veil with the sound of his mirthless
laughter. He said,
they are testing the sirens today. I am
happy. He really was lavish with words.
So happy, just being with you. But you,
you love another,
I know, he said, perhaps a handsome man,
a young and handsome man. Not young,
not handsome, I thought, just a filthy snob.
It's a onesided love,
I said. What can I do, or you? I smiled.
A smile is such a detached thing, I wear
it like a flower. Near the lake, a pregnant
girl bared her dusky
breasts and washed them sullenly. On the old
canon-stand, crows bickered over a piece

of lizard-meat, and the white sun was there
and everywhere.
I want your photo, lying down, he said,
against those rusty, nineteen thirty four guns.
Will you? Sure. Just arrange my limbs and tell
me when to smile. I
shut my eyes, but inside eye-lids there was
no more night, no more love, or peace, only
the white, white, sun burning, burning, burning . . . .

Ah, why does love come to me like pain,
again and again and again.

I Shall Someday

I shall someday leave, leave the cocoon
You built around me with morning tea,
Love-words flung from doorways and of course
Your tired lust. I shall someday take
Wings, fly around, as often petals
Do when free in air, and you dear one,
Just the sad remnant of a root, must
Lie behind, sans pride on double beds
And grieve. But I shall someday return losing
Nearly all, hurt by wind, sun and rain,
Too hurt by fierce happiness to want
A further jaunt or a further spell
Of freedom, and I shall someday see
My world, de-fleshed, de-veined, de-blooded,
Just a skeletal thing, then shut my
Eyes and take refuge, if nowhere else,
Here in your nest of familiar scorn . . .

Brief Encounter

Nagai Tatsuo

I MUST ASK you to read a part of my letter before you begin the story proper:

I received your letter and the enclosed money order. Thank you very much.

Thank you for the remarkable news that the ring I left with you has joined your engagement ring and been reborn as a tooth. I find myself less surprised and sorry than wanting to tell how much it helped with the fresh, new view of life I mentioned to you.

As you have shown in your own person, the gold tooth artlessly in place somewhere behind an eyetooth is especially pleasing when glimpsed in the smile of a woman in her middle twenties. (Was yours perhaps one into which your husband himself put all his affection and skill? Forgive me. I will say no more about your false tooth. Even by way of sympathy.) I only hope this: that the two rings, the symbol of your gloom and the symbol of my new, fresh mood, will become admirable new teeth for the good of the people of Tokyo.

It occurs to me, as I stop writing for a minute to light a cigarette, that letter-writing scenes are disappearing from the movies. To be sure, telephones and telegraphs are relieving the race of the troublesome chore; but I feel a certain nostalgia for the expression on her face for those few seconds when, having laid down the pen, she raises the envelope to her lips.

What was I going to say? At first, not used to the work, I was exhausted; but now a month has gone by, and, sound and healthy again, I am in with the youngsters, having the experience of life in the mines . . .

I had quite cleaned out the room.

The medium-sized boston bag that held my belongings lay in the middle of the alcove, and twenty or thirty books were stacked against the wall. There was a newspaper on the desk by the window. The bedding was folded neatly in front of the cupboard, with the pillow on top, as if to weigh it down.

I said good-bye at the main house, and when I came back to my six-mat room, somehow cut off, amputated from the human world, the red kitten was curled by the pillow.

I felt myself smiling. "And what do you think you're doing here?" In my hat and coat, I knelt by the bedding and stroked the animal softly. Its eyes still closed, rolled over on its back, and, in a most excellent mood, it purred for me.

It had been in the main house for three months or so, and it would come to see me several times every day. Although nearly forty, I had never kept a cat or a dog. This was the first time I had ever lived near a cat.

I put my ear to its stomach and listened for a moment to the purring. Then, going out to the corridor that faced the garden and led to the main house, I put on my shoes. I had a raincoat over my arm. They had told me in the main house that the forecast was for rain.

Since they had agreed to store everything I did not immediately need, the disposition of my assets could not have been simpler.

I left the door open a little, for the kitten.

Several days earlier I had told my brother that I thought I might go to see a foreign movie — I would be off in the mines for a while, and would not have another chance. This morning a note had come by messenger.

"I was not able to get tickets for 'The Best Years of Our Life.' I enclose instead tickets for 'Brief Encounter,' an English movie that is said to be very good, and with them an express ticket. The latter is for tomorrow. I will see you at the station."

The note was in my pocket when I got off at Shimbashi. I had come in from Hodogaya on the electric line and I had been wondering all the way what to do. There were two tickets to "Brief Encounter." * I had no idea what sort of movie it was, but that was the title. It seemed to tease me, to jeer at me, to prod me.

My brother was too serious a sort to be teasing me with the two tickets, that much was sure; but it was ironical all the same, sending two tickets to a bachelor in his late thirties. What was I to do with the other?

As I walked down the stairs at Shimbashi I decided to invite A, who worked in an office behind the Ginza.

I thought I would make a joke of it: "Someone gave me tickets to a movie called 'Brief Encounter,' and I have to get rid of them I know it's a little behind the times for two grown men to go to

---

* The Japanese title is *Aibiki,* "Assignation," which, it will be noted as the story progresses, invites more quips than the English title does.

that sort of movie together but I won't be seeing you again for a while. Come on along."

Unfortunately, A. was out. Very well; I would give the ticket to someone in front of the theater. I crossed the bridge in the direction of the H. Theater.

There were three or four people at the ticket window. I walked briskly up — and then changed my mind. There was a couple, and there were young girls. The expression "a man in his forties" had come into my mind, and the image of middle-age accosting youth. Derisively came those other terms that seemed applicable: "ex-soldier," "broken-down soldier," and the rest.

I went into the theater. The girl showed me to my seat. The next seat of course was vacant. As if asking them to sit down, I gave it to my hat and raincoat.

There was no reason at all to invite someone else just because I had two tickets. This was much better — I could spread out. The trouble with me was that I was still a prisoner of inflexible concepts.

People came in; the theater filled. The bell rang. The news went dizzily in review.

Why was it, my brother had remarked the other day, that there was always something stale and musty about newsreels even when they had the latest scoops? The destruction after the storm was the same, whether the scene was Japan or America. The American woman, blown down the street, clung precariously to a telephone pole, and, frowning at the storm turned to the camera and smiled a childlike smile, as if to say that people did have interesting experiences.

The lights went on again when the newsreel was over. I felt somehow isolated from the crowd, but then the lights dimmed and the words "Brief Encounter" flashed against the rising curtain. I planted my elbow firmly on the arm of the vacant seat.

I had the aisle seat, and I felt a sort of pressure on my right. Someone, bent slightly forward, was standing there in the dark, waiting to be allowed past.

Automatically I looked back, but the only vacant seat was the one beside me. The ticket for it was in my pocket. I picked up my coat and hat nonetheless and put them on my knee.

The person bowed and slipped adroitly past. It was a woman in foreign dress, leaving a faint perfume behind her. I heard her open her handbag. She seemed to be taking out her glasses. I felt even after she had sat down that she was fairly tall for a woman.

Life was new and fresh, clearly it was — I reaffirmed the philosophy I had acquired during the preceding half year. But how was one to explain the mystery of the seat beside me?

21

The dull confession of a plain, tired wife, in an atmosphere of indescribable gloom. It began to pull at me. At first I resisted, but presently I was caught up in it.

There is no need here to recount the plot or to give my reactions, and indeed I am not qualified to. When I thought of it again some days later on the train, I suddenly thought too of *Earth*, that somber Japanese novel of peasant life, a cheap edition of which I had borrowed from a young comrade when I was stationed on the southern front. The movie was about a secret affair of a nameless woman in a small town, and the views of an ex-soldier are of no importance.

Yet I must mention something I would rather not: I thought again, for the first time in a great while, of my ex-wife, whom, a year before, I had let go without a shade of regret. Although no one could know that I had thought of her, I felt most ashamed of myself afterwards.

I was lightly dissatisfied with the last scene, in which the amiable husband forgave the wife. She had not committed the final error, it is true, but the affair had left her an empty shell. Perhaps that was what made me remember my wife. On that point, at least, I was superior to the husband of the movie.

"Brief Encounter" was over. I seem to have lost myself in thought, for the woman was asking to be let by. I stood up. I followed her, and we were the last to leave the theater.

The weather forecast had been accurate. The exit was screened by a white curtain, a May rain. There were some ten young people caught without umbrellas.

I stepped beyond them and lighted a cigarette. I was ready for the rain, but felt no need to hurry. The woman too took a cigarette from a silver case. There was a subtle quickness in her gestures, the movement from gesture to gesture. She had on a dark green suit, and she was indeed tall for a woman. I had glanced at her as she looked up into the sky, and been struck by the lashes of the slightly narrowed eyes. A woman's age is among the things I am incapable of judging, but she was not yet thirty, of that I was sure. Perhaps twenty-four or twenty-five, perhaps twenty-seven.

"It's not going to stop, either," she said suddenly. The black eyes moved toward me as she spoke.

"I'm afraid not." I looked at the rain hitting the pavement. Now and then a couple under a single umbrella stumbled through the spray.

"I thought it was so near, and I wouldn't need an umbrella. Stupid of me." A mischievous laugh came into the eyes. There was a trace of lipstick on her cigarette. I had not realized that it was possible to color the lips such a calm, tranquil color.

"It's near, is it?"

"Just over there." The eyes, still smiling, and a finger pointed to the left. "Next door to the curio shop."

I spread open my raincoat. "I have this. I'm going in that direction anyway — suppose I stop by and have someone come with an umbrella."

"Please don't bother. It's so near. I'll run on when I've made up my mind to get wet. Really." She spoke briskly, but with no suggestion of wanting to brush me aside.

"Suppose I do it this way." I pulled the coat over my head like a photographer, and smiled at her. The people who were waiting for a lull in the rain looked at us curiously.

Cocking her head a little to one side, she smiled back. I seemed to have put her at ease.

"Really? I shouldn't ask you to — but may I?" She came a step or two nearer. "The building next to the curio shop. A dentist named Suematsu. If you could ask the girl at the reception desk to come with a coat and an umbrella, I'd really be most grateful."

It pleased me to think that I was helping someone I would never see again. I ran through the rain. But I still did not understand about that seat.

There was a compact little building some two hundred yards away, around the corner from the curio shop. I had no trouble finding the dentist's office on the second floor. 'Suematsu Shingo, Doctor of Dental Surgery; Suematsu Akira, Dentist," the sign said in horizontal characters. It also said that Sunday was a holiday, and that the office was open only until two on Saturdays. Today was a Saturday.

Just inside the door there was a little window over the reception desk, where a girl of eighteen or nineteen was sitting. I told her my business, and she answered quietly.

Feeling somewhat nostalgic at the antiseptic smell of the office, I closed the door behind me. As I started down I could hear the rain below.

"Excuse me." Someone was calling from the head of the stairs.

It was the reception girl. Two umbrellas and an oil-cloth coat in hand, she stood by the wall, waiting for me to come up again.

"If I leave there will be no one here. Would you mind waiting till I get back?"

"Not at all, not at all."

She seemed to think that I was a friend of the woman's. Such a calm girl — should she be so trusting? There was something heart-warming about her. I walked slowly up and down before the Suematsu door.

"What a rain, and no sign of letting up. When did it begin?" The bright voice of the woman came from the stairs. Then she saw

23

me, and once more I looked closely into her eyes. "Well! What a bother for you! That's our Miss Tateno, as easy-going as ever. She had you watch the place, did she? Come on in, now that you've gone to so much trouble. For just a minute. It would be strange to let him go like this, wouldn't it, Miss Tateno?"

Turning from me to the receptionist, she pushed open the door without letting me answer.

"It's strange to think it would be strange."

She laughed, and opened another door, to a clean little waiting room that could accommodate perhaps three or four people.

"Have a seat. I'll be back in a minute." I took off my wet coat and sat on the sofa.

In the quiet I could hear water, and, faintly, the sound of a comb running through someone's hair.

"What about the coffee in the thermos bottle? Yes, let's have that. You have some too." She spoke to the girl in a voice so quiet that I wondered how it could come from the same person. "It was a gloomy, gloomy movie. I'm exhausted." I next heard someone opening a can. "I don't say it wasn't interesting, but I wonder how it would be for a young person."

Miss Tateno looked much brighter when she came in with coffee. She had changed from her office uniform. The place seemed more like a parlor.

"I shouldn't have asked you to wait. You must forgive me." She had on a blouse, I suppose you would call it — a clear, pale cerulean blue. (I know, having investigated these colors.) The sleeves were short, and the brooch was an ivory flower set in gold. I stood up.

"There was a terrible rainstorm in 'Brief Encounter' too."

"Yes. I must look a little like the doctor."

"Maybe it feels good when you get as wet as that." The woman sat down lightly in the chair opposite me.

If one had praised the fairness of her complexion, she would probably have answered: "Oh? And I've never done a thing for it. You should praise my father and mother."

But since in her hair, for all the careful attention that had gone into dressing it, there was a faint touch of calculated disarray, as of a keystone pulled slightly loose, so that the hair set off the beauty of the throat — since there was this air about her whole person, one could not doubt that a considerable sum had been invested in the almost unpowdered whiteness of the skin.

"You're going shopping in the rain?" She cast a quiet glance over my shoulder. "You are? Well, don't worry about me. I'll sit here with this gentleman a little longer, and then close the office."

24

Miss Tateno said nothing, but I gathered that she was leaving. The woman got up and went toward her.

"I'm sorry I had to say such unpleasant things. You must forgive me."

"Please don't apologize."

"You're not to worry. Understand? I'm completely over it now. I'll be in early Monday morning, looking very cheerful." She laughed softly. "Bye-bye."

I sensed that she had taken the girl's hand by way of apology. The "Bye-bye" had a high, clear ring to it.

"Something unpleasant happened, and I ran out to the movie. I felt dreadful, it was such a dismal movie." She had sat down again, and her eyes were still on the silver case after she had offered me a cigarette and taken one herself.

I wondered what the unpleasantness might have been, but did not feel that I could ask. Instead I turned the conversation to the matter that puzzled me. "I had two tickets to the movie, and the second one was a problem. It made me feel very useless."

"You should have taken your wife."

"Well, you see, as a matter of fact — " It was not a subject I found easy to talk about.

"May I ask if you were in the service? In the Navy, perhaps?"

"Precisely."

"I had two cousins in the Navy. Up until a few years ago I was rather popular with the young officers." But I did not want to talk about the past.

"And what did you do with the other ticket?" she asked.

"I wanted to invite a friend — a man, of course — but he was out. I went by myself."

"What a pity. And for a 'Brief Encounter,' too."

"But here I am drinking coffee with you. Why did you take that seat?"

"That seat?" Her eyes narrowed questioningly, and there was a pause. "Oh! I took the wrong seat. How stupid of me!" For the first time I felt a touch of coquetry.

"I thought it a great privilege."

"I was upset and a little excited, and there was no usher. I go there often, it's so close, and I thought my seat ought to be about there. And I'm little near-sighted."

"I see." I saw everything. I saw too that a slight case of myopia could make a woman's eyes rather seductive.

"I think it's letting up. You said you had business on the Ginza?"

"Nothing of any importance." I too looked out the window.

"If you're in no hurry, stay as long as you like. I have nothing to do myself."

"I go away tomorrow."

"How I envy you. Where are you going?"

"I'll be in Kyushu for a while."

"Men have all the advantages. On business?"

"No money in it, as they say. I'm going to work. In a coal mine."

"Oh?"

"I've done all sorts of things to keep myself alive since I came back. I've come to the conclusion that it's not too difficult if keeping yourself alive is all you want. But everything seems so strange, now that the military blinkers are off. Everything seems so fresh and new, so alive, from the time I get up in the morning till I go to bed at night."

"You were a commander?"

"A lieutenant-commander at the end of the war. I didn't do so well when it came to promotions." I spoke rapidly. I did not want to talk about the past. "There was a kitten that used to come and see me all the time. It was very interesting. I had never liked cats — so cold and willful. But then I would watch that kitten, and it seemed strange that such an animal could have been born. Everything was interesting to it, even its own tail. It was never bored. If that liveliness to new impressions could go on say four or five years, a cat would be a remarkable beast."

"Isn't it the truth. They get so fat and sluggish when they are older. I kept three cats once, but then it came to me that it was not very good form for a childless woman to be fond of cats, and I gave them away."

"I want to have all the experiences I can before I get fat and sluggish myself. I'm in a great hurry."

"And that's why you're going into a coal mine?"

"I want to do away with the ex-soldier."

"You'll join the Communist Party, then, and the labor movement?"

"Possibly. But the Party is too much like the service. It has no respect for you as an individual." I sensed that I was being asked leading questions. And so I made a leading remark: "To someone like me it's a fairy story, a well-matched husband and wife running a clean little office together."

"A fairy story — it was at first." She looked at me again with that slightly quizzical expression, and immediately lowered her eyes. Her manner changed abruptly. She evidently did not mean to be taken by my lead. "You're kept busy, that's all, repairing bad teeth day after day. Unless someone has to have a difficult bridge made, you can hardly breathe for the boredom. I'd like to use heaps of gold and platinum on something really good."

26

With that, I remembered my business on the Ginza. I hesitated a second, then took a little wad of paper from my pocket. I had found it in the desk drawer when I cleaned the room that morning. "It's a little sudden but could you use this?"

The delicately manicured hand took up the paper, and from it came an engagement ring.

I explained in some confusion: "I found it this morning when I was cleaning up. I wondered if I might be able to sell it on the Ginza. I know it would be more dashing if I were to drop it into the river from Kachidoki Bridge or somewhere, but I've never much been one for romantic things, and I thought I'd put it up for sale instead."

"I could take it for you. Shall I?"

"It's been no use for a year — no, for much longer than that. It's not a question of the money." I added, when I saw a cloud come over her face.

The curve of her neck, slightly arched against the back of the chair, turned toward the window. She fingered the ring languidly. "Three grams, maybe four? Well, let me take it for you. I think the rain has stopped."

I too had been looking uncomfortably at the faint yellowish sunlight coming through the window. It was time to leave.

As the hand with the ring dropped to her lap, she took a deep breath, and two points came to life on her blouse. Then her face, propped on her other hand, turned to me with a delicate quickness, as if to dismiss something. "Excuse me. Here I am brooding when I have company." She hunched over, and the smiling face came nearer. "When I'm busy I usually have lunch just up the street. I've left a supply of rice there. I thought of having something today before I go home, and if you have nothing else to do, suppose you come along." Without waiting for my answer, she took her handbag from the little table. "The price of gold changes every day, but let me give you a thousand yen anyway. Business is business. I'll send the rest to your mine when I know exactly how much it comes to."

The frankness of the smooth-flowing words helped a little.

I waited in the hall.

She came out, her lips alive, and the office door closed sharply.

In the evening sunlight after the May rain, we crossed the bridge toward the Ginza. It is pointless, at such times, to describe life as "new and fresh."

She exchanged quiet greetings with the waiters and sat down opposite me.

"They say beer doesn't go well with it, but —" We emptied our glasses.

"Your husband?" The talk of drink gave me courage to mention something that had puzzled me.

27

"Oh, don't worry about 'your husband.'" As she poured more beer for me—indeed, by pouring more beer—she fended off my question. "Were you on the southern front for a long time?"

"Here and there for two years."

"And you were separated from your wife a year after you came back?"

"I guessed everything immediately. It wasn't fun, but I wanted to be rid of the past, and I made a clean break with her. But that isn't a very pleasant subject."

"I'm sorry. That last scene of 'Brief Encounter' —remember? Where the husband forgives the wife? It bothered me. It made me very sad to think how they would pass the years afterwards. And so I brought it up. But no more."

True, that ending was no ending. Might we not better have left the matter to the critics, however?

"We got nothing at all from military life. Or one thing only. We islanders without island minds can still remember Java or Luzon when we see a sunset like this. The sunrise some morning makes us all think of sunrises on the continent, while we plow our fields and row our boats. That is the one thing it gave us."

"Men have all the advantages." Her long eyelashes lowered, she watched the shining beads that rose from the bottom of the glass. It is dangerous to be too impressed by feminine poses at certain times. "Oh, yes. You mustn't forget to give me your Kyushu address."

I took out my card case. A long, narrow piece of paper came out with it.

She opened her handbag.

"I have a pen."

"Thank you." Idly, I turned over the piece of paper. It was the second theater ticket.

"Oh, good! Write on the back of that."

I looked at her and we laughed.

With a delicate fountain pen I wrote down the name of the mine and the dormitory.

"When I was in the south, the boys under me all had pictures of their girl friends and their fiancees and their brides, and whenever they had a spare minute they would take out their pictures and look at them and show them off to the others. It was very strange, though — the habit would make them forget the real women."

She did not answer.

" 'Hey! What was my old woman's face like?' someone would say, and someone else would say, 'Now that you mention it, I can't remember my girl's face either. Be quiet a minute while I close my eyes and think.' It happened all the time."

"Interesting."

"How shall I describe it? The impulse to beautify women is always at work, and it builds up an image that moves away from the actual person. Even at my age."

"May I ask you to do the same with your image of me?" She tilted her head slightly and smiled.

"It may well happen."

Amused, I had my longest look into her eyes.

We parted at Tokyo Station, she to take the Central Line, I the Yokosuka Line. The next day I left for this mine.

A month later I had a registered letter from her:

First, our business.

The enclosed money order covers what I owe you for the item you left with me. I talked with a man we do business with, and bought it at the price he quoted.

It is becoming the cap for a young lady's second molar. She is a very pretty young lady and she is soon to be married. The lower bicuspid next to it will be capped with platinum, and for that I mean to use my own engagement ring.

The day I met you in that strange way was the day I decided on a divorce, after a great deal of unpleasantness. The reason is a most ordinary one, which I shall leave to your imagination.

I hesitated for a time about capping the teeth of a young girl soon to be married with two unlucky engagement rings, but then I came to think that they might be a sort of mascot for her in her new life.

I work hard all day long. It is new and fresh, this not being anyone's wife.

I trust that you are taking care of yourself.

Have you noted any tendency to beautify my image?

The letter with which I began was my answer.

That is all there is to the story.

It would please me beyond measure if, among my readers, there should be some who felt like going back to reread the beginning.

Translated by E.G. Seidensticker

Prelude to Glory

U Win Pe

AT THE stroke of four in the morning the cheap alarm clock of ten years ago faithfully clanged its rasping bell. The monk stirred on his low, hard couch. He had been listening for the bell and turning over in his mind the verses he had learned the day before. "Thus was it heard by me. At that time the Buddha, the Blessed One, was staying at Rajagaha, on the Vulture-Peak Hill." He groped for the lighter on the couchside table, clicked it thrice to waken the flame, and lit the long-stemmed kerosene lamp. The smoky glow revealed a faded bookcase with carvings and three missing panes, a small round table with a square shelf between its four legs, leather-bound gold-lettered volumes, oilpaper-wrapped books, dark-green Bandoola exercise books at nine kyats a dozen, an orange robe on a line spanning a corner of the room, and a dim photograph of an elderly monk on the wall.

The monk arose, grasped the lamp, and opened the door of his cubicle. The creak of door leaves shuttled across the main room of the refectory and reverberated above four small figures lying on the floor just outside the door.

Four little boys huddled together with a coverless dirty pillow each, two blankets between the four, and no net to protect them from the savage hordes of mosquitoes that ravaged such places. They were close together to get the warmth of each other's bodies — which they did, along with the musty smell of their long unchanged, unwashed clothes. One of the boys, Tha Nu, had shed his share of the blanket and had a leg thrown over his mate, Khway Ni, who had an arm across Tha Nu's neck.

As the monk crouched to shake Tha Nu's shoulder, a mosquito whined past his face and away.

"Tha Nu. Get up," he said.

Tha Nu was away in yester-afternoon rewinning the three *gon-nyin* from his monastery schoolmates under the jackfruit tree.

"Tha Nu, wake up." The monk shook him vigorously.

Tha Nu sat up. "Yes, your reverence," he murmured.

He disentangled the blanket from a leg and turned to arouse the other boys. Tha Gi, the eldest, awoke easily. Sein Tint jerked up as Tha Nu had heard dead men do when their corpses are possessed by evil spirits, and for a moment a plug of fear choked his throat. Khway Ni refused to get up. Tha Nu got on his feet and dragged Khway Ni awake by a hand.

The monk had lighted another lamp, opened the front door, the upper bolt of which the boys could not reach, and had returned to his cubicle.

Tha Gi and Tha Nu gathered the pillows and blankets and, after opening the other door, put them in a corner of the back room. Sein Tint rolled up the mats. Khway Ni carried the lamp into the back room and placed it near the head of the steps. Then all the four boys ran down towards the back of the monastery.

The latrine was a short distance away, built over a brook which flowed beside the monastery compound. But that was too far for the boys. They stopped beside a clump of bamboo immediately beyond the refectory building where the swollen brook turned inwards and its water lapped the bamboo roots. The air was fresh and cold and there was the rumor of a moon somewhere behind the low-driving wrack of clouds. A gust of wind shook drops from the bamboo leaves. The boys shivered from the touch of the cold drips on bare, thin flesh and from release of tension.

They returned to the building and Tha Nu walked through to the vestibule, in which hung a large hollowed-out log of teak. Tha Nu picked up the stick of *yindaik* wood beside it and beat on the log. The blows boomed out heavily at first, with a long pause between each so that a listener might think they had stopped and would come no more, but then they called out faster and faster like the squawking of an ancient, deep-throated, long-billed bird disturbed in its sleep, anxious and then thoroughly frightened. The sound passed through the confines of the monastery to awaken the monks to prayer and praise and practice, crossed a patch of nursling paddy and into the village to call upon the villagers to arise and cook for alms-food and for the meal they will carry with them into the fields.

With the first few notes of the *on-maung*, one or two of the many dogs in the monastery set up a hesitant howl; as the notes came closer together all the dogs joined to howl in earnest. This daily booming and howling drove to nervousness the ghosts in the compound who would have shifted to somewhere else were not the trees here so broad and cool and the wooden buildings old and comfortable. Moreover, each monastery must have its ghosts, and so they stayed. The noise stopped. Tha Nu put back the beating stick. He could hear in the sudden quiet a passing cloud expend itself with a spatter on the thatch-roofs of the village.

He entered the main refectory room to join the others in prayer which they intoned in their childish voices. Tha Nu was nine come the month of Thadingyut and had been three years in the monastery. He was a spare, brown boy with a thin, serious face but constantly active and falling foul of the monk in charge of the refectory. He came of good stock. His parents were pious, hard working cultivators with a few acres of their own. The head man of the village tract in which the monastery was situated was a maternal uncle and another maternal uncle was a ward headman in the town on the railway. But the real pride of his people was that their members had swelled the company of the Sangha. Tha Nu could count three uncles and cousins who were monks and an aunt was a nun. One of them was abbot of a monastery with forty-three monks and countless novices and schoolboys. And he had heard his relatives speak often of a granduncle, his grandfather's youngest brother who had died as an abbot at thirty-two.

That was a young age for any monk to be an abbot but this granduncle had been exceptional and his practices and learning had been known and commended far and wide, even to Mandalay, it was said. He lived an ascetic life in a small hut with barely enough room for a sleeping mat and a low-writing desk. He studied, went the rounds for alms-food, took classes in Abhidhamma and Vinaya, meditated, preached. As his fame grew, more and more monks came to study under him till the existent monastery buildings could hold them no more. People began to see the need for more buildings. A rich devotee from the city visited the monastery and begged permission from the abbot to build a new dormitory.

Now, there are certain things for which some people are not worthy, and the abbot, who was well versed and farseeing in astrology, knew that he was not entitled to the new building and that if it was built he would have to pay for it with his life. And it was not proper for a monk to dissuade anyone from charity. Though he had asked the donor whether it could not be postponed for a season of rains, the donor had been eager and he had had to accept. He died before the buildings were completed.

Tha Nu was born about a year after the abbot had died. It was said that he resembled the abbot, his granduncle, in form and feature. And as he grew up similar mannerisms convinced his parents that he was his granduncle reincarnate. After that there was only one vocation for Tha Nu. His grandfather taught him the scriptures with the first few words he could speak. He attended the monastery school as soon as he could walk there by himself and return home at night.

At six years of age the monastery became his home. Come Tazaung-mon he would enter the Order of the Lord as a novice.

When the boys had finished their prayers Tha Gi and Khway Ni picked up brooms to sweep the refectory rooms. Sein Tint and Tha Nu carried the dishes to the tub at the back to wash them. Halfway through the washing they heard the monk in charge of the refectory come out. They stopped their low conversation about a hussy who had died recently in the village and was said to be haunting her house violently. They stopped because the monk, U Arseinda, had a terrible temper as well as because he was so good at exorcising evil spirits. Perhaps his temper fitted him to be so.

They remembered when one of the boys — who was a novice now — had been possessed by an evil spirit. He had been sent on an errand to the village and had returned at lamp-lighting time. He had come into the refectory where they were doing a chore under the fastidious eyes of U Arseinda and, instead of doing the customary obeisance to the monk, had said in a queer voice: "I want meat."

The boys had heard, but it seemed that U Arseinda had not for he raised his head towards the boy as though to ask him what he wanted.

"I want meat," repeated the boy.

"What are you saying, boy?" the monk asked, not surprised but unbelieving.

"I want meat," said the boy, firmly with a slight tinge of impatience.

The monk caught it this time and he saw into the eyes of the boy and grasped what was wrong.

"Tha Nu, fetch that piece of rope from the storeroom," he ordered.

"Come with me," he told the boy and took him to a post in the middle of the room. "Stand here."

He went into his cubicle and came out with a cane. Tha Nu had returned with the rope. He called Tha Gi and some other boys.

"All right. Tie him to the post," he said. After a short struggle the boy was tied with his face to the post.

The monk took the cane in his hand.

"What do you want? Say it again," he told the boy who was possessed.

"I want meat," the boy repeated in a hard voice of anger.

The monk swung the cane thrice at him. The boy winced at each thwack but kept a tight mouth.

"Do you still want meat?" the monk asked.

The boy did not answer.

The monk gave him a few more strokes. This time the boy howled.

"I have been wrong, your reverence. Please release me. I will never do it again," he pleaded.

The monk beat him some more and with each stroke he cried: "Want some more meat. Want some more meat. Ask for more meat. You can get meat in a monastery. Want some more meat."

The evil spirit in the boy howled, pleaded, begged till at last the monk stopped.

"Who are you?" he asked the evil spirit.

"I am from the mango tree on the road to the monastery. I was feeling hungry. The boy came by and I followed him in."

"I told you you could stay if you did not disturb the boys and the people who come to the monastery, and you promised. Now you have broken your word."

"I confess that I have, your reverence. I have committed a great wrong. I promise you I will never do it again."

On that promise the spirit was released with the order to take away with him the marks of the lashes. The boy was untied, weary but unhurt. This the boys remembered, and how they had held U Arseinda in awe ever since.

The monk spoke to the boys at the dishes.

"Has U Po Din arrived?"

U Po Din was a *kappiya*, the layman who did odd jobs in the monastery like boiling the tea water, cooking the rice, carrying water. He dwelt in a *zayat* within the monastery precincts.

The boys looked at the fireplace, dark and cold. They realized that U Po Din had not yet come.

"No, your reverence," replied Tha Nu.

"Go fetch him."

Tha Nu stepped out into the cold, wet air. The rain had blown over but the clouds were still moving after it. The wind still worried the rain-laden branches. The moon was a little brighter now.

As he approached the *zayat* he could see the old man sitting hunched in a far corner, while his huge shadow jumped and leaped above him in the wind-harried candle light. Tha Nu climbed into the *zayat* and sat on his haunches near the old man. The old man was rummaging in his bedroll.

"What are you looking for?" he asked.

"My cheroot stub," replied the old man feeling his pillow and running his hand inside the pillowcase. Through with the pillow he placed it behind him at the foot of the bedspread. He took the

34

blanket and shook it without unfolding it. He spread it on the floor and pressed it all over, feeling with his hands. He put it aside. Next he took the mosquito net and tried to shake it while sitting, but found the net too long for that. He made as if to rise, and a joint cracked somewhere in his frail, stiff body. He caught his back with a hand and an involuntary cry.

Tha Nu got up. "I'll do it for you," he said.

He took the mosquito net and shook it. A cheroot stub rolled out, together with pieces of its charred stuffing.

"There it is," he said eagerly.

The old man took it and laid it on the floor. He brushed off the cinders but some of the ash smeared his already dirty mosquito net.

Tha Nu helped him fold the net and replace the blanket and pillow. He did not wait to roll up the bed.

"*Upasin* sent me to fetch you," he told the old man. "I'm going back."

He ran back across the wet earth and around the refectory to the back. He climbed the two blocks of tree stumps that served as stairs and wiped his feet perfunctorily on a worn coir doormat. He returned to the dishes. As he sat down he felt that Sein Tint beside him was not working. He glanced towards him and saw in his hands a peeled banana already bitten off at the top.

"What's that?" he asked Sein Tint.

Sein Tint did not reply.

"It's a banana. Where did you get it?"

Sein Tint took another bite.

"Give me a bite, too," he said.

"No," said Sein Tint with his mouth full.

"Come on," said Tha Nu desperately.

"No," said Sein Tint.

"My turn I always share," he said, hurt.

Sein Tint had no reply to that.

Tha Nu looked at the half-eaten banana. In the dim light it looked like a stump of cream with pastry flowering at the base. Sein Tint was beginning to swallow his last bite. There was not much time for argument. Tha Nu's hand darted out, clutched the banana off from its peel and thrust it into his mouth, some of it oozing out between the fingers. Sein Tint made a grab for it but Tha Nu had jumped backwards and was now up and away over the creaking, thumping boards, and swallowing hard. Sein Tint went after him and there was a scuffle against the wall.

"Which boy is that?" They heard the voice of the monk above the sound of struggle and they stopped.

"Which boy is that? Can't you hear me? Come here that boy."

"You go," said Sein Tint.

Tha Nu nodded and as he turned through the door into the main room he saw U Po Din come up the step blocks. He moved reverently towards the monk who was leaning against the doorjamb of his cubicle.

Tha Nu bowed thrice, touching the floor with his forehead. As he bowed he thought of the whack he would receive. Would it be on his knuckles or on his shoulders? He might even be caned. It was true he had not noticed a cane beside the monk, but he could always be asked to fetch one.

"Fetch me the betel box," said the monk.

Tha Nu fetched it and offered it in the prescribed manner, lifting it a little higher and then letting it alight onto the monk's accepting hand.

Now he will ask me to fetch the cane, he thought.

Instead it was, "Has U Po Din come?"

"Yes, your reverend," he replied. So things would be all right this once.

"You may go," the monk said.

Tha Nu bowed thrice and left the room. Released and relieved he went up to U Po Din, who was kindling the fire and said saucily, "You took a long time coming."

Then he went to join Sein Tint at washing the last of the dishes.

"Did you get it?" Sein Tint asked him.

"No," he replied.

Sein Tint took out a dish from the washbasin, let the water drain off, and set it with the others on a low table beside them.

U Po Din's fire flared.

*   *   *   *   *

"Pleasant sensation, mendicant brothers, arises in dependence on contact pleasantly felt, and on the cessation of that pleasantly felt contact the pleasant sensation which arose in dependence on that pleasantly felt contact then ceases and subsides.

"For one thus regarding this with right insight as it really is there are no theories of the past; upon the disappearance of theories of the past there are no theories of the future; upon the disappearance of theories of the future there is no obstinate holding on; upon the disappearance of obstinate holding on, his mind becomes without passion for material form, for sensation, for perception, for composite unity, for consciousness, and having ceased to grasp is liberated from the defilements."

Koyin Thila recited the passage from the Sutras rapidly, his sing-song voice rising and dipping like the flight of a greenfinch. He was lying on his stomach on a mat in his part of the dormitory. The light from the open window which reached down to the raised wooden floor burnished the gold lettering on the black leather-bound volume before him. The volume was open at a section of the second of the Three Baskets of Learning but his eyes were not on the text. He was repeating the passage, running it over again and again, trying to memorize it. The rapidity with which he could recite it now showed that he had become fluent with it and would soon have it by heart. That night, after evening lessons and prayers, he would go over it again, fixing it once and for all in his memory.

It was midday of the cool season and a light breeze slipped in the fragrance of stubble from the paddy-fields and clematis on the monastery fence. The last meal of the day had been eaten an hour ago and for the rest of the day and the night he would partake of no food till the dawn meal at about six. He would take no liquids, except water.

This noon hour was for rest but he had not had any. After the morning meal the abbot had called him to his *kyaung* to dictate a letter to a layman, in the town on the railway, who had sent a gift of cooking oil. But as they had got to the *kyaung* from the refectory building they had found one of the village elders waiting for the abbot. He had come to seek the attendance of the abbot and four other monks three days hence at a feeding of alms-food in commemoration of his wife's death a year ago. This matter had been quickly taken care of but, as always happened, the talk had turned to a fine point of the law and it was another half hour before the elder had gone away satisfied. Fortunately the letter had been dictated, written, sealed, and addressed in another quarter of an hour and had been handed over to the refectory monk for dispatch with a boy to the village headman who would be going up to town next day. At the refectory he had met Koyin Sekkeinda and together they had walked back to the dormitory.

Though ten years had passed, Koyin Thila was still spare and brown and with the same thin face and serious eyes of Tha Nu. His body was lithe and supple but there was no sign in the senior novice of the agitated gestures of the monastery school boy of ten years ago. He walked with a simple grace accentuated by the flowing lines of the robe that dropped from his left shoulder. Youth's rawness shone in his face but at the same time it emphasized the gentleness and calm as of one who has glimpsed the goal and knows that his steps are in the right direction.

Ten years ago a boy had been accepted as a novice in the Order. In lay clothes but with shaved head he had placed a set of robes before the abbot and after making reverence, he had begged of the abbot, in his compassion, to bestow upon him the status of a novice. He had taken refuge in the Buddha, the Dhamma, and the Sangha and had vowed to keep the ten precepts. He had been permitted to don the robes and had been given his new name, Koyin Thila, the novice Thila.

The ten precepts are but a light rein compared to the 277 rules observed by monks, but the donning of the robes and the discarding of the lay name could not change a young boy overnight. Dutifully he had tried to understand the nature of the four articles a novice was permitted to have. That the robes are not to adorn the body but to hide its nakedness, protect it from heat and cold and the scourge of mosquitoes and gnats; that food is not to beautify the body but to keep away fatigue and illness in the practice of the Buddha's teaching; that the monastery is for protection against inclement weather, scorpions, snakes, mosquitoes, and gnats; that medicine is for the eradication of oppressive disease. Thus knowing their nature it had been expected that he would not become attached to them. Accordingly he had not cared much about robes, the monastery and medicine. With food it had been different. When sometimes he had accompanied the monks and older novices to a feast in the village and had met at table a big dish of pork cut up in large chunks and cooked with much oil and many condiments, he had forgotten that food was merely to keep away fatigue and weakness and had felt for it in engrossing fondness.

There were also those nights when a few young novices had got together secretly to share a few pieces saved from the forenoon meal. It had been exhilarating but he had immediately come to realize that this arose more from the furtive joy of breaking the precept of not eating after noon than from a real love of leftovers. Also it had been an act of heroism to display before the monastery boys. A novice who did not transgress that precept was not worthy to be a man. Invariably he had awakened the following morning sick in his conscience and his restlessness had not been allayed till he had confessed to one of the monks. The monk had then given him the ten precepts again and had made him fetch water from the well or sweep the grounds as a penance.

It was U Arseinda, the refectory monk, who had finally taught him detachment from food. U Arseinda had accidentally overheard him praise curry. It had been the day after the annual robe-offering ceremony in the monastery. He had been helping the men from the village count the dishes and stack them up again in the refectory storeroom. He had said: "That chunk of pork I had yesterday, as big as the cap of my knee, with three layers of fat and meat, so rich and so savory. I was so cloyed from the meal I could neither sit nor stand. Oh, can Bagyi Aw cook." Then he realized that U Arseinda had been standing at the door all the time.

And for the next few months whenever U Arseinda or other monks at their table had brought home pork curry from their begging rounds in the village they had sent a saucer of it to Koyin Thila at the novices' table. A good curry like that, sent down from the monks' table, had had to be shared with the other novices. Since what had been sent down had never been much, there had been little left for him after the others had taken a piece each. He had begrudged them their share but at the same time he could not have kept it all to himself. After a few such occasions he had begun not to care much and had been satisfied with just a taste of it. Then one day U Arseinda had sent the dish down again but this time to Koyin Sekkeinda and not to him. Koyin Sekkeinda had had it passed around to him. He had been piqued and had wanted to decline but finally he had taken a piece. He had eaten it slowly with his head full of hot thoughts. Then while chewing the pork which had tasted as good as ever, he had at last seen it for what it was. The pleasant sensation had arisen in dependence on the contact of the pork on tongue pleasantly felt.

After the meal he had gone to U Arseinda and had recounted his thoughts and feelings. The monk had listened to him calmly and had casually said: "Fetch me the betel box." And Koyin Thila had known.

Then there had been the usual texts to study. He had taken with a will to the "Compendium of the subject matter of the Ultradoctrine" which was a summarization of the psychological and logical teachings in the Third Basket of Learning. Its dry, terse categories, analytical enumerations, and mnemonic summaries had somehow appealed to him and he had been fascinated by the exposition of the cognitive process. It was held that however swiftly an act of sense perception may be performed, seventeen moments of consciousness took place in every such act, each moment involving the nascent, static, and dissolving time-phases. Koyin Thila had spent many hours working out the cognitive processes for the eighty-nine possible types of consciousness. He had read and studied and memorized the compendium; so also, the various exegetical literature, commentaries, subcommentaries, expositions, and the Little-Finger Manuals. He had memorized the book of verses called "The Footsteps of the Law," the Book of Relations, and had immersed himself in Kaccayana's Pali grammar and the Great Chronicle of the life of the Buddha.

Generally, he had found life pleasant as a novice though it was not for pleasure that he had chosen to continue in this life. He could have returned to lay life at any time had he wished to. He had only to change into lay-clothes and take again the five precepts that layfolk were expected to observe. But he had preferred this life where, untouched by the sorrows and selfishness, he could concentrate on learning and practices undisturbed.

He had had his crisis at seventeen, and now that he could look back on it he was glad that it had come early. He had fallen in love with a distant cousin. She had accompanied her parents to the monastery on the sabbath of the full and dark of the moon during the lent of that year. She had been introduced to him as a cousin born of a distant maternal aunt a year after him. She had been brown and pretty with a charm that graced only the brown and not the fair. But it had been the serenity in her face and the quiet tone of her voice that had moved him. Here in the calm glances of a girl was the peace he had been seeking. The shock of the thought and the obvious impossibility had aggravated the pain of longing. He had blackened his thoughts with a burn of passion for her. The robes had been to him a cloak of thorns, the monastery precincts a burning cage, and the food a corrosive as it slid down his throat to fester in his maw. Finally he had decided to tell the abbot that he would discard his robes and return to lay life. That night the monastery had been awakened by the sounds of a fire in the village. The next morning as he went round seeking alms-food he learned that the granary of the girl's parents had been consumed by the fire.

He had hurriedly returned to the monastery and had pleaded illness and absence from classes. He had felt responsible for the tragedy and had deemed that this was the retribution for deviating from the true path. He had wanted to atone for it. His thoughts had turned to the austerities exercised by the Buddha in the six years before the Enlightenment. The Holy One had set the teeth, pressed the tongue to the palate and had tried to restrain, crush, and burn out the mind with the mind. The Holy One had taken food only in small amounts, as much as a hollowed palm would hold. The bones of the spine had become like a row of spindles, the ribs had stuck out like the beams of an old shed, the skin of the head had withered like the bitter gourd that has been cracked and withered through wind and sun. Koyin Thila had thought to expiate his sins by the practice of such severe mortifications. But he had remembered that the Buddha had preached against such self-torture that was painful, ignoble, and useless and had said that happiness could come only to those who had extinguished the fires

40

of passion, illusion, pride, and false views. He could do no good by flagellating the body and mind. Also there was no need for penance nor atonement. The past was to be put aside and the future abandoned. His true vocation was to leave behind him both the pleasant and the unpleasant, to cling to nothing, in all ways, to be independent and without attachment. This realization had brought to him a moment of simple and transparent character. In this manner he had moved another step nearer to the final knowledge.

So here now was Koyin Thila, a senior novice, repeating his lessons in the dormitory and breathing in the smell of the afternoon fields. As a gust of breeze threw in a stronger puff of perfume, the koyin stopped and looked at the fields dancing in the haze. The sunlight was bright on the stubble and the heat was gently pressing to get in through the fence of bamboo and clematis. In his mind's eye, the koyin saw a vision of the fields two moons hence in the fairest month of Tabaung. The heat would have got through the fence by then but it would be lost in the mazes of the mango and the pleasances of the jackfruit trees. That was the month when he would depart on a journey from which there would be no return. He would become a *pabbaji*, a departer, a wayfarer, and he would not need to look back again upon the world.

Thinking of his forthcoming journey brought to mind another journey in another time taken by Buddha in such a month to beat the drum of the Law before his father, King Suddhodana of Kapilavatthu. The books say that when Suddhodana heard Buddha was preaching at Rajagaha he sent a courtier with a thousand men to invite him. These arrived while he was preaching and as they listened to the Doctrine they attained arahatship. Arahats are indifferent to worldly things, so they never gave Buddha the message. The king sent another courtier and a thousand men with the same result and so on for nine times. Then he sent Kaludayin, the playmate of Buddha, who promised to bring back Buddha. Though like the rest he entered the Order he waited until the full-moon day of Tabaung. Then Kaludayin, seeing that the time was suitable for traveling, uttered his invitation. Koyin Thila softly repeated the verses from the *Theragatha*.

> "Now crimson glow the trees, dear Lord, and cast
> Their aging foliage in quest of fruit.
> Like crests of flame they shine irradiant,
> And rich in hope, great hero, is the hour.
> Verdure and harvest time in every tree,
> Where'er we look, delightful to the eye,
> And every quarter breathing fragrant airs,
> While leaf is falling, yearning comes for fruit.

41

It is time, O hero, that we departed.
Not over hot, not over cold, but sweet,
O Master, now the season of the year."

In the silence of the pause, the slow beat of the wooden clapper was heard to announce the afternoon classes in the Doctrine. Koyin Thila arose and adjusted his robes. The classes would be on the Visuddhi-Magga, the Path of Purity, taken by the abbot himself; it would not do to be late. He picked up a notebook and pencil and stepped down the dormitory stairs onto the brick path leading to the abbot's *kyaung*. As he walked with unhurried steps he carried in his bearing the unmistakable signs of a scion of the Enlightened One.

The Wog

Khushwant Singh

"WHAT CAN I do for you gentlemen?"

Mr. Sen asked the question without looking up. He pushed the cleaner through the stem of his pipe and twirled it round. As he blew through it, his eye fell on the rose and marigold garlands in the hands of his callers. So they knew that he had been married that morning! He had tried to keep it as quiet as possible. But as he had learned so often before, it was impossible to keep anything a secret for too long in his nosey, native land.

He screwed on the bowl to the stem and blew through the pipe again. Through his lowered eyes, he saw his visitors shuffling their feet and nudging each other. He unwrapped his plastic tobacco pouch and began filling his pipe. After an uneasy minute of subdued whispers, one of the men cleared his throat.

"Well, Mr. Bannerjee, what is your problem?" asked Mr. Sen in a flat monotone.

"Saar," began the Superintendent of the clerical staff, "Whee came to wheesh your good shelph long liphe and happinesh." He beckoned to the Chaprasis: "Garland the Shahib."

The Chaprasis stepped in front with the garlands held aloft. The Sahib stopped them with a wave of his pipe. "*Mez par* — on the table," he commanded in his gentle but firm voice. The Chaprasis' hands came down slowly; their fawning smiles changed to stupid grins. They put the garlands on the table and stepped behind the semi-circle of clerks.

"If that is all," said Mr. Sen standing up, "we can get back to our work. I thank you gentlemen for your good wishes." He bowed slightly to indicate that they should leave. "Bannerjee, will you look in later to discuss the redistribution of work while I am away?"

"Shuttenly Saar."

The men joined the palms of their hands, murmured their "*namastes*" and filed out.

Sen joined his hands across the waist-coat and watched the smoke from his pipe rise in a lazy spiral towards the ceiling. A new chapter in his life had begun. That's how Hindus described marriage — the third of the four stages of life according to the Vedas. It was alarming, he reflected, how his thought processes slipped into cliches and how Hinduism extended its tentacles in practically every sphere of life. His father had not been a particularly orthodox Hindu and had sent him to an Anglo-Indian School where the boys had changed his name from Santosh to Sunny. Thereafter he had gone to Balliel. He had entered the Administrative Service before the Independent Indian Government with its new-fangled nationalist ideas had made Hindi and a vernacular language compulsory. His inability to speak an Indian language hadn't proved a handicap. As a matter of fact, it impressed most Indians. Although his accent and mannerisms made him somewhat of an outsider, it was more than compensated by the fact that it also put him outside the vicious circle of envy and back-biting in which all the others indulged. They sought his company because he was an ub-Indian Indian, because he was a brown British gentleman, because he was what the English contemptuously described as a Wog — a westernised oriental gentleman.

Sen's main contact with his country was his mother. Like an orthodox Hindu widow she shaved her head, only wore a plain white sari and went in bare feet. He was her only child so they both did the best they could for each other. She ran his home. He occasionally ate rice, curried fish and sticky over-sweetened confections she made on special occasions. Other times she had the bearer cook him the lamb chops and the shepherd pies he liked better. She had converted one of the rooms to a temple where she burnt incense and tinkled bells to a diminutive image of the black-faced, red-tongued goddess, Kali. But she never insisted on his joining her in worship. Although he detested Indian movies, he made it a point to take her to one every month. She, at her end, did not object to his taking his evening Scotch and soda or smoking in her presence. She never questioned him about his movements. They got on extremely well till she started talking about his getting married. At first he had laughed it off. She became insistent and started to nag him. She wanted to see him properly settled. She wanted to fondle a grandson just once before she died, she said with tears in her eyes. At last he gave in. He did not have strong views on marriage or on whom he would marry. Since he had come back to settle in India, he could not do worse than marry one of his countrywomen. "Alright Ma, you find me a wife. I'll marry anyone you want me to marry," he said one day.

His mother did not bring up the subject again for many days. She wrote to her brother living at Dehra Doon, in the Himalayan foothills, to come down to Delhi. The two drafted an advertisement for the matrimonial columns and asked for insertions in two successive Sunday editions of the Hindustan Times. It read: "Wanted a fair good looking virgin of a high class respectable family for an Oxford educated Bengali youth of 25 drawing over Rs. 1,000/-p. m. in first class gazetted Government Service. Applicant should be conversant with H. H. affairs. C and D no bar. Correspond with horoscope. P. O. Box No. 4200."

The first insertion brought over fifty letters from parents who enclosed not only the horoscopes of their daughters but their photographs as well to prove that they were fair and therefore good looking. A fortnight later the applications were sorted out and Sunny's mother and uncle triumphantly laid out nearly a hundred photographs on the large dining table. Their virginity and capacity to deal with household affairs had, of necessity, to be taken on trust. But despite the professed indifference to the C and D, the applicants selected for consideration were of the same caste as the Sens and whose fathers had made offers of substantial dowries. Now it was for Sunny to choose.

This was the first time that Sunny had heard of the matrimonial advertisement. He was very angry and acutely embarrassed as some anxious parents had travelled up all the way from Calcutta, bribed the clerks concerned at the newspaper office and called on him at the office. He told his mother firmly that if it did not stop, he would call off the whole thing. But as he had given his word, he would accept anyone chosen for him. His mother and uncle quickly settled the matter by selecting a girl whose father promised the largest dowry and gave a substantial portion of it as earnest money at the betrothal ceremony. The parties took the horoscopes of the affianced couple to a Pandit who consulted the stars and, having had his palm crossed with silver, pronounced the pair ideally suited to each other and the dates that suited the parties to be most auspicious. That was as much as Sunny Sen could take. He told them quite bluntly that he would be married at the Registry or not at all. His mother and uncle sensed his mounting irritation and gave in. The bride's parents made a nominal protest: the cost of a wedding on the traditional pattern which included feasting the bridegroom's party and relations, giving of presents and paying the priests could run into thousands of rupees. The registrar's fee was only Rs .5/-. That was how Srijut Santosh Sen came to marry Kumari Kalyani, the eldest of Srijut Profulla and Srimati Protima Das's five daughters. Mr. Das was, like his son-in-law, a first class gazetted Government servant.

The honeymoon also created difficulties. His mother blushed as if he had said something improper. The Das's were outraged at the suggestion that their daughter should go away for a fortnight unaccompanied by a younger sister. But they resigned their daughter to her fate. Her husband had been brought up as a Sahib and she must follow his ways.

Sen's thoughts were interrupted by his colleague Santa Singh bursting into the room. The Sikh was like the rest of his race, loud and aggressive: "Brother, you think you can run away without giving us a party?" he yelled as he came, "we insist on having a feast to welcome our sister-in-law."

Sen stood up quickly and put his hand across the table to keep the Sikh at an arm's length. Santa Singh ignored the proferred hand, came round the table and enveloped his friend in his arms. He planted his wet and hirsute kisses on the Sahib's cheeks. "Congratulations, brother, when are we to meet our sister-in-law?"

"Soon, very soon," replied Sen extricating himself from the Sikh's embrace and wiping his cheeks. And before the words were out of his mouth, he knew he had blundered: "As soon as we get back from our honeymoon."

"Honeymoon!" exclaimed Santa Singh with a leer; he took Sen's hands in his and squeezed them amorously. "I hope you've had yourself massaged with chamelion oil; puts more punch into things. You should also add crushed almonds in your milk. Above all, don't overdo it. Not more than . . ." There was no stopping the Sikh from giving unsolicited advice on how to approach an inexperienced virgin and the proper use of aphrodisiacs. Sen kept smiling politely without making comment. When he had enough, he interrupted the Sikh's soliloquy by extending his hand. "It was very kind of you to have dropped in. We will call on you and Mrs. Singh as soon as we are back in Delhi."

Santa Singh took Sen's hand without any enthusiasm. "Goodbye. Have a nice time," he blurted and went out. Sen sat down with a sigh of relief. He knew he had not been rude. He had behaved with absolute rectitude — exactly like an English gentleman.

A minute later the Chaprasi raised the thick curtains to let in Mr. Swami, the Director of the Department. Sen again extended his hand across the table to keep the visitor at arm's length: the native's desire to make physical contact galled him. "Good morning, Sir."

The Director touched Sen's hand with his without answering the greeting. His mouth was full of betel saliva. He raised his face to hold it from dribbling out and bawled out to the Chaprasi: "Hey, spitoon *lao*."

The Chaprasi ran in with the vessel which Sen had ordered to be removed from his room and held it under the Director's chin. Mr. Swami spat out the bloody phlegm in the spitoon. Sen opened

46

his table drawer and pretended he was looking for his match box. The Director sat down and lit his *bidi*. "Eh, you Sen, you are a dark harse. By God, a pitch black harse, if I may say so." Mr. Swami fancied his knowledge of English idiom. "So quietly you go and get yourself hitched. My steno says 'Sir, we should celebrate holiday to celebrate Sahib's marriage!' I say, 'What marriage, man?' 'Sir, Mr. Sen got married this morning.' 'By God', I said, 'I must get the truth, the whole truth and nothing but the truth right from the harse's mouth — the dark harse's mouth." The Director stretched his hand across the table. "Clever guy you eh?" he said with a smirk. Sen touched his boss's hand with the tip of his fingers. "Thank you, Sir."

"What for thank you? And you come to the office on the day you get married. Heavens won't fall if you stay away a few days. I as your boss order you to go back home to your wife. I will put in a demi-official memo. What do you say?"

The Director was pleased with himself and extended his hand. Sen acknowledged his boss's wit by taking his hand. "Thank you, Sir. I think I will go home."

"My God, you are a Sahib! I hope your wife is not a Mem Sahib. That would be too much of a joke."

The Director left but his betel-stained smirk lingered on like the smile of the Cheshire Cat and his last remark began to go round and round in Sen's head with an insistent rhythmic beat. "I hope your wife isn't a Mem Sahib, not a Mem Sahib, not a Mem Sahib. I hope your wife is not a Mem Sahib."

Would his wife be a Mem Sahib, he mused as he drove back home for lunch. It was not very likely. She claimed to be an M. A. in English literature. But he had met so many of his countrymen with long strings of firsts who could barely speak the English language correctly. To start with, there was the Director himself with his "okey dokes" and "by gums" who, like other South Indians, pronounced eight as yate, an egg as a yugg, and who always stumbled on words beginning with an 'M'. He smiled to himself as he recalled the Director instructing his private secretary to get Mr. M. M. Amir, Member of Parliament, on the phone. "I want Yum Yum Yumeer Yumpee." The Bengalis had their own execrable accent: they added an airy 'h' whenever they could after a 'b' or a 'W' or an 's'. A virgin sounded like some exotic tropical plant, "the Vharjeen," "will" as a wheel, and the simple simple as a "shimple."

*   *   *   *   *

There was much crying at the farewell and the bride continued to sniffle for a long time afterwards in the car. She had drawn her

47

sari over her forehead down to her eyes and covered the rest of her face with a silk handkerchief into which she blew her nose. When Sen lit his pipe, she firmly clamped the handkerchief on her nostrils. "Does the smoke bother you?" was the first sentence he spoke to his wife. She replied by a vigorous shake of the head.

They stopped at a mango orchard by the roadside to have lunch. His mother had made two separate packets with their names in Bengali pinned on them. The one marked "Sunny" had roasted chicken and cheese sandwiches. The other contained boiled rice and pickles in a small brass cup with curried lentils. His wife poured the lentils on the rice and began to eat with her fingers.

They ate without speaking to each other. Within a few minutes they had an audience of anxious passers-by and children from a neighbouring village. Some sat on their haunches; others just stood gaping at the couple or commenting on their being newly married. Sen knew how to deal with the rustic. "Are you people hungry?" he asked sarcastically.

The men turned away sheepishly; but the urchins did not budge. "Bugger off, you dirty bastards," roared Sen raising his hand as if to strike. The children ran away to a safe distance and began to yell back at Sen, mimicking his English. "Buggeroff, Buggeroff," they cried. "*Arey* he is a Sahib, a big Sahib."

Sen ignored them and spoke politely to his wife. "Pardon the language," he said with a smile. "Would you like to sample one of my sandwiches? I don't know whether you eat meat; take the lettuce and cheese; it is fresh cheddar."

Mrs. Sen took the sandwich with her curry-stained fingers. She tore a strip off the toast as if it were a *Chappati,* scooped up a mixture of rice, curry and cheddar and put it in her mouth. She took one bite and stopped munching. Through her thick glasses she stared at her husband as if he had given her poison. She turned pale and being unable to control herself any further, spat out the food in her mouth. She turned her face the other way and brought up the rice and curry.

"I am dreadfully sorry," stammered Sen. "The cheddar upset you. I should have known."

Mrs. Sen wiped her mouth with the end of her sari and asked for water. She rinsed her mouth and splashed it on her face. The lunch was ruined. "We better be on our way," said Sen, standing up. "That is if you feel better."

She tied up her brass cup in a duster and followed him to the car. They were on the road again. She fished out a silver box from her handbag and took out a couple of betel leaves. She smeared one with lime and catechu paste, put in cardamom and sliced betel nuts, rolled it up and held it out for her husband.

"I'm afraid I don't touch the stuff," he said apologetically. "I'll stick to my pipe if you don't mind." Mrs. Sen did not mind. She slipped the leaf in her own mouth and began to chew contentedly.

They got to the rest-house in good time. The rest-house bearer took in the luggage and spread the bedding rolls. He asked Mrs. Sen what they would like for dinner. She referred him to her husband. "Just anything for me," he replied, "omelette or anything. Ask the Mem Sahib what she would like for herself. I will take a short walk before dinner."

"Don't go too far Sahib," continued the bearer. "This is wild country. There is a footpath down to the river which the Sahibs who come to fish take. It is quite safe."

Sen went into the bedroom to ask his wife if she would like to come out for a walk. She was unpacking her things. He changed his mind. "I'll go for a short stroll towards the river. Get the bearer to put out the Scotch and soda in the verandah; there's a bottle in my suitcase. We'll have a drink before dinner."

His wife nodded her head.

The well-beaten fishermen's footpath snaked its way through a dense foliage of *sal* and flame of the forest, ending abruptly on the pebbly bank of the river. The Ganges was a magnificent sight; a broad and swift-moving current of clear, icy-blue water sparkling in the bright sun. It must have been from places like where he stood, he thought, that the sages of olden times had pronounced the Ganges the holiest of all the rivers in the world. He felt a sense of kinship with his Aryan ancestors, who worshipped the beautiful in nature, sang hymns to the rising sun, raised goblets of fermented soma juice to the full moon and who ate beef and were lusty with full-bosomed and large-hipped women. Much water had flowed down the Ganges since then and Hinduism was now like the river itself at its lower reaches — as at Calcutta where he was born. At Calcutta it was a sluggish expanse of slime and sludge carrying the excrement of millions of pilgrims who polluted it at Hardwar, Benares, Allahabad, Patna and other "holy" cities on its banks, and who fouled its water by strewing charred corpses for the fish and the turtles to eat. It had become the Hinduism of the Cow-protectors, prohibitionists — and chewers of betel leaves. That must be it, he thought cheerfully. His was the pristine Hinduism of the stream that sparkled before him; that of the majority, of the river after it had been sullied by centuries of narrow prejudices. He walked over the pebbled bank, took up a palmful of the icy-cold water and splashed it on his face.

The shadows of the jungle lengthened across the stream and the cicadas began to call. Sen turned back and quickly retraced his steps to the bungalow. The sun was setting. It was time for a sundowner.

Tumblers and soda were laid out on the table in the verandah. The bearer heard his footsteps and came with a bunch of keys in his open hand. "I did not like to open the Sahib's trunk," he explained. "Please take out the whiskey."

"Why didn't you ask the Mem Sahib to take it out?"

The bearer looked down at his feet. "She said she could not touch a bottle of alcohol. She gave me the keys but I don't like to meddle with the Sahib's luggage. If things are misplaced . . ."

"That's alright. Open my suitcase. The bottles of whiskey and brandy are right on the top. And serve the dinner as soon as the Mem Sahib is ready."

It was no point asking his wife to sit with him. He poured himself a large Scotch and lit his pipe. Once more his thoughts turned to the strange course his life had taken. If he had married one of the English girls he had met in his University days how different things would have been. They would have kissed a hundred times between the wedding and the wedding night; they would have walked hand in hand through the forest and made love beside the river; they would have lain in each other's arms and sipped their Scotch. They would have nibbled at knick-knacks in between bouts of love; and they would have made love till the early hours of the morning. The whiskey warmed his blood and quickened his imagination. He was back in England. The gathering bloom and the dark, tropical forest, accentuated the feeling of loneliness. He felt an utter stranger in his own country. He did not hear the bearer announcing that dinner had been served. Now his wife came out and asked in her quaint Bengali accent, "Do you want to shit outside?"

"What?" he asked gruffly, waking up from his reverie.

"Do you want to shit inshide or outshide. The deener ees on the table."

"Oh, I'll be right in. You go ahead. I'll join you in a second." Good lord! What would his English friends have said if she had invited them in this manner! The invitation to defecate was Mrs. Sen's first communication with her husband.

A strong sweet smell of coconut oil and roses assailed Sen's nostrils as he entered the dining room. His wife had washed and oiled her hair; it hung in loose snaky coils below her waist. The parting was daubed with bright vermillion powder to indicate her status as a married woman. He had no doubt that she had smeared her body with the attar of roses as her mother had probably instructed. She sat patiently at the table; being a Hindu woman, she could not very well start eating before her husband.

"Sorry to keep you waiting. You should have started. Your dinner must be cold."

She simply wagged her head.

They began to eat; he, his omelette and buttered slice of bread with his fork and knife. She, her rice and lentil curry mushed in between her fingers and palm of her right hand. Sen cleared his throat many times to start a conversation. But each time the vacant and bewildered look behind the thick lenses of his wife's glasses made him feel that words would fail to convey their meaning. If his friends knew they would certainly have a big laugh. "Oh Sunny Sen! How could he start talking to his wife? He hadn't been properly introduced. Don't you know he is an Englishman?"

The dinner was eaten in silence. Kalyani Sen emitted a soft belch and took out her betel-leaf case. She rolled a leaf, paused for a split-second and put it in her mouth. Sunny had promised himself the luxury of expensive Havana cigars over his honeymoon. He took one out of its phallic metal case, punctured its bottom with a gold clipper and lit it. The aromatic smoke soon filled the dining room. This time his wife did not draw the fold of her sari across her face; she simply clasped her hands in front of her mouth and discreetly blocked her nostrils with the back of her hands.

They sat in silence facing each other across the table; she chewing her leaf — almost like a cow chewing the cud, thought Sen. He, lost in the smoke of his long Cuban cigar. It was oppressive — and the barrier between them, impassable. Sen glanced at his watch and stood up. "News," he exclaimed loudly. "Mustn't miss the news." He went into the bedroom to fetch his transistor radio set.

Two beds had been laid side by side with no space between them; the pillows almost hugged each other. The sheets had been sprinkled with the earthy perfume of *khas* fibre and looked as if they also awaited the consummation of the marriage performed earlier in the day. How, thought Sen, could she think of this sort of thing when (they hadn't even been introduced! No, hell) barely a civil word had passed between them? He quickly took out his radio set and hurried back to the dining room.

He tuned in to Delhi. While he listened in to the news, the bearer cleared the table and left salaaming "Good night, Sir." Mrs. Sen got up, collected her betel-leaf case and disappeared into the bedroom.

The fifteen minutes of news was followed by a commentary on sports. Sen had never bothered to listen in to it. He was glad he did because the commentary was followed by the announcement of a change in the programme. A concert of vocal Hindustani music by Ustad Badey Ghulam Ali Khan had been put off to relay a performance by the Czech Philharmonic Orchestra from New Delhi. Ghulam Ali Khan was the biggest name in Indian music and even the Anglicized natives had to pretend that they admired the cacophony of gargling sounds he produced from the pit of his stomach. Members of the diplomatic corps were known to sit through four hours of the maestro's performances lest they offend their Indian hosts or be found less cultured than staffs of rival embassies. The Czech Philharmonic had come to India for the first time and the wogs who ran Delhi's European Music Society had got away with it. Pity, thought Sen, he wasn't in town; he could have invited the right people for dinner (tails, of course!) followed by the concert. How would his wife have fitted in a party of this sort?

The sound of applause came over the air, followed by an announcement that the opening piece was a selection from Smetana's The Bartered Bride. Sen was transported back to the glorious evening at Covent Garden and the Festival Hall. Smetana was followed by Bartok. The only thing that broke the enchantment was the applause between the movements. How could one expect the poor, benighted natives to know that the end of a movement was not the end of the symphony!

There was an interval of ten minutes. The last piece was Sen's favourite — Dvorak's Symphony No. 5 in E minor. He poured himself a liquor brandy (V.S.O.P.), drew a chair and stretched his legs on it. He had never heard Dvorak as well performed even in Europe. A Cuban cigar, an excellent Cognac and the world's greatest music, what more could one ask for! He gently decapitated the cigar of its ashy ahead, lay back in the arm chair and closed his eyes in complete rapture. By the final movement he was fast asleep with the cigar slowly burning itself out between his lips.

Neither the applause, at the end of the concert, nor the silence and the cackling of the radio woke Sen from his slumber. When the cigar got too hot, he opened his mouth and let it drop on his lap. It slowly burnt through his trouser and then singed the hair on his under-belly. He woke with a start and threw the butt on the ground.

Although the cigar had only burnt a tiny hole near a fly button, the room was full of the smell of burning cloth. That was a narrow escape, thought Sen. He switched off the transistor and glanced at his watch. It was well after midnight. He blew out the oil lamp and went to the bedroom.

An oil lamp still burned on the table. His wife had fallen asleep — obviously after having waited for him. She had not changed nor taken off her jewellery. She had put mascara in her eyes. Her tears had washed some of it on to her cheeks and the pillow had a smudge of soot.

Sen changed into his pajamas and slipped into his bed. He stared at his wife's gently heaving bosom and her open mouth. How could he? In any case, he didn't have the slightest desire. He turned the knob on the lamp. The yellow flame turned to a blue fluting on the edge of the wick, spluttered twice, then gave up the struggle and plunged the room into a black solitude.

The bearer came in with the tea-tray and woke him up. "Sahib, it is after nine. Mem Sahib has been up for the last four or five hours. She has had her bath, said her prayer and has been waiting for you to get up to have her *chota hazri.*"

Sen rubbed his eyes. The sun was streaming through the verandah into the room. His wife had made a swiss roll of her bedding and put it away on the top of her steel trunk. "I'll have my tea in the verandah," he replied getting up. He went into the bedroom, splashed cold water on his face and went out.

"Sorry to keep you waiting; I seem to do it all the time. You should really never wait for me." He stretched himself and yawned. "I am always ... what on earth."

His wife had got up and while his face was still lifted towards the ceiling, bent down to touch his feet. He was her husband, lord and master. He looked down in alarm. She looked up, tears streamed down both her cheeks. "I am unworthy," she said half-questioning and half-stating her fears. And before he could reply, she drew the flap of her sari across her eyes and fled inside.

"What the hell is all this?" muttered Sen and collapsed into an armchair. He knew precisely what she meant. He sat a long while scratching his head with his eyes fixed in a hypnotic stare on the sunlit lawn. He had no desire to go in and make up to his wife.

The bearer came, looked accusingly at the untouched tray of tea and announced that breakfast was on the table. Sen got up reluctantly. She would obviously not have anything to eat unless he cajoled her. And he was damned if he was going to do it. Again he was wrong. She was at the table. He avoided looking at her.

"Tea?" he questioned and filled her cup and then his own. Once again they ate their different foods in their different ways without saying a word to each other. And as soon as the meal was over, she went to her betel leaves and he to his pipe. She retired to her bedroom. He took his transistor and returned to the verandah to listen in to the morning news.

The arrival of the postman at noon put the idea in his head. It was only a copy of the office memorandum sanctioning him leave for a fortnight. He walked in waving the yellow envelope bearing the legend — "On India Government Service Only."

"I am afraid we have to return at once. It's an urgent letter from the Minister. He has to answer some questions in Parliament dealing with our department. I'll get the bearer to help you pack while I give the car a check up. Bearer, bearer," he yelled as he walked out.

Half an hour later they were on the road to Delhi; a little before sunset, Sen drove into his portico. The son and mother embraced each other and only broke apart when the bride knelt down to touch her mother-in-law's feet. "God bless you my child," said the older woman touching the girl on the shoulder, "but what . . .".

Her son pulled out the yellow envelope from his pocket and waved it triumphantly. "An urgent summons from the Minister. These chaps don't respect anyone's private life. I simply had to come."

"Of course," replied his mother, wiping off a tear. She turned to her daughter-in-law. "Your parents will be delighted to know you are back. Why don't you ring them up?" A few minutes later Mrs. Sen's parents drove up in a taxi. There were more tears at the reunion, more explanations about the letter from the Minister. There was also relief. Now that the bride had spent a night with her husband and consummated the marriage, she could return to her parental home for a few days.

Sen spent the next morning going round the local bookshops and coffee houses. The week-end followed. On Sunday morning, when his mother was at prayer, he rang up the Director at his home to explain his return and ask for permission to resume work. "My mother has been keeping indifferent health and I did not want to leave her alone for too long." He knew this line of approach would win both sympathy and approval. The Director expressed concern and spoke warmly of a Hindu son's sacred duty towards his widowed mother. "And we must celebrate your wedding and meet your wife . . . as soon as your mother is better."

"Yes, Sir. As soon as she is up to the mark, we will invite you over."

The mother being 'a bit under the weather' and 'not quite up to the mark' became Sen's explanation for cancelling his leave and not having a party. It even silenced Santa Singh who had planned a lot of ribaldry at Sen's expense.

Days went by — and then weeks. Kalyani came over with her mother a couple of times to fetch her things. She came when her husband was in the office and only met her mother-in-law. It was conveyed to Sunny Sen that, under the circumstances, it was for the husband to go and fetch his wife from her home. Sen put off doing so for some time — and then had to go away on a tour of inspection to Southern India. It was a fortnight after his return that his parents-in-law learnt that he was back in town. The relations between the two families became very strained. Nothing was said directly but talk about the Sens being dowry seekers and Sen's mother being a difficult woman started going round. Then Sunny got a letter from his father-in-law. It was polite but distinctly cold. From the contents it was obvious that it had been drafted and written on the advice of a lawyer with a carbon copy made for use if necessary. It referred to the advertisement in the matrimonial columns and the negotiations preceding the marriage, the money given on betrothal and in the dowry, the wedding and its consummation in the forest rest house on the Ganges. Sen was asked to state his intentions.

For the first time, Sen realised how serious the situation had become. He turned to his mother. A new bond was forged between the mother and son. "It is a matter of great shame," she said firmly. "We must not let this business go too far. You must fetch her. I will go away to my brother at Dehra Doon for a few days."

"No, Ma, I will not have anyone making insinuations against you," he replied, and pleaded "in any case you must not leave me."

"No one has made any insinuations and I am not leaving you. This will always be my home; where else can I live except with my own flesh and blood. But you must get your wife. Let her take over the running of the house and become its mistress as is her right. Then I will come back and live without worrying my head with servants and cooking and shopping."

Sen flopped back in his chair like one exhausted. His mother came over behind him and took his head between her hands. "Don't let it worry you too much. I will write to my brother to come over to fetch me. He will go to your father-in-law's and bring over your wife. Before we leave, I will show her everything, give her the keys and tell the servants to take orders from her. When you come back from the office you will find everything running smoothly." She kissed her son's hair. "And do be nice to her, she is only a child. You know how much I am looking forward to having a grandson to fondle in my lap!"

Sen found the whole thing very distasteful. He felt angry with himself for allowing things to come to such a pass. And he felt angrier with his wife for humiliating his mother and driving her out of her home. He would have nothing to do with her unless she accepted his mother. He instructed his cook-bearer about the arrangements of the bedrooms. If the new mistress asked any questions, he was to say that those were his master's orders.

On Monday morning, when the bearer brought him his morning tea, he told him not to expect him for lunch and to tell his wife not to wait for him for dinner as he might be working late in the office. He had breakfast with his mother and uncle. He promised to write to his mother everyday to tell her how things were going. "You must try and understand her point of view," admonished his mother. "She has been brought up in a different world. But love and patience conquers all."

Sen was the last to leave his office. He drove straight to the Gymkhana Club. For an hour he sat by the bathing pool, drinking ice-cold lager and watching the bathers. There were European women from the diplomatic corps with their children; there were pretty Punjabi girls in their pony tails and bikinis; there were swarthy young college students showing off their Tarzan-like torsos as they leapt from the diving board. This surely was where he belonged — where the east and the west met in a sort of minestrone soup of human limbs of many pigments, black, brown, pink and white. Why couldn't he have married one of these girls, taught her proper English instead of the Americanised chi-chi which they thought was smart talk.

The bathers went home. Sen got up with a sigh and went to the bar. He was greeted by several old friends. "Hi, Sunny, you old bastard. What's this one hears about you?"

Sunny smiled. "I don't have to proclaim everything I do from the house tops, do I?"

"Like hell you do. You stand drinks all round or we'll de-bag you and throw you out in front of all the women." Three of them advanced towards him.

"Lay off chaps. Bearer give these B. Fs. what they want. What's the poison?"

They sat on the high stools and downed their drinks with "Cheers," "here's mud in your eye" and "bottoms up."

"Where's your wife?" asked one. "Don't tell me you are going to keep her in the seclusion of the *purdah* like a native!"

"No ruddy fears," answered Sen. "She's gone to her mother's. Would you chaps like another?"

One round followed another till it was time for the bar to close. One of the men invited him home for dinner. Sen accepted without a murmur.

It was almost 1 a.m. when Sen drove back into his house. He was well fortified with Scotch to gloss over any awkwardness. He switched on the light in the hall and saw trunks piled up against the wall. His wife had obviously come back. There was no light in her bedroom. She must have gone to sleep many hours earlier. He

56

switched off the half-light, tip-toed to his bedroom, switched on the table-lamp, went back and bolted the door from the inside. A few minutes later, he was fast asleep.

The bearer's persistent knocking woke him up. His head rocked as he got up to unfasten the bolt. What would the bearer think of the Sahib bolting his door against his wife? He couldn't care less. The throbbing in his head demanded all his attention.

"Shall I take tea for the Mem Sahib?" he asked.

"She does not have bed-tea," replied Sen. "Isn't she up yet?"

"I don't know Sahib; she has also bolted her door from the inside."

Sen felt uneasy. He swallowed a couple of aspirins and gulped down a cup of strong tea. He lay back on his pillow to let the aspirins take effect. His imagination began to run away with him. She couldn't. No, of course not! Must have waited for him till midnight, was scared of being alone and must have bolted the doors and was sleeping late. But he had been nasty to her and she might be over-sensitive. He decided to rid himself of the thought. He got up and knocked at the door. There was no response. He went to the bathroom and then tried her door again. There was no sound from the inside. He went to the window and pressed it with both his hands. The two sides flew apart and crashed against the wall. Even that noise did not waken her. He peered in and caught the gleam of her glasses on her nose.

With a loud cry Sen ran back into the house and called for the bearer. The master and servant put their shoulders to the door and battered against it. The bolt gave way and they burst in the room. The woman on the bed didn't stir. A white fluid trickled from her gaping mouth to the pillow. Her eyes stared fixedly through the thick glasses. Sen put his hand on her forehead. It was the first time he had touched his wife. And she was dead.

On the table beside her bed was an empty tumbler and two envelopes. One bore her mother's name in Bengali; the other was for him. A haunted smile came on his lips as he read the English address:

"To
    Mr. S. Sen, Esq."

Three Million Yen

Mishima Yukio

"WE'RE TO MEET her at nine?" asked Kenzo.

"At nine, she said, in the toy department on the ground floor," replied Kiyoko. "But it's too noisy to talk there, and I told her about the coffee shop on the third floor instead."

"That was a good idea."

The young husband and wife looked up at the neon pagoda atop the New World Building, which they were approaching from the rear.

It was a cloudy, muggy night, of a sort common in the early-summer rainy season. Neon lights painted the low sky in rich colors. The delicate pagoda, flashing on and off in the softer of neon tones, was very beautiful indeed. It was particularly beautiful when, after all the flashing neon tubes had gone out together, they suddenly flashed on again, so soon that the after-image had scarcely disappeared. To be seen from all over Asakusa, the pagoda had replaced Gourd Pond, now filled in, as the main landmark of the Asakusa night.

To Kenzo and Kiyoko the pagoda seemed to encompass in all its purity some grand, inaccessible dream of life. Leaning against the rail of the parking lot, they looked absently up at it for a time.

Kenzo was in an undershirt, cheap trousers, and wooden clogs. His skin was fair but the lines of the shoulders and chest were powerful, and bushes of black hair showed between the mounds of muscle at the armpits. Kiyoko, in a sleeveless dress, always had her own armpits carefully shaved. Kenzo was very fussy. Because they hurt when the hair began to grow again, she had become almost obsessive about keeping them shaved, and there was a faint flush on the white skin.

She had a round little face, the pretty features as though woven of cloth. It reminded one of some earnest, unsmiling little animal. It was a face which a person trusted immediately, but not one on which to read thoughts. On her arm she had a large pink plastic handbag and Kenzo's pale blue sports shirt. Kenzo liked to be empty-handed.

From her modest coiffure and make-up one sensed the frugality of their life. Her eyes were clear and had no time for other men.

58

They crossed the dark road in front of the parking lot and went into the New World. The big market on the ground floor was filled with myriad-colored mountains of splendid, gleaming, cheap wares, and salesgirls peeped from crevices in the mountains. Cool fluorescent lighting poured over the scene. Behind a grove of antimony models of the Tokyo Tower was a row of mirrors painted with Tokyo scenes, and in them, as the two passed, were rippling, waving images of the mountain of ties and summer shirts opposite.

"I couldn't stand living in a place with so many mirrors," said Kiyoko. "I'd be embarrassed."

"Nothing to be embarrassed about." Though his manner was gruff, Kenzo was not one to ignore what his wife said, and his answers were generally perceptive. The two had come to the toy department.

"She knows how you love the toy department. That's why she said to meet her here."

Kenzo laughed. He was fond of the trains and automobiles and space missiles, and he always embarrassed Kiyoko, getting an explanation for each one and trying each one out, but never buying. She took his arm and steered him some distance from the counter.

"It's easy to see that you want a boy. Look at the toys you pick."

"I don't care whether it's a boy or a girl. I just wish it would come soon."

"Another two years, that's all."

"Everything according to plan."

They had divided the savings account they were so assiduously building up into several parts, labeled Plan X and Plan Y and Plan Z and the like. Children must come strictly according to plan. However much they might want a child now, it would have to wait until sufficient money for Plan X had accumulated. Seeing the inadvisability, for numerous reasons, of installment buying, they waited until the money for Plan A or Plan B or Plan C had accumulated, and then paid cash for an electric washing machine or refrigerator or a television set. Plan A and Plan B had already been carried out. Plan D required little money, but since it had as its object a low-priority clothes-cupboard it was always being pushed back. Neither of them was much interested in clothes. What they had they could hang in the closet, and all they really needed was enough to keep them warm in the winter.

They were very cautious when making a large purchase. They collected catalogues and looked at various possibilities and asked the advice of people who had already made the purchase, and, when the time for buying finally came, went off to a wholesaler in Okachimachi.

A child was still more serious. First there had to be a secure livelihood and enough money, more than enough money, to see that the child had surroundings of which a parent need not be ashamed of, if not, perhaps, enough to see it all the way to adulthood. Kenzo had already made thorough inquiries with friends who had children, and knew what expenditures for powdered milk need not be considered out of the question.

With their own plans so nicely formed, the two had nothing but contempt for the thoughtless, floundering ways of the poor. Children were to be produced according to plan in surroundings ideal for rearing them, and the best days were waiting after a child had arrived. Yet they were sensible enough not to pursue their dreams too far. They kept their eyes on the light immediately before them.

There was nothing that enraged Kenzo more than the view of the young that life in contemporary Japan was without hope. He was not a person given to deep thinking, but he had an almost religious faith that if a man respected nature and was obedient to it, and if he but made an effort for himself, the way would somehow open. The first thing was reverence for nature, founded on connubial affection. The greatest antidote for despair was the faith of a man and woman in each other.

Fortunately, he was in love with Kiyoko. To face the future hopefully, therefore, he had only to follow the conditions laid down by nature. Now and then some other woman made a motion in his direction, but he sensed something unnatural in pleasure for the sake of pleasure. It was better to listen to Kiyoko complaining about the dreadful price these days of vegetables and fish.

The two had made a round of the market and were back at the toy department.

Kenzo's eyes were riveted to the toy before him, a station for flying saucers. On the sheet-metal base the complicated mechanism was painted as if viewed through a window, and a revolving light flashed on and off inside the control tower. The flying saucer, of deep-blue plastic, worked on the old principle of the flying top. The station was apparently suspended in space, for the background of the metal base was covered with stars and clouds, among the former the familiar rings of Saturn.

The bright stars of the summer night were splendid. The painted metal surface was indescribably cool, and it was as if all the discomfort of the muggy night would go if a person but gave himself up to that sky.

Before Kiyoko could stop him, Kenzo had resolutely snapped a spring at one corner of the station.

The saucer went spinning toward the ceiling.

The salesgirl reached out and gave a little cry.

The saucer described a gentle arc toward the pastry counter across the aisle and settled square on the million-yen crackers.

"We're in!" Kenzo ran over to it.

"What do you mean, we're in?" Embarrassed, Kiyoko turned quickly away from the salesgirl and started after him.

"Look. Look where it landed. This means good luck. Not a doubt about it."

The oblong crackers were in the shape of decidedly large banknotes, and the baked-in design, again like a banknote, carried the words "One Million Yen." On the printed label of the cellophane wrapper, the figure of a bald shopkeeper took the place of Prince Shotoku, who decorates most banknotes. There were three large crackers in each package.

Over the objections of Kiyoko, who thought fifty yen for three crackers ridiculous, Kenzo bought a package to make doubly sure of the good luck. He immediately broke the wrapping, gave a cracker to Kiyoko, and took one himself. The third went into her handbag.

As his strong teeth bit into the cracker, a sweet, slightly bitter taste flowed into his mouth. Kiyoko took a little mouse-like bite from her own cracker, almost too large for her grasp.

Kenzo brought the flying saucer back to the toy counter. The salesgirl, out of sorts, looked away as she reached to take it.

Kiyoko had high, arched breasts, and, though she was small, her figure was good. When she walked with Kenzo she seemed to be hiding in his shadow. At street crossings, he would take her arm firmly, look to the right and the left, and help her across, pleased at the feel of the rich flesh.

Kenzo liked the pliant strength in a woman who, although she could perfectly well do things for herself, always deferred to her husband. Kiyoko had never read a newspaper, but she had an astonishingly accurate knowledge of her surroundings. When she took a comb in her hand or turned over the leaf of a calendar or folded a summer kimono, it was not as if she were engaged in housework, but rather as if, fresh and alert, she were keeping company with the "things" known as comb and calendar and kimono. She soaked in her world of things as she might soak in a bath.

"There's an indoor amusement park on the fourth floor. We can kill time there," said Kenzo. Kiyoko followed silently into a waiting elevator, but when they reached the fourth floor she tugged at his belt.

"It's a waste of money. Everything seems so cheap, but it's all arranged so that you spend more money than you intend to."

"That's no way to talk. This is our good night, and if you tell yourself it's like a first-run movie it doesn't seem so expensive."

61

"What's the sense in a first-run movie? If you wait a little while you can see it for half as much."

Her earnestness was most engaging. A brown smudge from the cracker clung to her puckered lips.

"Wipe your mouth," said Kenzo. "You're making a mess of yourself."

Kiyoko looked into a mirror on a near-by pillar and removed the smear with the nail of her little finger. She still had two-thirds of a cracker in her hand.

They were at the entrance to "Twenty Thousand Leagues Under the Sea." Jagged rocks reached to the ceiling, and the porthole of a submarine on the sea floor served as the ticket window: forty yen for adults, twenty yen for children.

"But forty yen is too high," said Kiyoko, turning away from the mirror. "You aren't any less hungry after you look at all those cardboard fish, and for forty yen you can get a hundred grams of the best kind of real fish."

"Yesterday they wanted forty for a cut of black snapper. Oh, well. When you're chewing on a million yen you don't talk like a beggar."

The brief debate finished, Kenzo bought the tickets.

"But it isn't bad at all. Just right when you're hungry."

"You've let that cracker go to your head."

"You just ate."

At a landing like a railway platform five or six little box cars, each large enough for two people, stood at intervals along a track. Three or four other couples were waiting, but the two climbed unabashedly into a car. It was in fact a little tight for two, and Kenzo had to put his arm around his wife's shoulders.

The operator was whistling somewhat disdainfully. Kenzo's powerful arm, on which the sweat had dried, was solid against Kiyoko's naked shoulders and back. Naked skin clung to naked skin like the layers of some intricately folded insect's wing. The car began to shake.

"I'm afraid," said Kiyoko, with the expression of one not in the least afraid.

The cars, each some distance from the rest, plunged into a dark tunnel of rock. Immediately inside there was a sharp curve, and the reverberations were deafening.

A huge shark with shining green scales passed, almost brushing their heads, and Kiyoko ducked away. As she clung to her young husband he gave her a kiss. After the shark had passed the car ground around a curve in pitch darkness again, but his lips landed unerringly on hers, little fish speared in the dark. The little fish jumped and were still.

62

The darkness made Kiyoko strangely shy. Only the violent shaking and grinding sustained her. As she slipped deep into the tunnel, her husband's arms around her, she felt naked and flushed crimson. The darkness, dense and impenetrable, had a strength that seemed to render clothes useless. She thought of a dark shed she had secretly played in as a child.

Like a flower springing from the darkness, a red beam of light flashed at them, and Kiyoko cried out once more. It was the wide, gaping mouth of a big angler fish on the ocean floor. Around it, coral fought with the poisonous dark green of seaweed.

Kenzo put his cheek to his wife's — she was still clinging to him — and with the fingers of the arm around her shoulders played with her hair. Compared to the motion of the car the motion of the fingers was slow and deliberate. She knew that he was enjoying the show and enjoying her fright at it as well.

"Will it be over soon? I'm afraid." But her voice was drowned out in the roar.

Once again they were in darkness. Though frightened, Kiyoko had her store of courage. Kenzo's arms were around her, and there was no fright and no shame she could not bear. Because hope had never left them, the state of happiness was for the two of them just such a state of tension.

A big, muddy octopus appeared before them. Once again Kiyoko cried out. Kenzo promptly kissed the nape of her neck. The great tentacles of the octopus filled the cave, and a fierce lightning darted from its eyes.

At the next curve a drowned corpse was standing disconsolately in a seaweed forest.

Finally the light at the far end began to show, the car slowed down, and they were liberated from the unpleasant noise. At the bright platform the uniformed attendant waited to catch the forward handle of the car.

"Is that all?" asked Kenzo.

The man said that it was.

Arching her back, Kiyoko climbed to the platform and whispered in Kenzo's ear: "It makes you feel like a fool, paying forty yen for that."

At the door they compared their crackers. Kiyoko had more than two-thirds left, and Kenzo more than half.

"Just as big as when we came in," said Kenzo. "It was so full of thrills that we didn't have time to eat."

"If you think about it that way it doesn't seem so bad after all."

Kenzo's eyes were already on the gaudy sign by another door. Electric decorations danced around the word "Magicland," and green and red lights flashed on and off in the startled eyes of a cluster of dwarfs, their domino costumes shining in gold and silver dust. A bit shy about suggesting immediately that they go in, Kenzo leaned against the wall and munched away at his cracker.

"Remember how we crossed the parking lot? The light brought out our shadows on the ground, maybe two feet apart, and a funny idea came to me. I thought to myself how it would be if a little boy's shadow bobbed up and we took it by the hand. And just then a shadow really did break away from ours and come between them."

"No!"

"Then I looked around, and it was someone behind us. A couple of drivers were playing catch, and one of them had dropped the ball and run after it."

"One of these days we really will be out walking, three of us."

"And we'll bring it here." Kenzo motioned toward the sign. "And so we ought to go in and have a look at it first."

Kiyoko said nothing this time as he started for the ticket window.

Possibly because it was a bad time of the day, Magicland was not popular. On both sides of the path as they entered there were flashing banks of artificial flowers. A music box was playing.

"When we build our house, this is the way we'll have the path."

"But it's in very bad taste," objected Kiyoko.

How would it feel to go into a house of your own? A building fund had not yet appeared in the plans of the two, but in due course it would. Things they scarcely dreamed of would one day appear in the most natural way imaginable. Usually so prudent, they let their dreams run on this evening, perhaps, as Kiyoko said, because the million-yen crackers had gone to their heads.

Great artificial butterflies were taking honey from the artificial flowers. Some were as big as brief cases, and there were yellow and black spots on their translucent red wings. Tiny bulbs flashed on and off in their protuberant eyes. In the light from below, a soft aura as of sunset in a mist bathed the plastic flowers and grasses. It may have been dust rising from the floor.

The first room they came to, following the arrow, was the leaning room. The floor and all the furnishings leaned so that when one entered upright there was a grating, discordant note to the room.

"Not the sort of house I'd want to live in," said Kenzo, bracing himself against a table on which there were yellow wooden tulips. The words were like a command. He was not himself aware of it, but his decisiveness was that of the privileged one whose hope and well-being refuse to admit outsiders. It was not strange that in the hope, there was a scorn for the hopes of others and that no one was allowed to lay a finger on the well-being.

Braced against the leaning table, the determined figure in the undershirt made Kiyoko smile. It was a very domestic scene. Kenzo was like an outraged young man who, having built an extra room on his Sunday holidays, had made a mistake somewhere and ended up with the windows and floors all askew.

"You *could* live in a place like this, though," said Kiyoko. Spreading her arms like a mechanical doll, she leaned forward as the room leaned, and her face approached Kenzo's broad left shoulder at the same angle as the wooden tulips.

His brow wrinkled in a serious young frown, Kenzo smiled. He kissed the cheek that leaned toward him and bit roughly into his million-yen cracker.

By the time they had emerged from the wobbly staircases, the shaking passageways, the log bridges from the railings of which monster heads protruded, and numerous other curious places as well, the heat was too much for them. Kenzo finished his own cracker, took what was left of his wife's between his teeth, and set out in search of a cool evening breeze. Beyond a row of rocking horses a door led out to a balcony.

"What time is it?" asked Kiyoko.

"A quarter to nine. Let's go out and cool off till nine."

"I'm thirsty. The cracker was so dry." She fanned at her perspiring white throat with Kenzo's sports shirt.

"In a minute you can have something to drink."

The night breeze was cool on the wide balcony. Kenzo yawned a wide yawn and leaned against the railing beside his wife. Bare young arms caressed the black railing, wet with the night dew.

"It's much cooler than when we came in."

"Don't be silly," said Kenzo. "It's just higher."

Far below, the black machines of the outdoor amusement park seemed to slumber. The bare seats of the merry-go-round, slightly inclined, were exposed to the dew. Between the iron bars of the aerial observation car, suspended chairs swayed gently in the breeze.

The liveliness of the restaurant to the left was in complete contrast. They had a bird's-eye view into all the corners of the wide expanse inside its walls. Everything was there to look at, as if on a stage: the roofs of the separate cottages, the passages joining them, the ponds and brooks in the garden, the stone lanterns, the interiors of the Japanese rooms, some with serving maids whose kimono sleeves were held up by red cords, others with dancing geisha. The strings of lanterns at the eaves were beautiful, and their white lettering was beautiful too.

The wind carried away the noises of the place, and there was something almost mystically beautiful about it, congealed in delicate detail there at the bottom of the murky summer night.

"I'll bet it's expensive." Kiyoko was once more at her favorite romantic topic.

"Naturally. Only a fool would go there."

"They say that cucumbers are a great delicacy, I'll bet, and charge some fantastic price. How much?"

"Two hundred, maybe." Kenzo took his sports shirt and started to put it on.

Buttoning it for him, Kiyoko continued: "They must think their customers are fools. Why, that's ten times what cucumbers are worth. You can get three of the very best for twenty yen."

"Oh? They're getting cheap."

"The price started going down a week or so ago."

It was five till nine. They went out to look for a stairway to the coffee shop on the third floor. Two of the crackers had disappeared. The other was too large for Kiyoko's very large handbag, and protruded from the unfastened clasp.

The old lady, an impatient person, had arrived early and was waiting. The seats from which the loud jazz orchestra could best be seen were all taken, but there were vacant places where the bandstand was out of sight, beside the potted palm probably rented from some gardener. Sitting alone in a summer kimono, the old lady seemed wholly out of place.

She was a small woman not far past middle age, and she had the clean, well-tended face of these plebeian lowlanders. She spoke briskly with many delicate gestures. She was proud of the fact that she got along so nicely with young people.

"You'll be treating me, of course, so I ordered something expensive while I was waiting." Even as she spoke the tall glass arrived, pieces of fruit atop a parfait.

"Now, that was generous of you. All we needed was soda water."

Her outstretched little finger taut, the old lady plunged in with her spoon and skillfully brought out the cream beneath. Meanwhile, she was talking along at her usual brisk pace.

"It's nice that this place is so noisy and no one can hear us. Tonight we go to Nakano — I think I mentioned it over the phone. An ordinary private house and — can you imagine it? — the customers are housewives having a class reunion. There's not much that the rich ladies don't know about these days. And I imagine they walk around pretending the idea never entered their heads. Anyway, I told them about you, and they said they had to have you and no one else. They don't want someone who's all beaten up by the years, you know. And I must say that I can't blame them. So I asked a good stiff price and she said it was low and if they were pleased they'd give you a good tip. They haven't any idea what the market rate is, of course. But I want you to do your best, now. I'm sure I don't need

66

to tell you, but if they're pleased, we'll get all sorts of rich customers. There aren't many that go as well together as you two do, of course, and I'm not worried, but don't do anything to make me ashamed of you. Well, anyhow, the woman of the house is the wife of some important person or other, and she'll be waiting for us at the coffee shop in front of Nakano Station. You know what will happen next. She'll send the taxi through all sorts of back alleys to get us mixed up. I don't imagine she'll blindfold us, but she'll pull us through the back door so we don't have a chance to read the sign on the gate. I won't like it any better than you will, but she has herself to consider, after all. Don't let it bother you. Me? Oh, I'll be doing the usual thing, keeping watch in the hall. I can bluff my way through, I don't care who comes in. Well, maybe we ought to get started. And let me say it again, I want a good performance from you."

It was late in the night, and Kiyoko and Kenzo had left the old lady and were back in Asakusa. They were even more exhausted than usual. Kenzo's wooden clogs dragged along the street. The billboards in the park were a poisonous black under the cloudy sky.

Simultaneously, they looked up at the New World. The neon pagoda was dark.

"What a rotten bunch. I don't think I've ever seen such a rotten, stuck-up bunch," said Kenzo.

Her eyes on the ground, Kiyoko did not answer.

"Well? Did you ever see a worse bunch of affected old women?"

"No. But what can you do? The pay was good."

"Playing around with money they pry from their husbands. Don't get to be that way when you have money."

"Silly." Kiyoko's smiling face was sharply white in the darkness

"A really nasty bunch," Kenzo spat in a strong white arc. "How much?"

"This." Kiyoko reached artlessly into her handbag and pulled out some bills.

"Five thousand? We've never made that much before. And the old woman took three thousand. Damn! I'd like to tear it up, that's what I'd like to do. That would really feel good."

Kiyoko took the money back in some consternation. Her finger touched the last of the million-yen crackers.

"Tear this up in its place," she said softly.

Kenzo took the cracker, wadded the cellophane wrapper, and threw it to the ground. It crackled sharply on the silent, deserted street. The cracker was too large for one hand, he took it in both hands and tried to break it. It was damp and soggy, and the sweet surface stuck to his hands. The more it bent the more it resisted. He was in the end unable to break it.

(*Translated by Edward Seidensticker*)

67

May Day Eve

Nick Joaquin

THE OLD PEOPLE HAD ORDERED that the dancing should stop at ten o'clock but it was almost midnight before the carriages came filing up to the front door, the servants running to and fro with torches to light the departing guests, while the girls who were staying were promptly herded upstairs to the bedrooms, the young men gathering around to wish them a good night and lamenting their ascent with mock sighs and moanings, proclaiming themselves disconsolate but straightway going off to finish the punch and the brandy though they were quite drunk already and simply bursting with wild spirits, merriment, arrogance and audacity, for they were young bucks newly arrived from Europe; the ball had been in their honor; and they had waltzed and polka-ed and bragged and swaggered and flirted all night and were in no mood to sleep yet — no, caramba, not on this moist tropic eve! not on this mystic May eve! — with the night still young and so seductive that it was madness not to go out, not to go forth — and serenade the neighbors! cried one; and swim in the Pasig! cried another; and gather fireflies! cried a third — whereupon there arose a great clamor for coats and capes, for hats and canes and they were presently stumbling out among the medieval shadows of the foul street where a couple of street-lamps flickered and a last carriage rattled away upon the cobbles while the blind black houses muttered hush-hush, their tile roofs looming like sinister chessboards against a wild sky murky with clouds, save where an evil young moon prowled about in a corner or where a murderous wind whirled, whistling and whining, smelling now of the sea and now of the summer orchards and wafting unbearable childhood fragrances of ripe guavas to the young men trooping so uproariously down the street that the girls who were disrobing upstairs in the bedrooms scattered screaming to the windows, crowded giggling at the windows but were soon sighing amorously over those young men bawling below; over those wicked young men and their handsome apparel, their proud flashing eyes, and their elegant mustaches so black and vivid in the moonlight that the girls were quite ravished with love, and began crying to one another how carefree were men but how awful to be a girl and what a horrid, horrid world it was,

68

till old Anastasia plucked them off by the ear or the pig tail and chased them off to bed — while from up the street came the clackety-clack of the watchman's boots on the cobbles, and the clang-clang of his lantern against his knee, and the mighty roll of his great voice booming through the night: *"Guardia sereno-o-o! A las doce han dado-o-o!"*

AND IT was May again, said the old Anastasia. It was the first day of May and witches were abroad in the night, she said — for it was a night of divination, a night of lovers, and those who cared might peer in a mirror and would behold the face of whoever it was they were fated to marry, said Anastasia as she hobbled about picking up the piled crinolines and folding up shawls and raking slippers to a corner while the girls climbing into the four great posterbeds that overwhelmed the room began shrieking with terror, scrambling over each other and imploring the old woman not to frighten them.

"Enough, enough, Anastasia! We want to sleep!"

"Go scare the boys instead, you old witch!"

"She is not a witch, she is a maga. She was born on Christmas Eve! ! !"

"St. Anastasia, virgin and martyr."

"Huh? Impossible! She has conquered seven husbands! Are you a virgin, Anastasia?"

"No, but I am seven times a martyr because of you girls!"

"Let her prophesy, let her prophesy! Whom will I marry, old gypsy? Come, tell me."

"You may learn in a mirror if you are not afraid."

"I am not afraid, I will go!" cried the young cousin Agueda, jumping up in bed.

"Girls, girls — we are making too much noise! My mother will hear and will come and pinch us all. Agueda, lie down! And you, Anastasia, I command you to shut your mouth and go away!"

"Your mother told me to stay here all night, my grandlady!"

"And I will not lie down!" cried the rebellious Agueda, leaping to the floor. "Stay, old woman. Tell me what I have to do."

"Tell her! Tell her!" chimed the other girls.

The old woman dropped the clothes she had gathered and approached and fixed her eyes on the girl. "You must take a candle," she instructed, "and go into a room that is dark and that has a mirror in it and you must be alone in the room. Go up the mirror and close your eyes and say:

> *Mirror, mirror,*
> *show to me*
> *him whose woman*
> *I will be.*

"If all goes right, just above your left shoulder will appear the face of the man you will marry."

A silence. Then: "And what if all does not go right?" asked Agueda.

"Ah, then the Lord have mercy on you!"

"Why?"

"Because you may see — the Devil!"

The girls screamed and clutched one another, shivering.

"But what nonsense!" cried Agueda. "This is the year 1847. There are no devils any more!" Nevertheless, she had turned pale. "But where could I go, huh? Yes, I know! Down to the sala. It has that big mirror and no one is there now."

"No, Agueda, no! It is a mortal sin! You will see the devil!"

"I do not care! I am not afraid! I will go!"

"Oh, you wicked girl! Oh, you mad girl!"

"If you do not come to bed, Agueda, I will call my mother."

"And if you do, I will tell her who came to visit you at the convent last March. Come, old woman — give me that candle. I go."

"Oh, girls — come and stop her! Take hold of her! Block the door!"

But Agueda had already slipped outside; was already tiptoeing across the hall; her feet bare and her dark hair falling down her shoulders and streaming in the wind as she fled down the stairs, the lighted candle sputtering in one hand while with the other she pulled up her white gown from her ankles.

She paused breathless in the doorway to the sala and her heart failed her. She tried to imagine the room filled again with lights, laughter, whirling couples, and the jolly jerky music of the fiddlers. But, oh, it was a dark den, a weird cavern, for the windows had been closed and the furniture stacked up against the walls. She crossed herself and stepped inside.

The mirror hung on the wall before her; a big antique mirror with a gold frame carved into leaves and flowers and mysterious curlicues. She saw herself approaching fearfully in it: a small white ghost that the darkness bodied forth — but not willingly, not completely, for her eyes and hair were so dark that the face approaching in the mirror seemed only a mask that floated forward; a bright mask with two holes gaping in it, blown forward by the white cloud of her gown. But when she stood before the mirror she lifted the candle level with her chin and the dead mask bloomed into her living face.

She closed her eyes and whispered the incantation. When she had finished, such a terror took hold of her that she felt unable to move, unable to open her eyes, and thought she would stand there

70

forever, enchanted. But she heard a step behind her, and a smothered giggle, and instantly opened her eyes.

"AND WHAT did you see, Mama? Oh, what was it?"

But Doña Agueda had forgotten the little girl on her lap: she was staring past the curly head nesting at her breast and seeing herself in the big mirror hanging in the room. It was the same room and the same mirror but the face she now saw in it was an old face — a hard, bitter, vengeful face, in white mask, that fresh young face like a pure mask that she had brought before this mirror one wild May Day midnight years and years ago. . .

"But what was it, Mama? Oh, please go on! What did you see?"

Doña Agueda looked down at her daughter but her face did not soften though her eyes filled with tears. "I saw the devil!" she said bitterly.

The child blanched. "The devil, Mama? Oh . . . OH!"

"Yes, my love. I opened my eyes and there in the mirror, smiling at me over my left shoulder, was the face of the devil."

"Oh, my poor little Mama! And were you very frightened?"

"You can imagine. And that is why good little girls do not look into mirrors except, when their mothers tell them. You must stop this naughty habit, darling, of admiring yourself in every mirror you pass — or you may see something frightful some day."

"But the devil, Mama — what did he look like?"

"Well, let me see . . . He had curly hair and a scar on his cheek —"

"Like the scar of Papa?"

"Well, yes. But this of the devil was a scar of sin, while that of your Papa is a scar of honor. Or so he says."

"Go on about the devil."

"Well, he had mustaches."

"Like those of Papa?"

"Oh, no. Those of your Papa are dirty and greying and smell horribly of tobacco, while those of the devil were very black and elegant — oh, how elegant!"

"And did he have horns and a tail?"

The mother's lips curled. "Yes, he did! But, alas, I could not see them at that time. All I could see were his fine clothes, his flashing eyes, his curly hair and mustaches."

"And did he speak to you, Mama?"

"Yes . . . Yes, he spoke to me," said Doña Agueda. And bowing her greying head, she wept.

"CHARMS like yours have no need for a candle, fair one," he had said, smiling at her in the mirror and stepping back to give her

71

a low mocking bow. She had whirled around and glared at him and he had burst into laughter.

"But I remember you!" he cried. "You are Agueda, whom I left a mere infant and came home to find a tremendous beauty, and I danced a waltz with you but you would not give me the polka."

"Let me pass," she muttered fiercely, for he was barring her way.

"But I want to dance the polka with you, fair one," he said.

So they stood before the mirror; their panting breath the only sound in the dark room; the candle shining between them and flinging their shadows to the wall. And young Badoy Montiya (who had crept home very drunk to pass out quietly in bed) suddenly found himself cold sober and very much awake and ready for anything. His eyes sparkled and the scar on his face gleamed scarlet.

"Let me pass!" she cried again in a voice of fury, but he grasped her by the wrist.

"No," he smiled. "Not until we have danced."

"Go to the devil!"

"What a temper has my serrana!"

"I am not your serrana."

"Whose, then? Someone I know? Someone I have offended grievously? Because you treat me, you treat all my friends like your mortal enemies."

"And why not," she demanded, jerking her wrist away and flashing her teeth in his face. "Oh, how I detest you, you pompous young men! You go to Europe and you come back elegant lords and we poor girls are too tame to please you. We have no grace like the Parisiennes, we have no fire like the Sevillias, and we have no salt, no salt, no salt! Aie, how you weary me, how you bore me, you fastidious young men!"

"Come, come — how do you know about us?"

"I have heard you talking, I have heard you talking among yourselves, and I despise the pack of you!"

"But clearly you do not despise yourself, señorita. You come to admire your charms in the mirror in the middle of the night!"

She turned livid and he had a moment of malicious satisfaction.

"I was not admiring myself, sir!"

"You were admiring the moon perhaps?"

"Oh!" she gasped, and burst into tears. The candle dropped from her hand and she covered her face and sobbed piteously. The candle had gone out and they stood in darkness, and young Badoy was conscience-stricken.

"Oh, do not cry, little one! Oh, please forgive me! Please do not cry! But what a brute I am! I was drunk, little one, I was drunk and knew not what I said."

72

He groped and found her hand and touched it to his lips. She shuddered in her white gown.

"Let me go," she moaned, and tugged feebly.

"No. Say you forgive me first. Say you forgive me, Agueda."

But instead she pulled his hand to her mouth and bit it — bit so sharply into the knuckles that he cried with pain and lashed out with his other hand — lashed out and hit the air, for she was gone, she had fled, and he heard the rustling of her skirts up the stairs as he furiously sucked his bleeding fingers.

Cruel thoughts raced through his head: he would go and tell his mother and make her turn the savage girl out of the house or he would go himself to the girl's room and drag her out of bed and slap, slap, slap, her silly face! But at the same time he was thinking that they were all going up to Antipolo in the morning and was already planning how he would maneuver himself into the same boat with her.

Oh, he would have his revenge, he would make her pay, that little harlot! She should suffer for this, he thought greedily, licking his bleeding knuckles. But — Judas! — what eyes she had! And what a pretty color she turned when angry! He remembered her bare shoulders: gold in the candlelight and delicately furred. He saw the mobile insolence of her neck, and her taut breasts steady in the fluid gown. Son of a Turk, but she was quite enchanting! How could she think she had no fire or grace? And no salt? An arroba she had of it!

". . . No lack of salt in the chrism
At the moment of thy baptism!"

he sang aloud in the dark room and suddenly realized that he had fallen madly in love with her. He ached intensely to see her again — at once! — to touch her hand and her hair; to hear her harsh voice. He ran to the window and flung open the casements and the beauty of the night struck him back like a blow. It was May, it was summer, and he was young — young! — and deliriously in love. Such a happiness welled up within him the tears spurted from his eyes.

But he did not forgive her — no! He would still make her pay, he would still have his revenge, he thought viciously, and kissed his wounded fingers. But what a night it had been! "I will never forget this night!" he thought aloud in an awed voice, standing by the window in the dark room, the tears in his eyes and the wind in his hair and his bleeding knuckles pressed to his mouth.

BUT, ALAS, the heart forgets; the heart is distracted; and Maytime passes; summer ends; the storms break over the hot-ripe or-

73

chards and the heart grows old; while the hours, the days, the months and the years pile up and pile up till the mind becomes too crowded, too confused: dust gathers in it; cobwebs multiply; the walls darken and fall into ruin and decay; the memory perishes . . . and there came a time when Don Badoy Montiya walked home through a May Day midnight without remembering, without even caring to remember; being merely concerned in feeling his way across the street with his cane; his eyes having grown quite dim and his legs uncertain — for he was old; he was over sixty; he was a very stooped and shriveled old man with white hair and mustaches, coming home from a secret meeting of conspirators; his mind still resounding with the speeches and his patriot heart still exultant as he picked his way up the steps to the front door and inside into the slumbering darkness of the house; wholly unconscious of the May night, till on his way down the hall, chancing to glance into the sala, he shuddered, he stopped, his blood ran cold — for he had seen a face in the mirror there — a ghostly candlelit face with the eyes closed and the lips moving, a face that he suddenly felt he had seen there before though it was a full minute before the lost memory came flowing, came tiding back, so overflooding the actual moment and so swiftly washing away the piled hours and days and months and years that he was left suddenly young again; he was a gay young buck again, lately come from Europe; he had been dancing all night; he was very drunk; he stopped in the doorway; he saw a face in the dark; he cried out . . . and the lad standing before the mirror (for it was a lad in a night gown) jumped with fright and almost dropped his candle, but looking around and seeing the old man, laughed out with relief and came running.

"Oh, Grandpa, how you frightened me!"

Don Badoy had turned very pale. "So it was you, you young bandit! And what is all this, hey? What are you doing down here at this hour?"

"Nothing, Grandpa. I was only . . . I am only . . ."

"Yes, you are the Great Señor Only and how delighted I am to make your acquaintance, Señor Only! But if I break this cane on your head you may wish you were someone else, sir!"

"It was just foolishness, Grandpa. They told me I would see my wife."

"Wife? What wife?"

"Mine. The boys at school said I would see her if I looked in a mirror tonight and said:

> "Mirror, mirror,
> show to me
> her whose lover
> I will be."

74

Don Badoy cackled ruefully. He took the boy by the hair, pull-ed him along into the room, sat down on a chair, and drew the boy between his knees.

"Now, put your candle down on the floor, son, and let us talk this over. So you want your wife already, hey? You want to see her in advance, hey? But do you know that these are wicked games and that wicked boys who play them are in danger of seeing horrors?"

"Well, the boys did warn me I might see a witch instead."

"Exactly! A witch so horrible you may die of fright. And she will bewitch you, she will torture you, she will eat your heart and drink your blood!"

"Oh, come now, Grandpa. This is 1890. There are no witches any more."

"Oh ho, my young Voltaire! And what if I tell you that I my-self have seen a witch?"

"You? Where?"

"Right in this room and right in that mirror," said the old man, and his playful and harsh voice had turned savage.

"When, Grandpa?"

"Not so long ago. When I was a bit older than you. Oh, I was a vain fellow and thought I was feeling very sick that night and merely wanted to lie down somewhere and die. I could not pass that doorway of course without stopping to see in the mirror what I look-ed like when dying. But when I poked my head in, what should I see in the mirror but . . . but . . ."

"The witch?"

"Exactly!"

"And did she bewitch you, Grandpa?"

"She bewitched me and she tortured me. She ate my heart and drank my blood," said the old man bitterly.

"Oh, my poor little Grandpa! Why have you never told me! And was she very horrible?"

"Horrible? God, no — she was beautiful! She was the most beautiful creature I have ever seen! Her eyes were somewhat like yours but her hair was like black waters and her golden shoulders were bare. My God, she was enchanting! But I should have known — I should have known even then — the dark and fatal creature she was!"

A silence. Then: "What a horrid mirror this is, Grandpa," whis-pered the boy.

"What makes you say that, hey?"

"Well, you saw this witch in it. And Mama once told me that Grandma once told her that Grandma once saw the devil in this mir-ror. Was it of the scare that Grandma died?"

Don Badoy stared. For a moment he had forgotten that she was dead, that she had perished — the poor Agueda; that they were at peace at last the two of them, and her tired body at rest; her broken body set free at last from the brutal pranks of the earth — from the trap of a May night; from the snare of summer; from the terrible silver nets of the moon. She had been a mere heap of white hair and bones in the end; a whimpering withered consumptive, lashing out with her cruel tongue; her eyes like live coals; her face like ashes . . . Now, nothing! nothing save a name on a stone; save a stone in a graveyard — nothing! nothing at all! was left of the young girl who had flamed so vividly in a mirror one wild May Day midnight, long, long ago.

And remembering how she had sobbed so piteously; remembering how she had bitten his hand and fled and how he had sung aloud in the dark room and surprised his heart in the instant of falling in love; such a grief tore up his throat and eyes that he felt ashamed before the boy; pushed the boy away; stood up and fumbled his way to the window; threw open the casements and looked out — looked out upon the medieval shadows of the foul street where a couple of street-lamps flickered and a last carriage rattled away upon the cobbles, while the blind black houses muttered hush-hush, their tiled roofs looming like sinister chessboards against a wild sky murky with clouds, save where an evil old moon prowled about in a corner or where a murderous wind whirled, whistling and whining, smelling now of the sea and now of the summer orchards and wafting unbearable Maytime memories of an old, old love to the old man shaking with sobs by the window; the bowed old man sobbing so bitterly at the window; the tears streaming down his cheeks and the wind in his hair and one hand pressed to his mouth — while from up the street came the clackety-clack of the watchman's boots on the cobbles, and the clang-clang of his lantern against his knee, and the mighty roll of his great voice booming through the night: *"Guardia sereno-o-o! A las doce han dado-o-o!"*

Clay Doll

Sata Ineko

WITHOUT DOUBT, Toshico was a burden to the Yashima family. However much her mother Oseki may have pitied her, the love of a strong-minded mother for a daughter who is weak in the head is apt to show itself in the form of irritability. Toshiko was twenty-two when they at last found someone to marry her. To talk of a family's "finding someone to marry" its only daughter sounds odd, but that was how it was with the Yashima's. It was certain that the local charcoal man, who was to marry her, had been approached in the first place by Oseki. The only breadwinner in the family at the time was the eldest son Kaneyuki, who worked in a large shipyard. They had no property left, either, so a dowry was out of the question. Toshiko, in fact, had her own body to offer, and that was all. The man, Harada by name, occupied himself fetching charcoal from somewhere or other and selling it to various households in the district. He was not so much a merchant, thus, as a charcoal burner — a fact which, together with his total lack of relatives, gave Oseki's proposals a faint suggestion that it was she who was conferring the favor. Kaneyuki paid no attention whatsoever to Toshiko's prospective husband, but for Oseki, and even for Kaneyuki himself, the discovery of someone who would marry her was undoubtedly a relief. Even Kaneyuki's daughter Hiroko, who was five at the time, knew that.

On the day of the marriage, they did Toshiko's hair up in the traditional fashion, dressed her in a rather special kimono, and sat her formally in the best room to wait till Harada should come to fetch her. Like Oseki, she was short of stature, but where Oseki was neat and trim, Toshiko was fat and generally rotund. Her nose was straight like Kaneyuki's and Oseki's, but her cheeks bulged and the flesh round her mouth was pudgy. Her hair was too frizzy to take the formal style properly. Sitting there round-shouldered, her kimono tied with a red-patterned sash, she looked for all the world like some rustic clay doll. There is a kind of doll they make in the country, of light-colored clay, crudely turned out in a round mould and patterned with red paint — that is just how Toshiko looked. Yet to Hiroko, who was only a child, she was a resplendent being, and she and her younger brother romped delightedly about the room where Toshiko had been put.

Beyond the broad verandah of the house lay the garden. There were a shaddock tree and a persimmon tree, and a pomegranate with fruit on its boughs. Beneath the shaddock stood a small Shinto shrine, and a small bowl of the red rice offered to guests on festive occasions had been set before it as a special offering to mark the day. Guests, though, there were none. Harada came and took Toshiko away with him: that was all. He was a tall, rough-featured man, but his character, it was not to be doubted, was good.

So Toshiko came to have her own household — albeit in a rented room in the back streets of a fishing town — and in due course gave birth to a son. He grew into a quick-witted, lively child, so that it was strange to see Toshiko sitting vacantly by his side and to think that she was his mother.

"Now, now, Ichiro," she would complain placidly in her thick country accent, "you mustn't get up to so much mischief."

There was a strange contrast between her slow speech and the way the boy rushed about, all flaying arms and legs, as though trying to get rid of surplus energy. Yet despite such things Toshiko managed, in a way, to have a life of her own until the time the child was two or three. Harada, however, was beginning to feel dissatisfied with her. Her general vagueness, which extended even to her management of their finances, made everyday existence difficult for them. Nevertheless, he was fond of his child, nor could he bring himself to send Toshiko back to her mother, and she had, accordingly, to bear the full brunt of his irritation. Day after day he would beat her, and Toshiko's plump form would roll about the floor emitting cries like a distressed animal. She probably did not even know why she was being beaten. Afterwards, she simply went back to her habitual placid, plump, insensitivity, the same as ever save for the bruises on her face and body.

"When Toshiko was a little girl," Oseki would tell her granddaughter Hiroko, "the nurse who was carrying her dropped her from the verandah. That's why she's a bit simple now, they say."

Toshiko's father had been a doctor, and during his lifetime they had been well off, so that the nurse was no mere figure of speech. Even so, it was more or less a social convention that any child who was deficient mentally should be declared to have been dropped by someone in its infancy. There was an old photograph showing Oseki and her three children. Taken just after she had been widowed, it showed her still young, erect, and dignified, her lips firmly compressed, determined henceforth to make her own way in the world. Kaneyuki too — a young lad in a summer kimono with a stiff formal

78

skirt — was holding his head high and alert. Even Toshiko's little brother Naoyuki, standing with one hand on his mother's lap, had an intelligent look in his eyes. But Toshiko, standing on the edge of the group, had an obviously stupid look which her bangs and the neatness of her dress could not disguise. It was as if she, alone of the four, had been born behind other people. Stupidity, however, did not mean that her behavior was eccentric, and, given instructions from Oseki, she was capable of kitchen work if nothing else. In practice, this only created a further source of irritation for Oseki, who was forever nagging and getting impatient with her. Kaneyuki was a part of this state of affairs, and Naoyuki was the same; the only difference to Toshiko was that one was her elder, the other her younger brother.

Oseki, realizing from Toshiko's swollen face and bruises that Harada was ill-treating her, appealed to Kaneyuki.

"Her face was all swollen — he must have hit her dreadfully, poor girl. Why don't you give him a piece of your mind?"

"What's the use of my saying anything? Toshiko's slow in the head, that's the trouble."

"I *know* she's slow. But Harada can't very well complain at this stage, can he?"

"I told you from the start, didn't I — I didn't like marrying Toshiko to a man like him. It was your doing, wasn't it?"

"I suppose so. But who else would have married her? Only that kind of man would have had her. But nowadays it seems he's going around telling people he was cheated. He's getting a bit above himself, that's the trouble."

"What are you making a fuss about then? Why don't you fetch her back? You've no need to let a man like Harada make a fool of you. Why don't you go and get her now — that would be best."

Kaneyuki spoke out like this half to spite Oseki; also, out of a desire to pay back Harada and out of anger at Toshiko's stupidity. In short, what he said was no more than the product of his own selfish emotions. Oseki was inclined to try bringing Toshiko home for a few days to see whether it would sober Harada up or not, and the result was that they fetched her back, leaving the child Ichiro behind. Toshiko, as might be expected, cried till her heavy eyelids were red, but she always let other people do with her as they pleased, and once her mother had brought her home she had not the energy to run back to her child.

One night, about ten days later, Harada came to apologize, carrying the child strapped on his back. Ichiro's eyes were roving in all directions above his father's shoulder as he stood in the hall. Oseki, pleading Kaneyuki's absence, would not let Harada come in, and he had to go back home for the moment. All the while, Toshiko was sitting on the other side of the sliding doors, her head hanging and her shoulders drooping more than ever.

She saw her husband and child no more, since shortly afterwards the whole family vacated the house and removed to Tokyo, whither Naoyuki had preceded them. Although, in taking Toshiko back from Harada, Kaneyuki had merely acted on the feeling of the moment, his suggestion that they should all go to Tokyo was motivated at least to some extent by apprehension at the idea of leaving his younger sister near her husband. So Toshiko was whisked off again by Oseki, to slave away by herself at work others would have done in a trice, her fate increasingly involved once more in that of the newly poor Yashima family.

Kaneyuki's sudden move to Tokyo with Oseki, Hiroko and his other child, and his younger sister Toshiko, though partly prompted by the death of his wife, was equally due to a characteristically capricious dislike he had taken to his job. In the depression of late 1929, however, it was difficult to find work in an unfamiliar district. He tried his hand as a clerk in a family-run iron works, as an insurance agent, and in other jobs found through newspaper advertisements, but nothing lasted long. Anger at Harada's brutality to Toshiko had been the ostensible reason for taking her away, but now he himself began to wreak his ill-humor on her when he was drunk. Toshiko was in a constantly cowed state, and nowadays whenever her brother was there her eyes would watch him darkly from under drooping lids. When he objected to her expression and boxed her ears, she would roll in a ball on the floor and shriek like a small girl.

"What have I done?" she would cry, the heavy fold of her eyelids drooping forlornly. "Why do you have to hit me?" At this Kaneyuki would give an oath and fly into a rage again, and she would give a wail, put her hands up to her face and shuffle on her knees into a corner of the room.

"I'm sorry, I'm sorry."

"What are you sorry about?" Kaneyuki would shout, as though her abject appearance ired him still further. "If you think you're sorry, go and find some work somewhere — anywhere. You're the only one who doesn't do anything for your keep. We can't afford it nowadays."

Oseki, unable to watch in silence any longer, would put off her lap the sewing which she took in to earn some extra money, and turn to Kaneyuki.

"What's the use of your saying things like that, either? You just work it off on Toshiko when you're bad-tempered and *then* you feel better, don't you."

"You don't understand, mother."

"What do you mean — don't understand? Toshiko gets things done in her own way, doesn't she?"

"What does she do? Just eat and hang around your apron-strings."

"Don't you think you've said enough?"

"No, I don't! Why, you . . ." He made to set on Toshiko again, but Oseki checked him and shouted at Toshiko, "Why don't you get out of the way somewhere? It's your own fault! If you just stick around there . . ."

But Toshiko, told to get out of the way, had nowhere to flee to. She crouched down in full view by the sink in the kitchen and wailed piteously.

Halfway through his college course, Naoyuki, the younger brother, had got himself involved in some student movement, and rarely came home to his brother's house in Takinokawa. Kaneyuki was docile in his behavior to his younger brother, and would lend a ready ear as the other talked in a low voice of ideologies and the like. He himself, however, would quite happily help himself to the money for his parent's and children's food and spend it on drink. Then, when he was drunk, he would be worse-tempered than ever.

On three occasions Toshiko was sent to work as a maid in the homes of acquaintances. But, left to herself, she had no idea whatsoever of what was to be done, and it always ended with her coming, or being sent, home. This suited Oseki quite well, since, though she complained that Toshiko was useless, Toshiko's presence relieved her of the drudgery around the house. A department store took the kimonos that she sewed, and nice things came in exchange, and she did not want to make her hands rough. Toshiko's work, thus, contributed in a sense to Oseki's income, which was larger than that of any of them, but this fact occurred to none of them, not even Oseki herself. In the gaps between his short-lived jobs Kaneyuki would sell or pawn Toshiko's — sometimes even the children's — clothing and he helped himself to the money Toshiko had earned as a maid. Toshiko herself lacked the art of complaining; so long as there was no actual trouble her expression remained as placid as ever. Even she, though, sometimes wanted to talk to people. Kaneyuki found her one day standing chatting to a neighbor, and she was beaten again. After that she spent almost all her time by Oseki, making paper bags with newspaper.

Nor did she ever, of her own accord, give any indication of her feelings about her husband, Harada, and her child, Ichiro. On the rare occasions when Oseki wondered aloud what they were doing nowadays, her face would light up and she would start talking about Ichiro. Her brain never got round to worrying over what had become of him; she was merely happy at the recollection of things past.

"There was a family called Yoshikawa on the corner near our house in the fishing town, you know," she would muse. "One day

Ichiro went up into their house without telling me, and I looked for him all over the place."

"Harada must have had a hard time since then, managing the child all by himself," Oseki would say. "Serves him right, I say!"

"He was fond of the kid, though. He wasn't a bad man, was he. Just a bit short-tempered . . ." She would gaze into space and her hands would stop moving as though she would never get off the subject.

"Come on, you've stopped working," Oseki would scold. "You stop working at the slightest excuse."

Toshiko's shoulders would immediately bend over her task again. Further conversation being impossible, she would carry on her work of cutting and folding the newspaper in silence, but her expression stayed happy indefinitely.

Eventually, Kaneyuki went to work in a ship-building yard in On-omichi, to which he was introduced by a friend in the shipbuilding yard for which he had originally worked. The women were left alone. Kaneyuki's daughter Hiroko, though still attending middle school, managed at the same time to lend Oseki a skillful hand with her needlework. The money which Kaneyuki was supposed to send obstinately refused to appear. This was a constant source of irritation to Oseki, and on top of it Kaneyuki's absence allowed her to give freer rein to her own tongue. Every morning Hiroko woke up to hear Oseki grumbling at Toshiko. Her brother, who was only fourteen, still had the quilts pulled up over his ears, deaf to such matters.

"Things'll never get done if you go about them in such a lack-adaisical way. I told you yesterday, didn't I — first you do this, then you do that, I told you properly. When did you last wash this chopping board — it's all slimy! How many years have you been doing the kitchen, I'd like to know? Just think — at your age you still can't do what people tell you. All you do is make more work for me. Look at Hiroko, now — how much younger she is than you. You might think about *that* a bit."

Oseki's complaints were not so much complaints as a kind of routine morning bad temper which made her want to quarrel. The words rolled on and on, the very tone of her voice depressing, but not a word was audible from Toshiko in reply. This did not mean, though, that Toshiko let the words pass over her in complete indifference. At such times she went on stirring the pickle-tub — or what-ever else she happened to be doing — with an embarrassed expression and deep furrows in her forehead, stirring and stirring as though she found it impossible to move on to the next action. Since she made no reply, Oseki's grumbling would go on unchecked, the sound of her own words adding fuel to the flames of her wrath, till finally her voice would rise to a hysterical pitch.

82

"Are you going to go on forever, just getting a little bit of pickle out? Hurry up with you, we haven't got all day! We've got to get finished and get down to work or we'll never get by. What with Kaneyuki forgetting all about us and Naoyuki in trouble with the police, what's going to happen to us? The whole pack of you depend on me. What do you think would happen to you, Toshiko, without me? You've got to get a bit more like other people, before it's too late. Look, now! You're spilling the water!"

Hiroko, who was a knowing child, was half inclined to dismiss Oseki's grumbling as a mere morning habit, a kind of outlet for all the things she thought about in bed between waking at dawn and getting up. Toshiko was the predestined target. Her sluggish movements and her plump face jarred on Kaneyuki's and Oseki's frayed nerves. Toshiko herself had never considered why she should always be being beaten and grumbled at. All she knew was that she was not like other people. When Oseki said so in front of other people, she would smile sheepishly and put on an expression which said, "she's right, you know."

As Hiroko grew up and showed more and more promise, Oseki came to praise her and deplore Toshiko quite openly in front of others. On one occasion the other person, taking pity on Toshiko said,

"Toshiko seems different because all the rest of you are so clever. I feel sorry for her, really. It's hard on someone when everyone around her's so bright — it makes her look stupid. Why, Toshiko manages everything fine, don't you, Toshiko?"

On that one occasion Toshiko answered like an ordinary person.

"I wish I could do things like Hiroko," she said, "but I've always been a bit backward."

Eventually, however, the continual comparisons that Oseki kept drawing awoke something resembling a sense of competition in Toshiko. One autumn, the time came to repaper the sliding doors, and Toshiko took off the old paper and washed the woodwork in readiness. However, when she was told that Hiroko was to stick the new paper on that evening, the veins stood out blue on her forehead.

"Even I can manage to stick a bit of paper on some sliding doors," she said, and brought out the paper in spite of all Oseki's protests. But the task was beyond her.

"There's something up with Toshiko these days," Oseki confided in Hiroko later. "Insisting she could paper the doors — the idea of it!"

Hiroko had already realized that Toshiko had developed a sense of rivalry towards her. As the infant Hiroko had grown up, Toshiko had, quite unconsciously, begun to be jealous. Her jealousy, however, was not the kind to show itself in her relations with Hiroko. By insensible degrees, Hiroko had risen to such a superiority over Toshiko that no grounds for antagonism were left. All Hiroko felt, as she pictured to herself Toshiko red-faced and flustered in the attempt to show she could repaper the doors, was a sense of pity. The feeling may have had its mixture of conceit, but Hiroko had no sense of having done her aunt down, and she completed the papering in an untroubled frame of mind. Toshiko stood by as she did it, her shoulders heaving in the fight against her sense of defeat.

Sometimes Hiroko would think that her aunt smelt. At such times she would make a wry face to herself and recall what had happened late one winter afternoon two years previously. Coming home late from school, she had found the house in darkness. She could hear voices inside, however — Toshiko's voice raised in urgent protest and a man's low tones trying to overcome her resistance. Shocked, Hiroko withdrew. The man's voice, beyond all doubt, was that of the husband next door, and Hiroko knew what had been about to happen. As she walked along the main street, past the nightstalls that were already opening, she called to mind the pale, moody face of the man, who was a plasterer, and it dawned on her that however dull-witted her aunt may have been born she was still in a man's eyes, a woman. The Toshiko who had been vainly resisting the man's advances was a woman in her own right.

When Oseki, who had been out on some errand, came back that evening she was angered to find dinner not yet ready; Toshiko as usual said nothing, but pottered about in the kitchen making the preparations. Hiroko did her best not to meet her aunt's eyes. The plasterer next door showed no sign afterwards that anything had happened, but went around with the same pasty face and moody expression as before. His wife knew nothing. Hiroko alone remembered what had happened, whenever she saw their neighbor and his wife together. On one occasion she was coming back from the bathhouse with her aunt when they met the plasterer in the street. Toshiko passed by with her eyes on the ground, and the plasterer pretended not to recognize them.

Whenever it seemed to her that her aunt's body smelt, Hiroko recalled this incident, but she said nothing. Nowadays though — when, for instance, Toshiko sucked at her teeth with a loud noise after a meal — she seemed to know how Kaneyuki had felt when he looked at Toshiko with a grimace at mealtimes. She let Toshiko wash all her clothes, even her underwear, as a matter of course. She did even less for herself once she started working for a trading company in the center of Tokyo. In a sense, Toshiko had acquired another mistress. Unlike Oseki, however, Hiroko did not grumble at her; in fact, she would buy Toshiko's wooden clogs and other necessities, and would send Oseki and Toshiko to the movies on her own days off.

On such occasions, Oseki would set off with Toshiko in attendance as though she were a servant.

Oseki's grumbling went on every morning as usual until one day, for some inexplicable reason, Toshiko rebelled. With a shriek as though she had gone mad, she seized a kitchen knife and flourished it before Oseki. Oseki fled, terrified at the extraordinary change in Toshiko's expression. Toshiko came after her as though Oseki's flight was a further incitement, and Oseki ran outside bare-footed. There was a great commotion in the alley outside, and when Hiroko came running out in her nightwear, Toshiko was being held by the old man from the house opposite, writhing and gasping out between her sobs.

"Every day I say nothing, but Mother keeps on at me all the time. Oh, what shall I do, what shall I do! I do my best in my own way. Oh, I'd rather die!"

Oseki was standing some distance away, her face ashen, her small frame shrunken still further, peering out at Toshiko from within a small group of people. The plasterer had moved to another district some time previously.

Nothing like this had ever been known before. Hiroko was forced to conclude that Toshiko, who normally was scarcely so much as sulky, must have been extraordinarily pent up inside to go chasing after Oseki brandishing a kitchen knife. It dawned on neither her nor Oseki that Toshiko was venting on Oseki her jealousy of Hiroko.

Ten years had passed since the Yashima family came to Tokyo. Kaneyuki still lived in Onomichi, where he had remarried. He had been to Tokyo once with his wife. On that occasion, he had seen how they lived, and had said — ignoring the fact that he had done almost nothing for them himself — "Well, things have turned out all right after all. But it's too bad of Toshiko — letting herself be kept at home all her life." He had acquired a certain self-possession, and his manner had a corresponding pomposity.

About five years previously, Naoyuki had been kept in jail for close on a year without trial. On his release he had got a job with a publishing firm, had married, and by now had children of his own. Hiroko's younger brother, Kenichi, had completed middle school and gone straight to work at a post-office in Oji. Already the threat of war was hanging over everything.

Toshiko was over thirty-five by now, but she still seemed to look the same. Her body was as plump as ever; the only difference was her complexion, which, once fair, had grown somewhat darker. She always wore a white apron and seemed to walk with a slight stoop.

From Kaneyuki in Onomichi came an unprecedented request that they send Toshiko to his house for a while. His second wife was having a late first child, and they felt they should take every precaution — which meant in effect that Toshiko was being summoned to substitute for a maid. Oseki, who always believed in her own mind that her eldest son ought, as a matter of course, to take care of them, saw in this a good chance to let him do so. Hiroko and her brother were disgruntled. Hiroko, who was used to having Toshiko do all her washing and generally behaving like the young lady of the house, was concerned at the inconvenience Toshiko's absence would cause her. The only emotion she showed on the surface, however, was discontent at her father's concern for his own interests.

"I call it selfish, when he's never done a thing for *us*. He's just inviting Aunt Toshiko to suit his own convenience. Uncle Naoyuki's the same — he got her to come and help when they had their baby, too. Just like a temporary home-help. All for a pair of clogs in return, too — they were just trying to get something on the cheap. That's father's idea too, you can be sure."

"Even if it is, it can't be helped. Either way he'll have to take care of us after you get married."

"I don't know why father wants a kid at this stage," declared Hiroko fiercely.

Oseki gave a little snort and looked down as though at a loss for a reply. She half shared Hiroko's opinion, and she guessed, too, that Hiroko's outspokenness against her father was motivated by resentment at his neglect of her since her childhood. However, it was a peculiarity of Oseki's psychology that though she quarreled constantly with Kaneyuki when they were together, she was inclined to take his part whenever he was far away. The reason was that Hiroko's power in the house was getting so much stronger that even Oseki sometimes felt it irksome.

Finally, Oseki decided that she would take Toshiko to Onomichi personally. She and Hiroko had words on the subject, but Toshiko's own wishes were not consulted, nor did she herself express any opinion.

"I'll soon be back, eh?" she said propitiatingly to Hiroko as she left.

She came back after about six months. Kaneyuki's wife had given premature birth and the baby had not lived. Toshiko was sent home without ceremony. The times, however, were catching up with their home in Tokyo. Kenichi was being drafted into the army, which, at that time, meant he must expect to be sent to the front. Moreover, a prospective husband had been found for Hiroko. Oseki, thus, could no longer get by on her own efforts alone. The idea that her favorite Kenichi was going into the army and would go to the front in a year's time was in itself enough to discourage her, and she was inclined to commit herself to Kaneyuki's care.

"Well, even after I got married I *could* take Aunt Toshiko, if it was just her," said Hiroki — which made it imperative that Oseki should go to her eldest son, if only for the sake of the "face" which people made so much of at that period. It was decided that this time she should invite herself to Onomichi without waiting to be asked; she had taken a fancy to Kaneyuki's house there, which she had seen when she had taken Toshiko there previously. As soon as Hiroko was married, at a ceremony attended only by Oseki and Naoyuki with his wife, she left, with Toshiko in attendance as ever. Remembering how she had been stared at ill-humoredly by Kaneyuki at mealtimes, Toshiko had developed again the habit of darting abject glances upwards from under drooping eyelids, a habit which she had lost recently. She could hardly object, however, since even Oseki was to be dependent on Kaneyuki henceforth. A cold wind was blowing through Tokyo station the night they left, and everywhere were crowds of people seeing off soldiers going to the front. They made no impression on Toshiko, but Hiroko, who had come to see them off, was all the time watching the crowds about her with an anxious expression. Kuwaki, her husband, was a druggist and had just got his own small store in the suburbs of Tokyo. Their marriage was in its third year when the Pearl Harbor attack launched the war against Britain and America. This time it was Hiroko who was pregnant, and she was already considering getting Aunt Toshiko to come, just as the others had done. Oseki and Toshiko were leading uneventful lives at Kaneyuki's, but sometimes the pencil written letters contained complaints too. It was dreadful, they said, the way Kaneyuki always grumbled at Toshiko over his evening bottle of *sake*. He would ask what the three women had been doing with themselves in the house alone after he had gone to work, and would glare around at them just as though they'd been loafing all day. Then he would find fault with the way Toshiko moved about; when she did the cleaning, he complained, it did the house more damage than good. Oseki seemed to have forgotten how she herself had once grumbled every morning.

Soon after the New Year, Toshiko came up to Tokyo unaccompanied. Hiroko saw her through the train window before she was seen by Toshiko. Toshiko's face was fat and vacant, her eyes dully apprehensive, but the moment she noticed Hiroko a slow smile spread across her features.

"Granny sent her love," she said. "She told me you're having a baby."

Toshiko's voice sounded rather older, and her manner of speaking was more that of an older woman. Her frizzy hair had gone thin at the hairline. She was just forty, and her plump shoulders and hips seemed to have set hard without changing their shape.

Hiroko gave birth to a boy. Fortunately, she was used to handling Toshiko, and her husband did not get irritated with her as Oseki and Kaneyuki had done. Toshiko held the baby clumsily, as if her arms were too short. When the baby began walking, she would take him to play in the open space in front of the station. Sometimes Hiroko would go by on an errand for the store, and would find the child crawling and toddling on the ground as if it was their own parlor floor, while Toshiko, apparently unconcerned, chatted with an old man who was also in charge of a child. Sometimes in the morning, when the child woke first, Hiroko would give him to Toshiko and have another nap herself. Toshiko would keep the child by her as she prepared the meals. The boy would seat himself on the boarded kitchen floor and amuse himself by dashing down on the floor a glass or whatever else came to hand.

"Naughty boy, Mummy will be cross with you," Toshiko would say placidly. But she would make no move to put out of his way any glass that might still be left, and soon that, too, would break with a second crash.

"What are you up to?" Hiroko, hearing the noise, would call from upstairs.

"He's breaking all the glasses," Toshiko would reply unconcernedly, as though it were the child's fault.

Food was scarce by now, and Toshiko's appetite sometimes annoyed Hiroko. She disliked herself for being annoyed, but still it got on her nerves; it irritated her that Toshiko should apparently not realize properly the seriousness of the food situation. Not that Toshiko was discontented with a diet of sweet potatoes — it was just the quantity of them that she ate.

"What — all gone?" Hiroko would exclaim ill-humoredly, peering into the potato basket.

Kuwaki got his papers in his turn, and Aunt Toshiko's presence was a godsend to Hiroko. The first time there was a bad air-raid, Toshiko was squatting down in the cupboard before anyone else, panting audibly. As each crash came she let out a wail. The wails came with such regularity that Hiroko, in the cupboard with her, would be seized with a sense of the ridiculous and her eyes would run tears in her effort to stifle a laugh.

In time, though, Toshiko must have got used to things, and her cries became more half-hearted. There was an aeroplane factory near their house, and the raids were intense, yet they reached the end of the war with their home intact, and Kuwaki, who had been stationed in Japan, soon came home safe and sound.

Food got scarcer and scarcer. One day, when Hiroko came into the back of the house from the shop, a beer-bottle full of unpolished rice stood on the verandah, but Toshiko was nowhere to be seen. Hiroko, assuming that Toshiko must have gone somewhere and forgotten to finish hulling the rice, was looking vaguely around the house when she heard a deep groan from the toilet. She opened the door, peeped in, and gave a cry to summon her husband. Toshiko was squatting inside, groaning. She had had a stroke and was unconscious. They put her to bed, still wearing the baggy trousers that all women wore in wartime, but the groans went on. They went on the next day too, though Toshiko did not regain consciousness. Gradually they became louder and more ominous, till they could be heard in the houses round about. As Hiroko gazed with a distressed expression into Toshiko's face, a dreadful thought came to her before she could stop it: what if she regained consciousness but remained paralyzed, so that they had to keep her in bed? At that moment, she felt she would like to stop up the nose and mouth that emitted the groans; she even felt that for her to do so, in fact, would be the happiest thing for Toshiko too. But the next moment she was appalled at the dreadfulness of her own thoughts.

Toshiko breathed her last on the third day. Naoyuki came and saw to all the arrangements for the funeral. When the perfunctory ceremony was over, and Hiroko, back from the crematorium, had the urn containing the ashes in her arms, it occurred to her for the first time that they were a great deal indebted to Aunt Toshiko. Kaneyuki had said that they would have to keep her all her life, and Hiroko had half shared his view: it was the usual arrogance of the normal human being towards the weak. Yet, in the end, she began to suspect, it was they who had made use of her and she — unobtrusively doing their bidding, striving never to be a trouble to others — who had been of use to them. With the urn weighing heavily, irrevocably, on her arms, Hiroko shut her eyes and prayed. It was, in a way, an apology to Aunt Toshiko for her life.

(Translated by John Bester)

Flight and Pursuit

Annada Sankar Ray

THE PRINCIPAL was playing billiards with the marker. He made a wonderful break. That evening there was no one in the club except the marker to congratulate him.

"Fine, Your Honour! Grand! Very first-class!" the marker complimented him, with a smile. He asked for the Principal's cue and rubbed chalk on its tip.

"Why is the Judge so late today?" the Principal asked the question for the third time.

"I'm afraid the Judge may not come today," answered the marker, and added, without waiting for the next question: "It's a very bad murder case, Your Honour."

The information did not surprise the Principal, but he lost interest in the game. The Judge would not be coming. How long could he go on playing with the marker? The man seemed determined to let him win. But this break had not been the result of the marker's manoeuvring. When the Principal played with the Judge, he seldom made one like it, however.

It was the marker's turn. He had been playing billiards since his boyhood and was an expert. He had only to touch the white ball with his cue slowly, nonchalantly, and it would begin to roll steadily and smoothly over the green baize of the table. His aim was unerring. He made pots and in-offs and cannons as he pleased. But he deliberately kept his points down. It was not his policy to defeat the Principal. He kept himself in the background very skillfully.

The Principal won when he played with the marker but he felt none of the exhilaration of winning. He played for a while longer that evening and handed in his cue. The marker was eager to get off early. He suppressed a smile and said: "It's most regrettable, Your Honour, the Judge has not come today. Meanwhile, is there anything I can bring you, Huzoor?"

The Principal stood himself a drink. "Water," he said.

"Very good, Sir." The marker salaamed and disappeared.

The sound of a car outside diverted the marker's attention. He hurried in its direction.

"Hello, Principal."

"Hello, Judge."

They held out their hands. Both were pleased. Their marker showed more pleasure than they did, but he was disappointed. There was no hope of his getting away early now. If the Judge and the Principal started playing, it would be nine o'clock before he was free. He would have to stand on one side and applaud, "Grand!" and then go around to the other side and exclaim, "Splendid!" From time to time, he would have to rub chalk on the tips of their cues. And, when they consulted him, he would have to suggest which moves to make. If they disagreed, he acted as umpire. Every half hour he had to remember to salaam and ask, "Is there anything I can bring for Your Honour?" and fetch the drinks they ordered.

The Judge and the Principal chose their cues and called: "Marker!"

The marker presented himself and salaamed. Pointing to one another, they said, simultaneously: "Ask him."

The poor marker was in a dilemma. If he asked the Judge first, it would be obvious that he gave the Principal precedence over him. And, if he asked the Principal first, it would be obvious that he gave the Judge precedence. The marker had held his job for a long time. It would not be taken away from him lightly. For what was the good of giving offence to anyone? All his sons, sons-in-law and nephews were well-employed, thanks to the good offices of his bosses. Not one had been left unprovided for. As soon as the cool weather came to an end, in a couple of months, a punkapuller would be required for the Judge's office. Would he then not have to approach him for the post on behalf of one of his relatives?

The Principal was learned no doubt, and learning is to be respected wherever it is found. The marker knew that. But the Judge was the dispenser of punishment. He could, if he wished, send a man to the gallows. Within his jurisdiction the greatest deference was due to him.

"Is there anything I can bring you, Huzoor?" he turned to the Principal.

"Lemon squash," said the Principal and laughed. It was as he had expected.

The Judge said: "Gin."

They then gave themselves up to the game. They spoke only of the moves they made. When they disagreed, they summoned the marker. His opinion was authoritative and his verdicts were impartial, without respect for personalities. He also had his code. A look at him showed that he was conscious of his role. He would not compromise. Though his salary was a mere fraction of the Judge's he would not help even the Judge to win by unfair means. All the

91

sahebs were afraid of rubbing him the wrong way. They would not get another man who knew the game as well if he threw up his job.

The game did not go well that evening. The Judge was inclined to be absent-minded. Again and again he miscued, or his ball missed the one at which he aimed. The marker kept the score. The Judge shuddered when he looked at the board: minus twenty! "No luck," he said and gave up.

"What's the matter, Sur?" the Principal was concerned. "You aren't playing at all."

"Why talk about it. Maitra," the Judge answered. He was pale. "How can a person play games when the life of a man is at stake? You teachers are the ones who can afford to play games. You are the lucky ones."

The Principal protested. "Anyone can sentence a man to the gallows," he said, "but how many can develop manhood in the sons of men? Yet teachers are paid less than anybody else."

"Anybody can send a man to the gallows?" the Judge was astonished. "The power to do so has been given to only one of the two million two hundred thousand inhabitants of these two districts. I am one in two million."

The Judge's hair was as white as a yaktail fan, but he was not old. He had barely entered his forties. The flesh of his face was firm. His lips were as fresh as a hibiscus; he never took betel, so their colour was natural. His complexion was fair for a Bengali. He was in the habit of spending some time in England every three or four years. He had not married. When questioned about it, he would say: "I'll think about getting married when I have saved something."

The Principal was a grass widower. His wife and children lived in Calcutta. He had been appointed Principal and sent to this country town after many years of teaching at Presidency College, in Calcutta. He would go back to his old post if this town did not suit him, foregoing his promotion. But, if he found it congenial, he planned to bring his family later. At one time, he had studied in London. The Judge had been his classmate.

"Why do you worry so much about it?" the Principal asked, casting a significant glance at the Judge's white hair. "You do not give the verdict. The jury is there. If the jury says the accused is guilty under Section 302 and if you agree, the death sentence is passed in accordance with the law. That is, if you can find no grounds to lighten the punishment. If you can, the accused is given transportation for life. To this extent you have a free hand. There is no responsibility where there is no freedom. You are responsible only to the extent that you act as a free agent."

Maitra had practised as a barrister for a time. He did not find a good practice. By nature he was a scholar. He had a good degree. His appointment letter followed closely upon his interview with the Director of Public Instruction. He opted for the life of a teacher before he had passed the age limit for Government service. Otherwise, he would have felt as frustrated as Michael Madhusudan Dutta, and, like him, cried: "Alas! Strange was the fruit for which I strove, misled by hope."

They left the billiard-table and seated themselves on the high bench at the end of the room, still holding their cues. They continued to argue. The marker, assuming that they would resume their game shortly, coughed and went outside for a chat with the chauffeur.

The Judge sighed and said: "My dear friend, if only it were as easy as that. How can I make you understand that my responsibility for the consequences of the verdict is greater than that of the jury. What you have said reminds me of what someone else once told me. It is God who kills a man destined to die. Such a man is dead even before he is brought to trial. I, like Arjuna, am no more than an instrument in His hand. *Nimittamatro bhava Savyasachi.*"

"The Gita has the last word. The responsibility belongs entirely to that fellow, God. What have you or I got to do with it? Why should we be in such deadly earnest about it? Hundreds and thousands of people die every day. What does one more or one less matter?" The Principal was indifferent.

"Let them die if they must. But why at my hands? They may die because of their own bad luck, their own adverse fate. But why should they die because of an error of judgment, a miscarriage of justice? Not a single innocent person should be unjustly punished. This is the basic tenet of a judge's moral creed. Whose headache is it if not mine? I take it very seriously." The Judge was unyielding.

"Fine! Your worry is your worry. But my evening is spoiled. Marker! Now where has that fellow gone?"

The marker had taken off his turban and was resting. He hurried back, tying the turban around his head as he came. The Principal said: "Ask him."

"No, no, it's my turn, not yours. Marker!"

The marker obeyed. He went up to the Principal and salaamed.

"Orange!" said the Principal.

The Judge ordered a chhota peg.

"Cheerio!" they raised their glasses and drank. But they made no move to get down from their lofty perch. The poor marker was at a loss to know what to do.

93

The Judge's eyes fell on the marker's face. With his intuitive un derstanding of men, he at once realised the fellow's plight. Raising his right hand, he said: "Enough."

The marker took the cues and hung them in the rack. He col lected the balls, arranged them in the centre of the table, and switch ed off the strong light over it. But he was not free to go as long as the sahebs were in the club and might wish to order drinks. It was not yet nine o'clock, but the night was a dark one and it seem ed later than it actually was. The town was quiet.

"What's the use of detaining this poor fellow?" the Judge said. "Nobody seems to want to come to the club after tennis nowadays." And he added, in English: "What is there to attract them? Where are the fair enchantresses? All the ladies in this station are *purdah*. This is what Indianisation has brought us to."

"And Islamisation," added Maitra, also speaking in English. "But that is not the only reason, Sur. You've not married. The Civil Sur geon is also a bachelor. How long does it take for a club to close down if its members work against it? Society itself may close down, too."

The Judge laughed. "We are the enemies, are we? Ha! Ha! Come on, come on! Let's go over to my place. I'll be pleased to have you as my guest for dinner."

The two friends got into the car and let the marker go.

THEY chatted about many things as they dined. Then they car ried their cups of coffee into the living-room and seated themselves beside the fire. The weather had turned cold, but Sur's English habits were an even stronger incentive than the weather. He enjoyed sitting by the fireside as he listened to the B.B.C. His pet dog, Jolly, lay at his feet.

"Maitra," Sur came back to the subject they had been discussing, "could you send a man to the gallows yourself? That is, could you, if you were a judge, pass the death sentence?"

"Certainly," Maitra answered, without any hesitation. "It's not I who pass the sentence. It is the law. If the Government abolishes capital punishment, I'll not have to pass such a sentence."

"But that other person, the person who advised me to regard my self only as an instrument, said he could not do it. When I asked him the question I have just asked you, he retreated. Then he told me a story, the story of his life."

The Judge again grew absent-minded. His memory went back to the early days of his career.

"The case did not come to my court and I do not recall the de tails," he spoke, slowly, as he thought back and pieced together what he could remember, stopping frequently, correcting himself, and protesting against what he was saying. What emerged was more or less as follows:

"When Neogy was the District Judge of Rajshahi, a murder case was brought to trial in his court. Engrej Mollah had been killed. The accused was none other than his son, Gopal Mollah. Gopal was eighteen or nineteen years old. His mother was dead. He was a spoilt boy and got whatever he wanted. His father had never been able to deny him anything. Gopal was a boy of some taste. He organised a troupe of *alkap* players in his village. (*Alkap* is a variety of *jatra*.) Day and night he busied himself with it. He was handsome and had a good voice. Many girls were attracted to him. Their husbands became his enemies. But Gopal was a good boy. Nobody was able to make allegations against his character.

"One day Gopal announced that he wished to marry a certain widow. Who was she? Shonabhan. Shonabhan was older than Gopal. She was good-looking and voluptuous. She had a bad reputation. She was very wealthy and therefore much sought-after. Engrej said: 'No.'

"Gopal got out of control. Engrej was still vigorous and strong. He was also wealthy and a Member of the Union Board. In order to protect his son, Engrej married Shonabhan himself. He had hoped that Gopal would accept the situation and marry some nice good girl. But Gopal quarrelled with his father and left the village. The *alkap* troupe was taken over by his bosom friend, Kalu.

"Engrej was quite happy. Another son was born to him. One dark night a person entered his room and attacked him with a sharp weapon. Engrej called out: 'Gopal, you!' The neighbours heard his cry and came running. They found him unconscious. He died shortly after. None of them actually saw Gopal, but they had heard Engrej cry out: 'Gopal, you.'

"SHONABHAN was not at home at the time. She was attending an *alkap* performance. Gopal was arrested the following day at the meeting-place of the *alkap* players. He said: 'When I left home I left it for good. Why should I go back?' Circumstantial evidence was against him. A handkerchief had been picked up, a handkerchief that Shonabhan had given to Gopal. There was blood on it.

"In a murder case, the jury is usually reluctant to invite trouble. When they feel any hesitation about acquitting a person outright, they turn his offence into one under Section 304 instead of Section 302. In this instance, the jury could have reduced the gravity of the offence if they had wished to do so, but guilt was established under Section 302. The public prosecutor explained to them, very convincingly, that if a wife dies another wife can be found, if a child dies another child may be born, but when a father dies he cannot be replaced. There is no crime greater than patricide. 'If Gopal has not committed this heinous crime in the hope of obtaining his stepmother, set him free. If there is any reasonable doubt in your minds, give him the benefit of the doubt. But,' the public prosecutor declaimed, theatrically, 'if the person who murdered Engrej Mollah is his son, Gopal, and nobody else,' — he wiped the tears from his eyes as he addressed the jury — 'your duty is a stern one. You should not allow any superstitious consideration to sway your judgment. Engrej's line will not become extinct if Gopal goes. You are educated Hindus and Muslims. A word to the wise is sufficient.' "

Maitra could not restrain himself any longer. "The judge," he said, "certainly took the tender age of the accused into consideration and did not send him to the gallows, but sentenced him to transportation for life. Is that it?"

"No, my friend, Gopal was no longer a boy. He had become a major. His age could not be made an extenuating circumstance. Neogy concurred with the verdict of the jury and passed the capital sentence. A good lawyer might have been able to save the boy. But the boy's maternal uncle was poor. He stood aside. A lawyer was assigned to the case from the official defence panel, as provided by the law. At Government expense. For a nominal fee. No good lawyer puts his name on the panel. The lawyer assigned to Gopal was no match for the Public Prosecutor. What could Neogy do? He sent him to the gallows," Sur concluded, pathetically.

"Ah, the gallows!" Maitra shuddered. "Did the High Court confirm the sentence?"

"Listen to what happened after that. The boy heard the sentence in silence. He did not cry or throw himself about. He folded his hands in an attitude of prayer and raised them heavenwards, looking up once. That was all. Then the trial of the judge began. When he returned to his bungalow, he found that he could not put his mind to anything. He had no appetite. He woke from a nightmare and could not go to sleep again. A few days later, on the excuse of inspecting the jail, he visited the prison in order to talk to Gopal. He said: 'Gopal, I'm sorry for you with all my heart. Tell me, what can I do for you? I also am afraid of making a mistake.'

"Gopal answered: 'Your Worship is the dispenser of justice. But on the day of the Last Judgment, Allah will be my judge. He will sit in judgment on the witnesses also, on the jurors and on Your Worship.'

"Neogy was upset. 'Gopal,' he said, 'appeal.'

" 'Can an appeal save a man whose own father has condemned him?' Gopal asked. 'And I want to die. Is it possible for a man to marry a woman who has been his stepmother? I could not have shown my face in the village again if I had been acquitted. People would still have thought that I had killed my father in order to marry my stepmother.' "

Maitra interrupted: "That is what is known as an Oedipus complex."

"THE boy's words rang so true," Sur went on, "that it seemed to Neogy everybody else in the drama had been only acting. Gopal was the only one who had not been pretending. He forgot time and place and pleaded with Gopal. 'Gopal,' he cried, 'for God's sake tell me what actually happened.'

"Gopal answered: 'God is my witness. I did not go to the house. Shonabhan gave me the handkerchief before she married my father. After the ceremony, I threw it at her and walked out. Allah alone knows how the blood got on it.'

"Gopal refused to say anything more. Neogy did not question him. The doubt that had entered his mind stuck there. He wrote to the Government, asking for leave, saying that when he returned to duty he did not wish to be appointed to the post of Judge. He felt that if he were made a judge again he would have a nervous break-down."

Maitra interrupted again: "He wasn't fit to be a judge! Such a credulous fellow! He believed anything he was told. It's not strange that a man condemned to death should fabricate an alibi."

"Have you ever heard of a man condemned to death who refused to appeal?" Judge Sur asked.

"Do you ask me to believe that Gopal didn't appeal?" Maitra countered.

"No, friend, Gopal didn't appeal. It was such an unnatural thing that others besides Neogy were upset. Even the Public Prosecutor was dumbfounded. Just listen to what followed. Neogy was granted leave. On its expiry, he was sent back to the same district to officiate as Magistrate. He took the opportunity to go to Badalgachhi on his way to see the stupa at Paharpur. Like Haroun-al-Rashid he began making enquiries incognito. From the village watchman and local police sub-inspectors he learned that a certain Halim Mirdha had, as it were, killed two birds with one stone — the father and the son. He wanted Shonabhan and her property for himself. The affair had been going on for a long time. Mirdha had looked after Shonabhan's property before her marriage. Shonabhan would have married him if he had not already had a wife. Engrej Mollah had snatched his prize away from him. Mirdha had been trying to devise a way to get rid of him ever since. One dark night, he had called out, 'Father!', entered Engrej's room and killed him. Groggy with sleep, Engrej had cried out, 'Gopal, you!' Shonabhan was not there. Mirdha was gone before anyone could reach the place."

"Opium, opium!" Maitra commented, sarcastically. "I've heard that hemp is grown at Badalgachhi. Neogy got a strong whiff of it."

"Halim Mirdha went into hiding and stayed away for a long time," Sur went on. "He returned to the village only after Gopal had been sentenced. But the villagers looked upon him with suspicion. He was very careful in his movements. He was planning to marry Shonabhan after Gopal was executed. When Neogy got back to headquarters, he was running a temperature of 102 degrees. He went to see the new judge in spite of it. 'There is still time,' he said. 'Let's try to save the boy from the gallows.'

"The new judge was McGregor. He was not easily persuaded. 'I did not try the case,' he said. 'I have no *locus standi* in the matter. And you are no longer the judge. You are *functus officio*. The papers have been sent to the High Court. The High Court may not confirm the sentence. In that case the boy will not die.'

" 'If and when the sentence is confirmed,' Neogy protested, 'the case will be practically lost.'

"McGregor said: 'If a mercy petition is sent up to the Governor, the Governor can, in consideration of the boy's age, waive the death sentence. There are precedents.'

" 'Will a boy who has refused to appeal submit a mercy petition?' Neogy asked. 'To do that would be to admit his guilt.'

"McGregor said: 'He'll have to admit it if he wants to live. Fourteen years pass very quickly. It is not very difficult to start life over again at the age of thirty-three. He is a farmer's son. Nobody is going to outcast him if he settles in some other village.' "

"That's right." Maitra applauded. "McGregor was fit to be a judge. What happened next?"

"The inevitable. Gopal had not appealed. The High Court confirmed the sentence. There was not a soul to stand up and say a word on Gopal's behalf. Neogy visited the prison again in order to see Gopal. Gopal refused to submit a mercy petition. Why should he beg for mercy when he had not committed the crime? Then Neogy did something unprecedented. He wrote a letter to the Judicial Secretary, telling him all about the case. In reply, he was informed that no action could be taken upon any information an ex-judge might happen to obtain outside his court. Unless a mercy petition was submitted, it would be assumed that the accused was unrepentant. In that case, no mercy was called for. Neogy gave up. His term as officiating Magistrate ran out before the date set for the execution. He was transferred. He took to drinking and began to gamble at the races. And he began to read the Gita. He hoped to save himself by such means."

"Why?" Maitra asked, in surprise. "Did he lose his life?"

"Oh, wait," Sur went on. "Hear me to the end. When I first made his acquaintance, he was officiating as a Commissioner. How could he have risen so high in the Service if he had not lived? When I told him that I found the work of a judge disagreeable and the post of a magistrate a doubtful blessing, he said to me: *'Nimitta-matro bhava Savyasachi.'*

"But, when he told me this story, I became apprehensive that I, too, might punish an innocent man and regret it for the rest of my life. It was his testimony. Whenever a murder case comes to my court I sit down with the Gita. But I find no solace or peace of mind in it. It is an open question whether anyone called God exists or not. I cannot put my conscience to sleep with the thought that I am an instrument in His hands. A judge has to be alert always, vigilant, in order to prevent the innocent from being punished. Why should the innocent be sent to prison? Why to the gallows? As long as a trial is in progress, I have no rest and no peace. I, the Judge, am more on trial than the accused. When it is over, I experience a feeling of immense relief. But a doubt always lingers. Who knows what the truth is? Pilate's question. I am as sceptical as Pilate. Pilate did not become a believer even though the Son of God Himself appeared before him. There is no way for me to know what actually happened in any particular case. I am helpless. If I did not realise that, what good would it do me to think of myself as an instrument of justice?"

"IT will be good for society, if not for you," Maitra said, after some thought.

"From one point of view, yes. Unless a show of justice is maintained, people will take the law into their own hands. Every individual will become both judge and executioner. But I want certainty. A hundred per cent certainty. The certainty that the person I punish is not another Gopal. But, of course, I have never run across a boy like Gopal, a boy who refuses to appeal, who will not submit a mercy petition, who can leave the Last Judgment to God and die quietly. I forgot to tell you that, before he left the district, Neogy went once again to the prison to see Gopal. This time he begged, pitifully. 'Forgive me, Gopal,' he said. 'I'm only a misguided human being. All men make mistakes.'

"Gopal answered: 'Your Worship, you are not to blame. What is there to forgive you for? No one can harm a man whom Allah protects. And no one can save a man whom Allah does not protect.

May Allah have mercy on Your Worship! May He make you a Governor!' "

"The boy was really a good boy. One has to admit it," Maitra conceded.

"Quite right," Sur assented, absent-mindedly, "but how tragic! Why should such things happen? What is a man born into the world to do? How? Why is he punished? Is he punished for something he has done in this life, or in some other life? Or is it in preparation for a future life? How can you justify such things to those who do not believe either in reincarnation or in life after death?"

Maitra sat on without speaking. Sur said: "There is good music on the radio tonight. Shall I tune in on the B.B.C.?"

"No, let it be," Maitra gestured.

The atmosphere in the room was oppressive and tense. Maitra at length broke the silence. "Sur," he said, "you ought to get married."

"Why? Tell me, has anybody asked you to play the matchmaker?"

"No, but it will be good for you. Your hair is white, but you have a fine physique. A lot of people marry at your age. And are happy."

"Ha! I haven't told you what Mrs. Neogy said to me, have I?"

Maitra was embarrassed. "What did she say?"

"She said that, since I had honoured her by calling her my elder sister (Didi), she wished to take the liberty to say something. She said: 'Never marry. Spare your wife.' "

"What? Did she, really?"

"Not only that. One day she came to my bungalow. She said she had come for legal advice. She was too shy to approach a lawyer. I was, she said, a brother to her. What was there to be shy about before a brother? She said she hoped I would give her the same advice I would my own sister in similar circumstances."

MAITRA grew restless. "What was it all about?" he asked.

"It was serious. Mrs. Neogy said that she had done her utmost to reform Mr. Neogy. She was forced to admit that she had failed. Drinking and gambling at the races could be forgiven. But he was also selling his country to the British. She had read his official papers. His subordinates, encouraged by his acquiescence, were following an unchecked policy of oppression and repression. Whenever she said anything, her husband got furious. She wanted to know if she could make that a valid ground for divorce."

"No, no! It can't be true! It's impossible!" Maitra flinched.

100

"I explained that to her. I even threatened her a little. To read official documents secretly could also be made a ground for divorce," Sur smiled.

Maitra's face had withered. "It's bad, very bad, to do something like that. But can it be made a ground for divorce? Or are you joking? You know how much I dislike the idea of divorce."

"You have not realised what I was doing, Maitra," Sur said. "I did not want the life of a man — for whom I had so much respect, a man who had given me so much sound advice — to be made more unbearable than it already was. I did not give her the least encouragement. Your society was perfectly safe in my hands."

"Do you know what I would have done?" Maitra took up the threads of the conversation. "I would have psycho-analysed the lady. Why was she so annoyed with her husband that she sought legal advice about divorce? What was at the root of it? Was it mistrust arising from a difference in attitude to the country, or something else?"

"There, now! You've started your theorising," Sur laughed. "A person in grave trouble comes to me in the hope of finding a way out of her dilemma, and I sit down to psycho-analyse her in an effort to discover an academic truth! If I had done that, I might have detected all sorts of complexes. I don't know how many complexes you have on your list. Perhaps hers was a Jupiter complex."

They both laughed. Then Sur said: "What I understand as the truth is something quite different. Gopal may have had an Oedipus complex — that is, if he committed the murder at all. But I would not have used your psycho-analytical methods if I had been his judge. That is not my way of ascertaining the truth. The question I ask is: 'What was the situation?'

"What solutions of the situation were possible or likely? There are situations of which the only possible outcome is a tragic one. The only way out is through tragedy. Men sometimes murder and pay the penalty because there is no other escape for them from a situation that is unendurable. No one is going to trust a judge enough to tell him what the situation was, nor are people often able to grasp a situation clearly enough to describe it. To them I am Yama incarnate. Actually, I am a man's friend. I embrace and press to my heart the man I send to the gallows. There is no more terrible punishment. Yet I pronounce the sentence with love. To me all murderers are Gopal. The true verdict will be given on the Day of Judgment. What takes place here takes place in the interests of society, according to the law as prescribed and approved by society."

Maitra, overcome with emotion, grasped Sur's hand. Neither spoke. When they regained their composure, Maitra asked: "What happened in the end? Was it divorce or separation?"

101

"Neither." Sur paused. "They spent another seven years together. Then —" Sur's voice hoarsened.

"Say it, say it! Out with it!" Maitra was consumed with curiosity.

"He lost his footing and fell, late one dark night. He died in a gutter. I heard it was drink."

"Ah, he died!" Maitra was deeply moved. He seemed to be in a dream.

Sur shook him and said: "So, you see, marriage is not a panacea for all evils. Even a woman cannot save a man. Nor can the Bhagavad Gita. I have found only one solution — not to engage in dangerous work of this kind. It is less dangerous to work in the pit of a mine. But, if I become a pitman, no girl of respectable family will marry me. And how can I support such a girl? But you not only permit me to engage in the far more dangerous work of a judge or a magistrate, but you approve so heartily that you take my ladder away as soon as I am well up in the tree. As a judge, I may convict one innocent man among ten guilty ones. I may order the police to fire on an unruly mob. Among the people who are shot may be an innocent boy or girl. My wife will at once rebel against me. How can I convince her that I am not a bad man, that my job is to blame. If it were possible, I would resign and step out of all this. If there is a girl who would be willing to marry a *fakir* and live with him under a tree like a *fakirini,* I might consider marrying her."

MAITRA was listening with rapt attention. The fire was about to go out. Sur dumped more coal into it and stirred it up. It seemed symbolic of his life.

"Now tell me about yourself. Is there anything I can do for you?" Maitra asked when Sur resumed his seat and was quiet once more.

"Thank you, my friend, but nobody can save me except myself. I accept one thing the Gita says, if nothing else: *Uddharedatmanat-manam.*"

They were silent for a long time after that. Then Sur began to speak quietly, relating the story of his own life. Maitra listened without comment.

"What did I know of the world when I was your classmate in London? All I thought of was how to do well in my examinations, get a good job and come back to India. I had to relieve my father who was getting old. Should he pauperise himself for my sake? I did not worry too much about the nature of the jobs offered me, nor wonder which would give me peace of mind and which would be dis-

102

tasteful. The day I set my father free from all financial obligations towards me by becoming a member of the Indian Civil Service — the thought from which I derived the greatest satisfaction — came the realisation that henceforth I was my own master. In due course, I returned to India and joined my post. I enjoyed it. The only fly in the ointment was political disaffection. When the British found that I was hesitant about carrying out their policies, they put me in the judiciary. I became even more independent in consequence.

"But, gradually, I began to feel that I was losing my mental health. The people who were my constant associates, in whose company I spent my days and nights, were people accused of robbery, of murder, of rape. They belonged to the slimiest layer of society. Those who handled their cases also dirtied themselves. The slime was on their hands and feet, on their persons. At times, I have compared their faces. I have been unable to distinguish a policeman's face from the face of a criminal. On visits to the prison, I have seen that the faces of the warders are in no way different from the faces of the convicts. The faces of lawyers are frightening. Their dress differs, but their faces are the faces of criminals. Anyone touched by crime takes on the expression of a criminal. How could I protect myself from this all-defiling slime? How could I live in it with the impunity of a mud-fish? I studied my own face in the mirror. I was afraid.

"One day, O'Neill, a Member of the Board of Revenue, visited my station. At one time he had been my superior officer. We met again. In the course of conversation, he asked: 'Sur, do you like judging? I had an idea that you preferred the executive.'

" 'You're right,' I answered, 'but I don't want to go back to it.'

"O'NEILL left. I could not get rid of the thought that he had put into my mind. I had tried very hard to keep myself well-posted on executive procedure. By temperament I'm an executive. But there had been a four-year break. I could not have taken up the threads again if I had gone back. Political differences were at their height, not only between the British and the Indians, but between the Hindus and the Muslims as well.

"Still it was better to go back, even into all the unrest, than become a criminal among criminals. I wrote to the Chief Secretary. Must I be a judge always? Against my inclination? The Chief Secretary had been my guest. He answered sympathetically. He had been through my papers. It had been decided from the outset that the place for me was the judiciary. It was my fate, whether I liked it or not. Good judges were needed. He hoped that I would realise that the public interest was more important than personal likes and dislikes. He wished me success.

"It took me a long time to reconcile myself to the idea. I don't know how I managed to do it. Just imagine, even skulls are sometimes produced in court as evidence! Clothes stained with blood and semen are an everyday affair. I have to inspect such articles. The police handle them. Doctors are called in to describe the nature of the injuries on a body. They relate what they are able to discover by autopsy. I have to write down the evidence with my own hand, in all its revolting detail. More revolting still is the report on the body of a woman in a case of rape. It is barely tolerable coming from even a doctor. But to hear a woman herself describe in full a beastly outrage on her person . . . The lawyers dig for details to find out whether the case belongs under Section 379 or not. Did penetration take place? I feel like caning them. They try to prove even a good girl is not pure. As if a woman has no will of her own once she has been touched. As if any beast is entitled to abuse her. Behind this attitude are the moral values of our unequal society. An unfortunate girl, who has slipped once, is fair game for anybody, at any time, by general consent. But a man is carefully protected by the law, no matter if he slips a thousand times over.

"Who is there to protect these unfortunate girls in a society like ours if I don't? Among all these 2,200,000 people? And not only these women. Who trusts a man who has been convicted of stealing once? Does he obtain normal employment? He is forced to steal again. The second offence brings double punishment. We often find that the second offence is of a lighter character than the first. But our magistrates double the first sentence blindly. I reduce the sentence on appeal. I say that, if the current offence calls for six months, the magistrate can, taking a previous conviction into consideration, make it a year. But, for the first offence, an accused may have been given ten months by a different magistrate in totally different circumstances. To double it mechanically and give the man twenty months is to mete out punishment out of all proportion to the offence. The magistrates are not always to blame. The Court Sub-inspectors tell them that it should be done.

"Whenever I get the opportunity I reduce such a sentence, invoking the curses of the police. I also set up an organisation to help men who have served a term in prison to find normal employment. Nobody wants to give them a job. If they do, they attract the attentions of the police. And who can really trust such a man? He may disappear any day, taking things with him. If such a theft is reported to the police, they only say: 'Didn't we warn you?' If I dare to engage an ex-convict as my gardener and he lets me down, the Superintendent of Police will say: 'Rightly served. Can you straighten a dog's tail?'

"Good judges are needed by society. The idea is inadequate. Another must be appended to it. Without the addition of the second, people like me would find it very hard to go on living. I have to deal with what is ugly, with what is false, with what is bad. Should I then draw the conclusion that there is no beauty, no truth, no good? From my dwelling-place in Hell, it is difficult to believe that a Heaven exists at all, or a God. It is obvious that man exists. But does man look as though God has created him in His own image? What proof of His paternity is there that we attribute Fatherhood to Him?

"I HAVE been a worshipper of beauty from my boyhood. Beauty is not just an empty word to me. I looked for it everywhere when I was young. I did catch glimpses of her, the hem of her dress, a curl of her hair. But how can she beckon to me in this Palace of the Underworld? Where is her glance? Often and often I have bewailed her absence from my life as a judge. I have almost given up in despair. It was ten years before my inner vision developed. At last I became convinced. She exists.

"She exists. The road she travels passes through all this anguish, across this garbage, through a narrow mountain-gorge overhung by broken men and fallen women. This road is her road. In following it, I am following in her footsteps. I shall find her. I shall see her. She goes ahead of me. She moves through the air without touching the ground. She is like the daughter of the sun, Tapati. And I, in pursuit of her, wade through mud and water, climb up banks, run and stumble over rough ground. I am like King Sambaran. My gaze is fixed on heaven. The road I must travel, the road that is hers, is the shadowy dark way of frightful ugliness and evil.

"It is as though she throws dust in my eyes lest I see her too clearly, in order that I may not recognise her. Or the dust flies up of itself, in the wake of her passing. I see darkness. The name of that darkness is harsh reality, the reality which continually overwhelms me with new and newer offences. Only the other day a young mother was brought to my court. She had strangled her babe with her own hands. Before her there came a friend, a friend who had enticed a boy into a vacant house and murdered him in his sleep. He cut off his head and buried it in sand beside a river. I shall say nothing about the person whose case is being tried at this moment. It is *sub judice*. But it is still another revelation of cruel reality. I wonder silently if she is there, on the other side of this darkness. Will she answer if I call? I cannot see her with my eyes. Yet I turn my eyes to her, in her direction, away from all this.

"No, this cruel, very frightful, reality of yours does not blind me, even though the sight of it may distress me. I can always see beyond it, through it. My feelings transcend it. My feet kick it aside. I have no illusions about it. I am not involved with it. I do not look upon it as good. I only accept it. There was a time when I vowed not to accept anything without scrutinising it first — not God, not life after death, not reincarnation. I am still unable to accept the basic tenet of the Gita. Like Arjuna, I cry in fear and trembling, 'I lose my sense of direction and can find no peace when I behold Thy terrible fanged mouths, like the devouring flames of Time.' I omit the rest.

"Reality is cruel. I admit it. But reality is not the last word. My eyes are fixed on the one who has thrown it into my face. She is not a ferocious deity with terrible fangs. Her face does not devour with its flames. She is very, very close and dear to me, very much my own. I am hers. My relationship with her is a permanent relationship. Not a day passes but the sound of her footsteps comes to my ears. The sound of her wings in flight is audible over the subdued, confused noise of the court-room. I cannot leave the Judge's chair. I am pinned to my seat. My ears are turned to the witness or the accused, to the defence lawyer or the public prosecutor. But the ankle-bells of an unseen presence tinkle for me. Another person exists. She exists. She exists. The one who protests against all this reality. One who is not less real nor less actual. One who can be caught if one knows how, who can be touched if one knows how.

"Neogy's wife could not save him from the gutter. But my beloved has kept me out of the slime. I am alive only by her grace. She has done what no wife could do. Why then should I think of marriage? In what way are you better off than I am? In what way am I the loser? My white hair is not a flag of surrender. I do not admit defeat. Every day I engage in battle with this deadly reality. I am undefeated, not by virtue of the strength of my own arm, but by virtue of the magic charm she has given me. A man wants invincibility. The woman who helps him to remain undefeated is the one he seeks. What does it matter whether she exists in the flesh or not?

"Maitra, perhaps you consider me unfortunate. There is no one to cook Bengali delicacies for me. A Muslim cook cannot even prepare bitter gourd properly. My taste in food, like that of Lord Sinha in the Government House at Patna, is Bengali, no matter how Anglicised I may otherwise be. I also considered myself unfortunate at one time. I tried to find a solution. I did not find it in marriage. Man does not live by bread alone. Likewise, man does not live just for a wife. He has to establish a harmony between the contradictory aspects of his life, between the beautiful and the ugly, between the best and the worst. I have not been able to do it. Amidst all the outward comfort of my way of living, I have burned. Now I have at last found a kind of solution. I do not burn any more. I am at peace. My solution lies not in flight, but in the pursuit of one who flies in front of me."

IT was late. Maitra said in a drowsy voice: "Sur, you've told me a very nice fairy-tale tonight. You are good at making things up."

Sur laughed. "How did you like the story?" he asked.

"Straight evasion." Maitra yawned. "I hoped you'd tell me about the secret sad romance of your life, about the lady you couldn't marry, for whose sake you've remained a bachelor. I believe in the existence of such a lady. If not in this count , abroad. The person you describe is no imaginary. Some day she'll materialise."

"No, no. That'll never happen. She's foregone her place. The lady of my dreams has superseded her entirely. I'll tell you about it some day, if you want to know."

With that, Sur saw Maitra to the car.

"The Principal's residence," he said to the chauffeur.

His valet came and helped him out of his dinner-jacket. He put on his pyjamas and sat down to study the papers of the case under trial, far into the night.

(Translated from Bengali by Lila Ray)

The Bread of Salt

N.V.M. Gonzalez

USUALLY I was in bed by ten and up by five and thus was ready for one more day of my fourteenth year. Unless Grandmother had forgotten, the fifteen centavos for the baker down Progreso Street — and how I enjoyed jingling those coins in my pocket! — would be in the empty fruit-jar in the cupboard. I would remember then that rolls were what Grandmother wanted because recently she had lost three molars. For young people like my cousins and myself, she had always said that the kind called *pan de sal* ought to be quite all right.

The bread of salt! How did it get that name? From where did its flavor come; through what secret action of flour and yeast? At the risk of being jostled from the counter by other early buyers, I would push my way into the shop so that I might watch the men who, stripped to the waist, worked their long flat wooden spades in and out of the glowing maw of the oven. Why did the bread come nut-brown and the size of my little fist? And why did it have a pair of lips convulsed into a painful frown? In the half-light of the street, and hurrying, the paper bag pressed to my chest, I felt my curiosity a little gratified by the oven-fresh warmth of the bread I was proudly bringing home for breakfast.

Well I knew how Grandmother would not mind if I nibbled away at one piece; perhaps, I might even eat two pieces, to be charged later against my share at the table. But that would be betraying a trust; and so, indeed, I kept my purchase intact. To guard it from harm, I watched my steps and avoided the dark street corners.

For my reward, I had only to look in the direction of the sea-wall and the fifty yards or so of river bed beyond it, where an old Spaniard's house stood. At low tide, when the bed was dry and the rocks glinted with broken bottles, the stone fence of the Spaniard's compound set off the house as if it were a castle. Sunrise brought a wash of silver upon the roof of the laundry and garden sheds which had been built low and close to the fence. On dull mornings the light dripped from the bamboo screen which covered the veranda and hung some four or five yards from the ground. Unless it was August, when the damp northeast monsoon had to be kept away from the

108

rooms, three servants raised the screen promptly at six-thirty until it was completely hidden under the veranda eaves. From the sound of the pulleys I knew it was time to set out for school.

It was in his service, as a coconut plantation overseer, that Grandfather had spent the last thirty years of his life. Grandmother had been widowed three years now. I often wondered whether I was being depended upon to spend the years ahead in the service of this great house. One day I learned that Aida, a classmate in high school, was the old Spaniard's niece. All my doubts disappeared. It was as if before his death Grandfather had spoken to me about her, concealing the seriousness of the matter by putting it over as a joke. If now I kept true to the virtues, she would step out of her bedroom ostensibly to say Good Morning to her uncle. Her real purpose, I knew, was to reveal thus her assent to my desire.

On quiet mornings I imagined the patter of her shoes upon the wooden veranda floor as a further sign, and I would hurry off to school, taking the route she had fixed for me past the post office, the town plaza and the church, the health center east of the plaza, and at last the school grounds. I considered whether to try to walk with her and decided it would be the height of rudeness. Enough that in her blue skirt and white middy she would be half a block ahead and, from that distance, perhaps throw a glance in my direction, to bestow upon my heart a deserved and abundant blessing. I believed it was but right that in some such way as this her mission in my life was disguised.

Her name, I was to learn many years later, was a convenient mnemonic for the qualities to which argument might aspire. But in those days it was a living voice. "Oh that you might be worthy of uttering me," it said. And how I endeavored to build my body so that I might live long to honor her. With every victory at singles at the handball court — the game was then the craze at school — I could feel my body glow in the sun as though it had instantly been cast in bronze. I guarded my mind and did not let my wits go astray. In class I would not allow a lesson to pass unmastered. Our English teacher could put no question before us that did not have a ready answer in my head. One day he read Robert Louis Stevenson's *The Sire de Maletroit's Door*, and we were so enthralled that our breaths trembled. I knew then that somewhere, sometime in the not too improbable future, a benign old man with a lantern in his hand would also detain me in a secret room and there daybreak would find me thrilled by the sudden certainty that I had won Aida's hand.

It was perhaps on my violin that her name wrought such tender spell. Maestro Antonino remarked the dexterity of my stubby fingers. Quickly I raced through Alard — until I had all but committed two-thirds of the book to memory. My short brown arm learned at last to draw the bow with grace. Sometimes, when practising my scales in the early evening, I wondered if the wind carrying the straggling notes across the pebbled river did not transform them into a Schubert's *Serenade*.

At last Mr. Custodio, who was in charge of our school orchestra, became aware of my progress. He moved me from second to first violin. During the Thanksgiving Day program he bade me render a number complete with pizzicati and harmonics.

"Another Vallejo! Our own Albert Spalding!" I heard from the front row.

Aida, I thought, would be in the audience. I looked quickly around but could not see her. As I retired to my place in the orchestra I heard Pete Saez, the trombone player, call my name.

"You must join *my* band," he said. "Look, we'll have many engagements soon. It'll be vacation time."

Pete pressed my arm. He had for some time now been asking me to join the Minviluz Orchestra, his private band. All I had been able to tell him was that I had my school work to mind. He was twenty-two. I was perhaps too young to be going around with him. He earned his school fees and supported his mother hiring out his band at least three or four times a month. He now said:

"Tomorrow we play at a Chinaman's funeral. Four to six in the afternoon. In the evening, Judge Roldan's silver wedding anniversary party. Sunday, the Municipal dance."

My head began to whirl. On the stage, in front of us, the Principal had begun a speech about America. Nothing he could say about the Pilgrim Fathers and the American custom of feasting on turkey seemed interesting. I thought of the money I would earn. For several days now I had but one wish, to buy a box of linen stationery. At night when the house was quiet I would fill the sheets with words that would tell Aida how much I adored her. One of these mornings, perhaps before school closed for the holidays, I would borrow her algebra book and there upon a good pageful of equations, there I would "slip my message, tenderly pressing" the leaves of the book. She would perhaps never write back. Neither by post nor by hand would a reply reach me. But no matter; it would be a silence full of voices.

That night I dreamed I had returned from a tour of the world's music centers; the newspapers of Manila had been generous with praise. I saw my picture on the cover of a magazine. A writer had described how many years ago I used to trudge the streets of Buenavista with my violin in a battered black cardboard case. In New York, he reported, a millionaire had offered me a Stradivarius violin, with

110

a card which bore the inscription: "In admiration of a genius your own people must surely be proud of." I dreamed I spent a week-end at the millionaire's country house by the Hudson. A young girl in a blue skirt and white middy clapped her lily-white hands and her voice trembling, cried "Bravo!"

What people now observed at home was the diligence with which I attended to my violin lessons. My aunt, who had come from the farm to join her children for the holidays, brought with her a maid-servant, and to the poor girl was given the chore of taking the money to the baker's for roll and *pan de sal*. I realized at once that it would be no longer becoming on my part to make these morning trips to the baker's. I could not thank my aunt enough.

I began to chafe on being given other errands. Suspecting my violin to be the excuse, my aunt remarked:

"What do you want to be a musician for? At parties, musicians always eat last."

Perhaps, I said to myself, she was thinking of a pack of dogs scrambling for scraps tossed over the fence by some careless kitchen maid. She was the sort you could depend on to say such vulgar things. For that reason, I thought, she ought not to be taken seriously at all.

But the remark hurt me. Although Grandmother had counseled me kindly to mind my work at school, I went again and again to Pete Saez's house for rehearsals.

She had demanded that I deposit with her my earnings; I had felt too weak to refuse. Secretly, I counted the money and decided not to ask for it until I had enough with which to buy a brooch. Why this time I wanted to give Aida a brooch, I didn't know. But I had set my heart on it. I searched the downtown shops. The Chinese clerks, seeing me so young, were annoyed when I inquired about prices.

At last the Christmas season began. I had not counted on Aida's leaving home, and remembering that her parents lived in Badajoz, my torment was almost unbearable. Not once had I tried to tell her of my love. My letters had remained unwritten, and the algebra book unborrowed. There was still the brooch to find, but I could not decide on the sort of brooch I really wanted. And the money, in any case, was in Grandmother's purse, which smelled of "Tiger Balm." I grew somewhat feverish as our class Christmas program drew near. Finally it came; it was a warm December afternoon. I decided to leave the room when our English teacher announced that members of the class might exchange gifts. I felt fortunate; Pete was at the door, beckoning to me. We walked out to the porch where, Pete said, he would tell me a secret.

111

It was about an *asalto* the next Sunday which the Buenavista Women's Club wished to give Don Esteban's daughters, Josefina and Alicia, who were arriving on the morning steamer from Manila. The spinsters were much loved by the ladies. Years ago, when they were younger, these ladies studied solfeggio with Josefina and the piano and harp with Alicia. As Pete told me all this, his lips ash-gray from practising all morning on his trombone, I saw in my mind the sisters in their silk dresses, shuffling off to church for the evening benediction. They were very devout, and the Buenavista ladies admired that. I had almost forgotten that they were twins and, despite their age, often dressed alike. In low-bosomed voile bodices and white summer hats, I remembered, the pair had attended Grandfather's funeral, at old Don Esteban's behest. I wondered how successful they had been in Manila during the past three years in the matter of finding suitable husbands.

"This party will be a complete surprise," Pete said, looking around the porch as if to swear me to secrecy. "They've hired our band."

I rejoined my classmates in the room, greeting everyone with a Merry Christmas jollier than that of the others. When I saw Aida in one corner unwrapping something two girls had given her, I found the boldness to greet her also.

"Merry Christmas," I said in English, as a hairbrush and a powder case emerged from the fancy wrapping. It seemed to me rather apt that such gifts went to her. Already several girls were gathered around Aida. Their eyes glowed with envy, it seemed to me, for those fair cheeks and the bobbed dark-brown hair which lineage had denied them.

I was too dumbstruck by my own meanness to hear what exactly Aida said in answer to my greeting. But I recovered shortly and asked:

"Will you be away during the vacation?"

"No, I'll be staying here," she said. When she added that her cousins were arriving and that a big party in their honor was being planned, I remarked:

"So you all know about it?" I felt I had to explain that the party was meant to be a surprise, an *asalto*.

And now it would be nothing of the kind really. The women's club matrons would hustle about, disguising their scurrying around for cakes and candies as for some baptismal party or other. In the end, the Rivas sisters would out-do them. Boxes of meringues, bonbons, lady-fingers, and cinnamon buns that only the Swiss bakers in Manila could make, were perhaps coming on the boat with them. I imagined a table glimmering with long-stemmed punch glasses; enthroned in that array would be a huge brick-red bowl of gleaming china with golden flowers round the brim. The local matrons, however hard they tried, however sincere their efforts, were bound to fail in their aspiration to rise to the level of Don Esteban's daughters. Perhaps, I thought, Aida knew all this. And that I should share in a foreknowledge of the matrons' hopes was a matter beyond love. Aida and I could laugh together with the gods.

At seven, on the appointed evening, our small band gathered quietly at the gate of old Don Esteban's house, and when the ladies arrived in their heavy shawls and trim *pañuelos*, twittering with excitement, we were commanded to play the "Poet and Peasant" overture. As Pete directed the band, his eyes glowed with pride for his having been part of the big event. The multicolored lights that the old Spaniard's gardeners had strung along the vine-covered fence were switched on and the women remarked that Don Esteban's daughters might have made some preparations after all. Pete hid his face from the glare. If the women felt let down, they did not show it.

The overture shuffled along to its climax while five men in white shirts bore huge boxes of food into the house. I recognized one of the bakers in spite of the uniform. A chorus of confused greetings, and the women trooped into the house; and before we had settled in the *sala* to play "A Basket of Roses" the heavy damask curtains at the far end of the room were drawn and a long table richly spread was revealed under the chandeliers. I remembered that in our haste to be on hand for the *asalto*, Pete and I had discouraged the members of the band from taking their suppers.

"You've done us a great honor!" Josefina, the more buxom of the twins, greeted the ladies.

"Oh, but you have not allowed us to take you by surprise!" the ladies demurred in a chorus.

There were sighs and further protestations amid a rustle of skirts and the glitter of earrings. I saw Aida in a long, flowing white gown and wearing an arch of *sampaguita* flowers on her hair. At her command two servants brought out a gleaming harp from the music room. Only the slightest scraping could be heard because the servants were barefoot. As Aida directed them to place the instrument near the seats we occupied, my heart leaped to my throat. Soon she was lost among the guests, and we played "The Dance of the Glowworms." I kept my eyes closed and held for as long as I could her radiant figure before me.

Alicia played on the harp and then in answer to the deafening applause she offered an encore. Josefina sang afterward. Her voice, though a little husky, fetched enormous sighs. For her encore, she gave "The Last Rose of Summer"; and the song brought back snatches of the years gone by. Memories of solfeggio lessons eddied about us, as if there were rustling leaves scattering all over the hall. Don Esteban appeared. Earlier, he had greeted the crowd handsomely, twisting his mustache to hide a natural shyness before talkative women. He stayed long enough to listen to the harp again, whispering in his rapture: "Heavenly, heavenly . . . "

By midnight the merry-making lagged. We played while the party collected around the great table at the end of the *sala*. My mind travelled across the seas to the distant cities I had dreamed about. The sisters sailed among the ladies like two great white liners amid a fleet of tugboats in a bay. Someone had thoughtfully remembered — and at last Pete Saez signalled to us to put our instruments away. We walked in a single file across the hall, led by one of the barefoot servants.

Behind us a couple of hoarse sopranos sang "La Paloma" to the accompaniment of the harp, but I did not care to find out who they were. The sight of so much silver and china confused me. There was more food before us than I had even imagined. I searched in my mind for the names of the dishes; and my ignorance appalled me. I wondered what had happened to the boxes of food that the Buenavista ladies had sent up earlier. In a silver bowl before me, I discovered, there was something that seemed like whole egg yolks that had been dipped into a bowl of honey and peppermint. The seven of us in the orchestra were all of one mind about the feast; and so, confident that I was with friends, I allowed my covetousness to have its way and not only stuffed my mouth with this and that confection but also wrapped up a quantity of those egg yolk things in several sheets of napkin paper. None of my companions had thought of doing the same, and it was with some pride that I slipped the packet under my shirt. There, I knew, it would not bulge.

"Have you eaten?"

I turned around. It was Aida. My bowtie seemed to tighten around my collar. I mumbled something, I did not know what.

"If you wait a little while till they've all gone, I'll wrap up a big package for you," she added.

I brought a handkerchief to my mouth. I might have wiped away bits of food there, if only I were certain there were such telltale signs. But there were none; and if I had said "No, thank you," I might have honored her solicitude adequately and even relieved myself of any embarrassments. I could not quite believe that she had seen me, and yet I was sure that she knew what I had done; and I felt all ardor for her gone from me entirely.

114

I walked away to the nearest door, praying that the damask curtains hide me in my shame. The door gave on to the veranda, where once my love had trod on sunbeams. Outside it was dark, and a faint wind was singing in the harbor.

With the napkin balled up in my hand, I flung out my arm to scatter the egg yolk things in the dark. I waited for the soft sound of their fall on the garden-shed roof. Instead I heard a spatter in the rising night-tide beyond the stone fence. Farther away glimmered the light from Grandmother's window, calling me home.

But the party broke up at one or thereabouts. We walked away with our instruments after the matrons were done with their interminable goodbys. Then, to the tune of "Joy to the World," we pulled the Progreso Street shopkeepers out of their beds. The Chinese merchants were especially generous. When Pete divided our collection under a street lamp there was already a little glow of daybreak.

He walked with me part of the way home. We stopped at the baker's when I told him that I wanted to buy with my own money some bread to eat on the way to Grandmother's house at the edge of the sea-wall. He laughed, thinking it strange that I should be hungry. We found ourselves alone at the counter; and we watched the bakery assistants at work until our own bodies grew warm from the oven across the door. It was not quite five, and the bread was not yet ready.

Going Back

Gunadasa Amarasekara

WHEN my mother left the school at Yatalamatta where she taught for twenty-six years the people of the village gave her a big farewell. I had an invitation from the organizing committee. It said that the function would be on March 25th and that a group photograph would be taken afterwards. I didn't go. I can't say this was for lack of leisure. Some time ago I had taken part in a ceremony of this kind where Mr. Wiratunga of the boys' school was leaving. I am still nauseated when I remember the blubbering and the blathering on that occasion. I knew there would be the same sort of exhibition when Mother was leaving. I had no stomach for such silliness; village folks who wore their hearts on their sleeves seemed to me clods who were incapable of thinking rationally. Even as I took up the invitation I could imagine Mother trying to make a speech and breaking down; her eyes running with tears and her voice shaken by sobs. "What a blessing that I can stay here and not be mixed up in such stuff and nonsense," I said to myself.

It was for this reason that I went home during the holidays only a week before the Sinhalese New Year. When I got home, the first thing both Mother and Nangi asked me, even before I could change my clothes, was why I hadn't come to the function.

"It was very rude of you," Mother said, "You shouldn't have stayed away when they sent you a letter all the way to the University."

"Quite so, if Podi Aiya had been there everything would have been just perfect," Nangi joined in.

"Yes, if I'd come I could have cried, too," I said.

"Of course, you would have been the first to cry, if you'd come," Nangi retorted. "In spite of all your big talk, I know you'd have cried before anyone else."

"Don't talk nonsense! These farewells are good for women who are waiting to turn on the tap," I said angrily. Nangi's remark seemed to me an insult to my mature intelligence.

"He has got these ideas into his head after he started reading big books," said Nangi. "But when we were at Ratnasara together,

116

he'd be all of a twitter at the very mention of home. When we'd gone back after the holidays he'd talk of nothing else for two or three days.

"Do you hear, Mother?" she went on. "He talks like a lord now but when we were children he'd chatter to me all the time about home once you'd left us at school. 'Now Mother must be going back.' 'Now she must be gathering vegetables in the back garden.' 'Now she must be offering flowers at the shrine.' That's all he'd talk about. But now he can't come back to the place where we'd lived for twenty-six years even on the day we are leaving."

I hid my blushes.

"It wasn't really because of my exam that I stayed away," I said in irritation. "It is because I didn't want to watch that sort of comedy."

"Never mind the function. You must come with me to Yatalamatta before the New Year. I had nobody to go with. I was waiting for you," said Mother.

"Why do you want to go back to the village you have left? There is none of your family there," I said scowling.

"That's not the point. But at least on New Year we must call on people who were our neighbours for so many years."

"I can't. I have a lot of work to get through. I've brought down all my books."

"Well, if you can't, I'll go alone. It wouldn't be very difficult for me to take the jeep that goes to Yatalamatta early in the morning." Mother said to me in a reproachful manner.

She said no more at the time. But after lunch the next day, I heard her talking again to Nangi about the journey. I was at the dining table, reading a book, and I could hear them talking in the bedroom.

"It's the seventh today — nearly two weeks since we came away — and I haven't still been able to go," Mother was complaining.

"Much use it was waiting for Podi Aiya!" I heard Nangi say. "The only thing to do now is to go by yourself, Mother."

"I don't know what kind of state the place is in already. When we left I told the school-mistress from Hettihena to open the doors of the school every few days and sweep the front garden at least. It is the season now when the rubber leaves fall and the whole garden must be covered with them."

"If the Hettihena teacher isn't ill she won't fail to do as you said," Nangi answered her.

"It is all right if she does it. But I am not sure. When I was there things got done because people were afraid. I'd make a fuss, but it won't be the same now. And I couldn't get the gate repaired before I came away. Both posts were rotted. If that wretch of a bull from Pelawatta had got into the garden, he'll have ruined everything. A fine state things must be in."

I was both amused and provoked by this conversation.

"Why give yourself all this trouble? When you left you should have brought the school here — garden and all. Then you wouldn't have had all this worry. It won't do the Government good to have you always hanging around like a creditor," I said mockingly.

The two of them went on talking as if they hadn't heard me.

The next evening Mother spent on preparations for the visit to Yatalamatta. She got ready some sheaves of betel leaves as gifts for several people there.

"But betel leaves alone won't do. I must take a tin of biscuits, too, to Rukmalgoda," she remarked to Nangi while putting the betel together.

"And Brampy! you can't sleep late tomorrow. We must take the jeep early in the morning. We'll have to get to Unanvitiya and walk from there," she added to our servant who was nearby.

"Why get off at Unanvitiya?" asked Nangi. "You can go straight to Yatalamatta."

"How? The Anguruvela bridge is broken down and the jeep now runs on the Unanvitiya road. But it is nothing to walk the three miles from there. We can be at Yatalamatta by ten anyway," Mother replied enthusiastically.

"If there is any trouble it'll be crossing the edanda at Danduvana," she went on. "It'll be a good thing if the water has come up to the edanda. Otherwise I'll feel giddy when I see the bottom. Still, I'll get across somehow. Or if I can't, I'll at least get the Kumara girl to help me over by way of Mahahena."

Mother's voice was so eager that I felt she was already making the journey in her imagination.

"If we have to walk from Unanvitiya we should get to Yatalamatta before eleven or twelve," complained Brampy.

"Twelve or two — what does it matter? We are going back to the place which was our home, aren't we?" Mother replied.

That night, before going to bed, Nangi came up to me when I was studying.

"If you don't go with Mother tomorrow, she'll get into a lot of trouble," she said. "Now she wants to take that fool Brampy. If she goes with him, she will fall off an edanda and break her neck. So please go," Nangi pleaded.

"That would serve her right for having the nerve to plan these jaunts," I said.

"That may be. But please go with her, Podi Aiya. Otherwise she will get into some trouble."

"I don't want to go on this ridiculous journey! I must finish this book before the holidays are over. If I go, tomorrow will all be spent on the trip. The day after, I'll have to rest my legs. I shan't be able to do any work."

"Anyway, please go, Podi Aiya," Nangi repeated.

"No, I can't. She can take anybody she has asked. Let her go and learn a lesson."

In spite of what I said then, I decided, after Nangi went away, to accompany Mother after all. If Mother got an idea into her head, she would carry it out, somehow. I too felt that if she went with Brampy she might get into some mess. So, while still inwardly murmuring against it, I decided reluctantly to go.

Although we left home the next morning before dawn, it was about seven when the jeep arrived. Mother had several parcels in her hand, but I didn't want to help her with any of them because of the resentment in my heart. We were the only passengers in the jeep. Mother took a seat at the rear, while I sat by the driver. Until we reached Unanvitiya Mother was silent, perhaps because she felt that talk would make me angrier.

The gravelled road from Hammeliya to Unanvitiya passed through some pretty country. On one side of the road lay fields of open heath, on the other side, low hills covered with tea bushes, coconut, breadfruit or jack trees. Houses lay almost at the edge of the road, with some of the gardens marked off by a hedge of green stakes or flowering plants. As we passed by in the jeep, my eyes would rest instinctively from time to time on a young girl sweeping her garden. When we approached Yatalamatta the fields that we had so far seen on one side of the road gave place to the Gin Ganga and its pleasant river bank.

The charm of these surroundings softened my ill temper. When the jeep stopped at the Unanvitiya market place, with its row of shops and its suspension bridge, I alighted with some cheerfulness and took one of the parcels that Mother was carrying.

Yet my feeling of pleasure slowly lessened. Post Estate, which was once full of rubber trees was now a desert without tree or leaf. I hadn't known that the rubber trees had been uprooted because the land was to be planted with tea. I held the parcel over my head and walked on with quick strides. It was now about eleven; the sun beat on us like fire and the sandy road too was getting hotter. My

119

body was dripping sweat. Both of us hastened on without exchanging a word. Post Estate stretched about a mile and ended at the village of Yatalamatta. That mile seemed to me like ten.

"It's a mercy it'll be shady from here on," said Mother when we got to the Danduvana edanda.

It had been raining in the hills and, as Mother had hoped, the stream was about half full. I took all the parcels from her and went ahead. In place of the bamboo stem that had once served as a hand rail, there was now a fairly thick trunk of an arecanut tree, so crossing the edanda was not very difficult.

As we reached the other side, we met Mr. Kumara. "It looks as though you've come visiting friends and relatives," he said.

"Yes — how can we forget them so soon?" said Mother, smiling broadly.

"Yes, yes of course. You may go anywhere, but this village is your real home. Podi Mahattaya's especially," he added turning to me. "You were born here; weren't you?"

"Well, wherever I live is home to me," I said with deliberate indifference.

"Don't say that. When you are a big man someday and people say you were born here, we'll all be honoured."

Everybody we ran into thereafter had the same thing to ask, "Ah, coming back to visit your old home?" "Of course, how can you forget so soon a place where you lived so long?" Some of our acquaintances turned to me and asked, "Has Podi Mahattaya just come home for the holidays?" By the bridge we encountered Hichchi Mahattaya who said, "It was very bad of you not to have come even when we sent you a letter." He had been on the farewell committee. It seemed to me that all this was foolishness and empty chatter. "What a pack of sentimental idiots," I said to myself.

Near the bridge we met also Loku Mahattaya of Pelawatta. "We were saying only yesterday that you'd be sure to come today or tomorrow — before the New Year anyway," Loku Mahattaya exclaimed loudly when he was still some way off Pelawatta. His property was next to the school.

"Ah well, it's only today I was free to come," said Mother. "How are things at the school? I told the school mistress from Hettihena to go every two or three days and see that the place was kept clean. I don't know whether she has done that."

"I haven't seen her. I couldn't go there myself after you left. Are you going straight to the school or to Rukmalgoda?" he asked, "But why go to the school? There is nobody there now."

"We'll go to Rukmalgoda first and have something to eat. Then we must go to the school," Mother said.

Her eagerness seemed to me to have grown with these encounters and conversations on the way and she had grown more talkative too.

It was almost twelve when we reached Rukmalgoda.

"We thought you wouldn't fail to come today," said Akmeemana Hamine as soon as she saw us. "We waited for some time before sitting down to lunch. And when did Podi Mahattaya come home?"

After we had washed our faces, we were taken to the dining table. Even while eating, Mother kept asking Akmeemana Hamine questions about the school.

"Haven't you seen that girl from Hettihena going that way?" she asked.

"How should she be going there? As soon as the holidays began her husband came down and took her off to Hikkaduwa," answered Akmeemana Hamine.

"Well, well, with all my pleading I haven't been able to make her spend the holidays here!"

"Good Lord, school teachers today don't do anything except for pay! You won't find teachers like yourself now!"

"That foolish generation is gone now!" I answered.

Although by the end of the meal I was so drowsy that I could hardly keep my eyes open mother set out for the school without wasting a moment.

"I've never got mixed up in such an annoying business before," I grumbled to myself as I accompanied her. The school was about half a mile from Rukmalgoda. Fortunately, the fierce glare of the sun had somewhat lessened now and there was some shade; yet the tarred road seemed as hot under our feet as if it had been on fire.

As we passed the bend in the road near the temple, we caught sight of the school garden and the high walls of the school house. From the first glimpse, they had the air of a place deserted. Coming closer we could distinguish the fence of *Rukattana* trees and the gate. The trees with their wildly overgrown branches pushing out above the road, made my first impression stronger. We came up to the gate and I drew aside with my hands the bamboo poles which served as bars. In the enveloping stillness, the grating sound of the bamboo seemed to resound loudly. "No one has even stepped in here since we left!" Mother remarked as we passed through the gate. "Just look how grass has overgrown the garden in a few days!"

The garden was covered not only with grass, but also with dried rubber leaves blown by the wind.

121

The door of the school house creaked as I opened it. As always during the holidays, desks and benches were piled in the hall. Scattered here too on the floor were leaves and litter carried by the wind.

What I needed most was a short nap. I put two benches together, took off my coat and lay down. "Wake me when the sun is low," I told Mother.

Lying there, I could look up at the school roof. It shared in the desolation of a place where no one had set foot for some time. Large cobwebs hung here and there and, while I looked, two white-bellied mice ran idly between the rafters. Soon my eyes closed.

When I woke, I must have been asleep for over an hour. I had slept so long because I was tired and felt in my body a sluggishness that made the thought of getting up uninviting. I lay where I was and glanced around. Mother was working in the garden with a mamoty. "Cease, cease — " I listened to the rasping sound of the mamoty as it struck the hard earth in a monotonous rhythm, On the roof, the two mice I had seen before I fell asleep were still gambolling among the rafters. "How many cobwebs there were up there!" I thought. I felt sleepy again, as if my tiredness had grown.

"Dear, dear, who would have thought the place would come to this?" Mother was muttering to herself as she worked.

I turned my head and looked through the large window. The sun had now set on the hills which lay beyond the road, and they looked faded and weary after the long scorching.

I rose unwillingly and began to walk up and down the schoolhouse to rid myself of the sluggish feeling in my body. Mother was still working in the garden.

"Cease, cease — " the sound of the mamoty alone broke the surrounding silence.

I strolled about aimlessly for a short time, then leant against a parapet and looked on. At the other end of the parapet lay a blackened clay lamp and a basket with withered flowers in it. It occurred to me that Mother must have lit the lamp before she came away.

"What's this lamp?" I asked her.

"Which one? The one on the wall? That's the lamp we lit for the gods before we left."

I threw the dried-up flowers out of the basket and put it back on the parapet. Then I thought it shouldn't be left lying there and put it inside a cupboard.

The schoolroom felt lonelier than ever and I stepped out into the garden. Tufts of grass had sprouted everywhere, and there were marks left by rain water which must have flooded the garden some days before. I sat down on the plinth. Only the orange tree was as I remembered it. I gazed at the big roots which stood up out of the earth. What memories that tree held for me — memories of the hours that we had spent, Nangi and I as children sitting at its foot. Was it really the same tree? I looked at it again. One or two of its branches were dying. Some one had told me that fruit trees did not flourish where no human voice was heard. I got up and went where Mother was working.

"Who would have thought this place would come to such a state? It'll take a month to clear it. I started working with this mamoty because I couldn't bear to see things as they were," she said to me, as I stood there silent. "It should be nearly five now. Shouldn't it? This part at least looks all right now."

She took the mamoty in and left it inside the school. She seemed tired as she came back and sat down on the front step wiping her face. I sat down by her and both of us were silent for some time.

"How long is it since we first came here! Then there was only this one schoolroom." Mother broke the silence.

"These walls, none of this was here then. None of it would have been put up but for me." She went on talking, and I listened.

"I got this plinth made when I was expecting your sister — the one who died. I spent three years getting these walls and fences up, and filling the swamps down there. That piece of flat land was a thicket with bushes up to a man's head. Ah, well, the place is going back to what it was. That wall has been cracked by the rain water a few days ago."

While she was talking, I felt a pang that would not be put into words. This decay — was it not going on before my eyes. As I contemplated the trees, the schoolroom, the walls? They were shrinking into a desolation which touched my heart.

Mother began to speak again, pausing from time to time.

"You were a child just beginning to run about, when I finished all this work, built that room and cemented the school floor. The footprints you left in the cement should be there even now. One day, when the cement was still wet, we had gone to Galle. When we got back, we went round to the back door and opened it, and you ran into the schoolroom before I could stop you. The marks you left must be there, clear as ever," she said, and rising, went up to the door opening from the schoolroom into the headmistress' quarters.

"There you see — there are your prints," she said, pointing. "I shouted, 'No, no, son this way!' Those are the marks you made running back." She showed me another line of footprints in the opposite direction. "They'll remain there till the floor is cemented again."

I was bending over to look at the prints. They made me want to touch them. I bent right down and felt them with my hands. The big toe, the other toes, the heel — they were all there. I turned my head and looked at my feet. A strange happiness passed me, like falling in love. "They are mine! Dear God! Aren't these all mine," I said to myself. My eyes were wet. Everything around me seemed to dissolve in the flood of tenderness that swept my heart.

"It's time to go. I want to take this lime plant home and grow it. If you can uproot it without hurting the roots we can replant it there." Mother said, getting up from the step.

"I'll take it out of the ground," I said. I brought the mamoty and uprooted the plant, leaving a clod of earth sticking to the roots. Mother wrapped it in a large leaf and tied it. "Let's wash our faces and get ready to go."

I went down to the well with Mother and washed. The water was very cold against my face — refreshingly cold. I dipped my face into the hollow of my hands filled with water and also drank several mouthfuls.

"I must drink some of the water too, before going, however cold it is," said Mother.

As I put the bamboo back into place on our way out, I felt a sharp pain within me. Something seemed to fall away from my heart — something that would be lost to sight forever. It was now almost twilight.

We walked silently until we passed the boundary of the school garden and more than once I looked back.

"Let me see that lime plant," said Mother, who had not spoken a word till the school was out of sight. She took the plant from me and examined it.

"A fine plant. It will grow nicely in our front garden."

I looked back again after we had turned the bend. The high cream-coloured walls of the school could just be seen through the trees.

We waited at the corner of the road for the jeep more than half an hour. It was about seven when it arrived at last. There was another young man waiting with us. He was going to Colombo by way of Baddegama; he had a suitcase in his hand, and he wore a pair of white slippers that would have suited a woman better than a man. There was an old woman with him and from their conversation I realized that she was his mother and had come to see him off.

"When you get there you must write to us every two or three days," she kept saying.

The young man made no reply for some time. At last he said angrily, "What's the use of making the Postal Department richer? Colombo isn't a far off country, as you imagine. I shan't have the leisure to write so often."

His words made me smile. The jeep arrived and we got in — the three of us.

"Such foolish women — these village folk," the young man remarked to me after the jeep had started. "They don't give you any peace from the time you leave home."

The headlights were bad and the jeep moved slowly. There were many ruts too in the road, and whenever a wheel went into one of them we were shaken. Each time this happened, the thorns of the lime plant scraped my feet.

Little by little, the jeep filled up with passengers. Among those who got in were several people I knew. Two of them, the registrar from Unanvitiya and the retired police officer spoke to me.

"How long is it till your final exam?" the registrar asked me in a respectful tone.

"Another year," I said.

"And then you'll be a doctor. Good for us too," he remarked. "So many rich men there have been in these villages, but none of their sons could pass a decent examination."

"What's this you are taking?" He was pointing to the plant at my feet. "A lime plant, isn't it? What? Carrying away an ordinary lime plant?"

"Yes, Mother wanted to take it home from Yatalamatta," I said with assumed nonchalance.

Both my acquaintances got off at the next stop. I moved into a corner of the jeep and reflected. If I had stayed at home, I could have worked at my books the whole day. This journey had been a waste of time. How silly my behaviour had been earlier in the evening! My mind shrank from recollecting it and I was ashamed of myself. How immature I had been!

The jeep jerked us from side to side, and the lime plant kept knocking against my feet. Everytime it touched me, I was irritated. I put it in a corner but with the shaking of the jeep it rolled back to my feet.

The jeep stopped for somebody to get out. I took the plant and stealthily threw it far out of the window.

When we reached home, it was about eight-thirty. My head was aching, so I went to my room and stretched myself out on the bed feeling out of humour. I could hear Mother at the dining table talking to Nangi.

125

"The whole place is a jungle. Grass grown wild in the garden, the lamp and flowers we left in the schoolroom still there, leaves and dust, and rubbish all over. I could have cried when I saw it. Lord, to think that was the place I kept so well!"

I tossed in my bed, as if in pain, and cursed. I cursed myself and my miserable education.

But Mother's voice was flowing as if infused with new life.

(Translated by Reggie Siriwardena)

Surabhi

Gulabdas Broker

SURABHI HEARD the sound of approaching footsteps. She rushed out to the entrance of the compound and discovered that it was only the gardener. Disappointed, she returned to the drawing-room and threw herself on the sofa.

Her mouth and throat were dry. She picked up the half-finished glass of water from the teapoy and touched it to her lips. The touch brought a rush of memory. She closed her eyes in ecstasy and her cheeks turned pink. She gave herself to the pleasant sensation for a few minutes. Then suddenly, shamed by her own lasciviousness, she opened her eyes wide and emptied the glass of water at one stretch.

She tried to sound indignant as she muttered: "Shameless brute! How dare he take liberties with me?"

Unable to bear the load of her thoughts, Surabhi got up from the sofa and began to pace the room restlessly. Her mind, however, was taking longer strides in various directions:

"Of course, he knew that my protests were weak and meaningless."

"That's not true. I really didn't like his doing it, but he is so bold! How shamelessly he laughed when I turned my angry eyes at him!"

"Why, I wouldn't have left the place at once if I had been a willing participant!"

This last thought gave her solace, but not for long. Soon another accusing thought tormented her.

"Did you really not like it? Why have you then been so eager to see him again? Why have you been rushing out every time you hear a sound? Why do you get disappointed when it turns out to be someone else? Why? Why? Why?"

A face floated before her eyes — handsome, delicate features, wavy black hair, dreamy, eloquent eyes — and she heard a question: "Shall I take another — just once?"

Her lips trembled.

127

Wave after wave of memory engulfed her, making her skin tingle, tickling her mind . . .

* * * * *

It was evening. The sky was resplendent with the glow of the setting sun.

It was the first occasion that she had been out with Suryakant. They had not intended to take a long walk, but somehow discussing various topics they had lost count of time and distance until they were at the beach. Warned by the long shadows of evening she had wanted to return home, when Suryakant had said, "Let us watch the sunset for a while."

"No, no, it is getting late," she had protested sincerely.

"Oh, a few minutes aren't going to make much difference."

Next moment he had thrown himself on the sands. With a woman's intuition she had looked around, weighing the situation. It wasn't after all a very lonely place. A few yards away a group was enjoying the seascape. But as she sat down, a couple of feet away from Suryakant, she had deliberated: "What will my husband have to say about this? He will not like it. But why should he object? After all Suryakant is not a stranger. Besides this is all so innocent."

* * * * *

Before they were aware of it, the evening glow had withdrawn itself and the moon had emerged, in her full splendour, to meet the night. The sands and the sea lay cloaked in her soft light.

Suddenly Suryakant had said: "I am told you sing beautifully."

"How do you know?"

"An angel whispered it to me. Isn't it true?"

"Of course not. I don't know how to sing." But her laughter had all the melody of chiming anklet bells and contradicted her statement.

"You sing to me, then I will tell you if you are a good singer or not," he had said, moving closer to her, looking at her with meaningful eyes. She had been frightened by what his eyes were really trying to say.

Of course, this was not the first time that she had noticed him look at her thus. He was almost a regular visitor to their house. Often her husband, tired and bored, would retire for the night, leaving them to finish a discussion. But, on such occasions, secure within the four walls of the house and with the assuring presence of her husband in the next room, she had felt no cause for anxiety.

This evening, however the sense of security had been absent. She had been conscious of his nearness and the romantic surroundings. She had said firmly: "Let us go. It is getting awfully late."

128

Suryakant did not make any move to get up. "No, I am not inclined to leave unless you sing me a song. I know you sing beautifully."

"What does all this mean?" she had asked sharply, rising to her feet.

"It only means that you must meet my request, if you want me to do what you want. Come on." With these words he had pulled her down.

Seeing his determination she had then decided that it was best to comply with his wish to hear her sing. And even before she could think of a song he had placed his hand on hers and pleaded in a caressing voice: "Please. A girl should not be so hard-hearted!"

She withdrew her hand. "What shall I sing?"

"You know the song — 'The flame of your love burns in your eyes'?"

She nodded.

"Sing it, then."

She had not been pleased with his choice. The song was too sickeningly romantic. But she did not want to delay returning home any longer and so she cleared her throat and began to sing.

She had a sweet melodious voice, full of emotion. Soon the atmosphere was resounding to the sentiments expressed in the song and since she was very fond of music she was lost in her own world. He had broken the trance by saying, "Why do you stare at the horizon? Look at me. I wish to see the flame in your eyes. I wish to see peacocks dancing in them. Please look at me."

She had looked at him disapprovingly and he had smiled, staring at her with his dreamy eyes.

Even she had felt sorry when the song ended and the last notes dissolved into the coolness of the night.

When she had turned to look at him again she had seen stars shining in his eyes! And, in his caressing voice, he said: "How utterly beautiful! You carry honey in your throat. I must show you my appreciation in some way. I must offer you a gift!"

"I do not want any gift. Come on. It is frightfully late."

"Oh, but I cannot let you go without showing you how much I have admired your singing."

"What will you give me?" she had said, momentarily carried away by his playfulness.

"This," he had said as he had pulled her towards him and placed his lips on hers in a fleeting kiss.

At first she had been too stunned to think clearly, but when she had recovered from the shock her first concern was about the onlookers. Had anybody seen it happen? Who were the two men who had just then passed by? Her brow was quickly dotted with sweat in spite of the cool breeze.

Indignant, she had lashed out at him: "Shameless brute! How dare you . . . .!"

"Why am I shameless?" he had asked in an innocent tone, laughing away her annoyance.

"I would have never agreed to sing you a song if I had known your intentions. How dare you take such liberties!"

"Are you really annoyed? Be honest. Shall I kiss you once more, just once more? Then, you can be sure." He laughed again, as he spoke.

"You are shameless!" she said, infuriated by his obvious disbelief in her protests. "Don't ever talk to me again — never — never."

After that she had not even waited to see if he would accompany her home. But he had. Not a word, however, was exchanged between them on the way. Only when they were very close to her house had he said: "Whatever you may say to the contrary, I feel you will remember this evening. You are not really displeased. I shall see you soon — very soon. Cheerio!"

She had been too annoyed to look back.

*　*　*　*　*

An indistinguishable, faint sound broke the chain of her thoughts. In spite of a strong determination to hold on to her seat, Surabhi rushed out. A dog was scratching at the gate.

Once again, disappointed, she returned to the sofa and moaned: "Oh, what a woman am I! Why do I still pine for him? Why am I expecting him with such eagerness in spite of that evening? Or is it because of it?"

Surabhi paused for a while to find shelter from her own accusations. But this proved a short-lived escape.

"Even my husband has noticed a change in me. The other day he had asked, 'Suru, whom are you thinking about so much?' Oh, God! Oh, God!"

"And I lied shamelessly. I said, 'Who else except you, of course!' Oh, what a horrible woman am I!"

The shadow of shame covered her face. "And still I continue to think of Suryakant! I still long to see him! But then he is so romantic, has such a poetic mind and is so sure of himself. And his eyes, oh..."

Footsteps were again heard outside but this time Surabhi remained sitted. "No, no. I shall not bother. I don't care who it is." The sound came nearer and nearer. Surabhi held her breath but her thoughts defied her. "It is him, it is Suryakant. I am sure. Oh, thank God!"

Hurriedly she tidied her hair with her hands. She rearranged the folds of her sari quickly. With a pounding heart she awaited his appearance.

A familiar voice said, "Postman!"

Surabhi felt lifeless as she got up to receive a letter. She returned to the sofa as she surveyed the envelope. It was addressed to her husband. The word "Confidential" stared at her accusingly. Suddenly a thought gripped her like the clutching fingers of danger: "Who could have sent the letter? Oh, God! Could it be one of the two men who had seen it all? They could be known to my husband."

She carefully examined every inch of the envelope. She held it against the light but nothing was revealed. Even the postmark could not be deciphered. She was sure that the postal authorities had co-operated with the writer in guarding an evil secret!

It was five o'clock. In another hour her husband would be home. In another hour she would be exposed for what she was — a shameless, fickle-minded, unfaithful woman! In another hour she would be lost to the love and respect which she had enjoyed in the house until then.

A tear rolled down her cheek. How wonderfully happy her one and a half years of marriage had been. Her husband had always been so tender and considerate. Not once had he spoken a harsh word to her. Yet soon — in an hour — a volcano would erupt and the molten lava of his hatred and contempt would reduce her existence to nothing.

*   *   *   *   *

She shuddered at the thought of facing her husband. She knew his capacity to be calm even in the face of tragedy. Supposing he only said sadly, resignedly: "Surabhi, Suru, why did you do it? I had placed the honour of my house in your hands. I had so much trust in you. What have you done? Oh, Surabhi, what have you done?"

She would never be able to bear such cool condemnation.

She surveyed the letter once again. The writer had taken every precaution to shield the contents. What if she destroyed it? But she must know the contents first. Yes, that was it; she would read the letter and then destroy it.

What if it were a business letter? How could she do such a mean thing? Her husband had never even once opened her mail. Hadn't she cheated him enough already? Hadn't she sinned against him enough?

With a final resolve she flung the letter away — as far away as possible. It slid under an almirah.

Surabhi straightened herself and muttered: "I am building a mountain out of a molehill. If the two men were my husband's acquaintances I would certainly have known them."

Once again she thought of Suryakant, then hurriedly turned her thoughts to her husband. Two faces swam before her: one handsome, romantic, delicate, with dancing, mischievous eyes; the other — calm, cool, collected and trusting. Both were smiling — one with desire, the other with affection and reliance.

"Oh, God! God!" Surabhi wailed.

She got up from the sofa. She must drown herself in work. She ran into the kitchen.

It was nearly six-thirty. Her husband should have returned by then. Every minute seemed to her like an hour.

Six-thirty-seven-seven-thirty-seven-forty-five . . .

What could have possibly delayed him? Had someone already told him? Other men, in similar circumstances, would drive the woman away. But her husband would not think of such a drastic punishment. He would atone for her sins himself. He would suffer, himself.

Tears of remorse streamed down her face.

"Please God, please bring him home safe. Don't let any harm befall him. I promise I shall never betray his trust again."

Eight-fifteen-eight-thirty . . .

Surabhi said prayer after prayer to the Almighty, "bribing" the Lord with many promises.

Eight-forty-five — nine o'clock . . .

Surabhi was in utter despair born out of remorse for her thoughtless behaviour. "Let him come home safe and I swear I shall tell him everything — everything. I shall make a complete confession. I shall willingly face his condemnation. I shall submit to any punishment that he thinks fit for me. I shall even leave the house . . ."

※   ※   ※   ※   ※

Familiar footsteps sounded on the gravel in the compound. Surabhi, tumbling against objects, blinded by tears of shame and guilt, ran into the bathroom and quickly washed her face. She hurried out to receive her husband.

He looked extremely tired. In a tone as calm as she could manage she asked him with a forced smile: "Why so late?"

"Oh, a lot of work — all urgent," he said wearily as he threw himself into a chair. He closed his eyes and said nothing further. Her worst fears seemed to have proved true. But she was determined to abide by her vow. The confession had to be made at any cost.

Her husband opened his eyes, smiling wanly, and said, "Come on, Suru, let us have our dinner."

"Have a wash. Everything will be laid by then."

Her conscience nagged at her. "What about the confession, Surabhi?" She hesitated for a few seconds and then said with courage. "There is something I have to tell you. Can we postpone the dinner for a while?"

"All right. What is it, Surabhi?"

She swallowed the lump in her throat and tried to speak out her thoughts but no sound came.

"What is it, Suru?"

"Oh, nothing, just this letter!" She picked up the letter from under the almirah and handed it over to him. She could hear her heart pounding like a gigantic clock. She tried to hide her trembling hands.

She nearly collapsed at his feet as he silently began to read the letter. She could not take her eyes off his face, thought the slightest change in his expression frightened her. At last he had finished reading the letter. Wearily he said, "Always someone or other!"

Surabhi held her breath. It was coming — she knew it — she knew it.

"Suru, how many can we help?" He sounded so tired. "Now this Kanti wants a loan."

"Does he say anything else?" she asked cautiously.

"Nothing much of importance." Then he saw the fear in her eyes. Tenderly he touched her shoulder and said, "Why do you look so scared, Suru? Has anything frightened you?"

The words, spoken fondly brought her instant relief. She dug her head into his lap and a sob escaped her throat. Soon her whole body was shaking convulsively.

Her husband gently lifted her chin up and asked softly, "What is this, Suru? Why are you crying?"

She looked at him with love-filled eyes. Now was the time to make the confession. She opened her lips, swallowed the lump in her throat, but once again no words came. Only tears glistening like large pearls rolled down her cheeks.

Greatly worried and perturbed, her husband fondly stroked her hair, feeling its silkiness under his hands.

"Please, Suru, what is it? Tell me. Trust me."

She was overwhelmed by his goodness. Impulsively, she embraced him. At last she found her voice, but she only said: "I wish you would come home early. I get so worried and frightened."

(*Translated by Snehprabha Pradhan*)

The Enchanted Plant

Bienvenido N. Santos

THE COUPLE had known difficult times, especially during the war. The mere fact that they had been residents long before the outbreak of the war, did not save them from the usual annoyances, even dangers, that were the lot of citizens from the enemy country. Yet, they had been living all along like natives; they spoke the language well enough to pass for Japanese, to belong, as it were, to this valley of little box houses and flowering gardens, where they had exiled themselves in search of the happiness that they thought neither could have without the other.

During the war, they seldom left their house, and whenever they had to go out, they walked along the tortuous Wakabayashi-sho, affecting the quick mincing steps of the natives, their heads bowed as though against strong winds from the bay. Everybody in Setagaya-ku must have known who they were, but nobody molested them. In fact, many of the villagers wondered how there could be war between the two countries when there was no rancour in their hearts, no private grudges.

The meaning of war, Sol and Isabel realized, went over the heads of these people. It did not make sense — victory and conquest, new lands, other than what they knew were theirs, on which the flag of the rising sun now flew amidst great shouting and greater silences. What made sense was death, its shadow dimming the skies over the pleasant valley — boys who had romped these streets, touching fences as they walked or pausing to peer into the faces of passengers in cabs, smiling at their thoughts, now unheard from, who, perhaps, would never come back. They had such smiles when they left, their eyes mere slits of light, it didn't make sense that they were not coming back.

But even then, Isabel and Sol had different times. It was all right when everything went well, before the war. They had money and could go places they had seen in pictures and buy whatever they fancied. They spent week-ends outside the city, in low cottages overlooking valleys, with hot baths right in their room, seafoods and drinks served by neat attendants with knowing smiles. It was bliss. The past lay behind them like a nightmare. Villa Magdalena was only a picture, a page in an album, stowed away in a corner among back issues of magazines from home and travel folders colorful with pictures of faraway lands.

Sol realized how hard Isabel had tried to make him forget as if she herself had no memories that plagued her with the insinuating thrusts of guilt. She lavished gifts on him, her gift of self not the least of these in what seemed an attempt to blindfold his mind and numb his heart with the fierce delights of the present. Sometimes he would wake up in the middle of the night and find her also awake; and when he started to talk about what they had left behind, she would turn to him, blurring his words with kisses, while her hand sought his body and soon her hair would be spilling over his eyes and he would feel his fingers sinking into her flesh and it would be again, as it had always been since that time in the shuddering house of the dead.

During the war, Sol had to give up his job in the city as assistant mechanic in a bicycle shop. He stayed home spending his time translating Japanese stories and poems in the dialect. Most of his Japanese materials were already in English translations. Isabel stayed in the house, watching time pass, by a wall clock, by the shadows and the sun. Weather permitting, she stayed in the garden, tending her flowering plants, root crops, and vegetables. Sol called to her sometimes to listen to his completed translations. He was just starting a dictionary in the dialect, using a Webster's dictionary as reference, when he was stricken with a sickness that lasted practically throughout the war. It left him thin and emaciated. It was then that he realized how much he meant to her. It must have been at this time, too, when, whatever he had originally felt for her, gratitude for her gifts, compassion for her plight, vanity for her worship of him, must have turned into love or whatever it was that transcended the desires of the flesh, that was stronger than pity, deeper than habit.

Sol was never too ill to notice Isabel's grief every time he appeared to worsen. Once, he told her that one of the clearest memories he had of his mother was the old woman's singing to him as he lay sick in bed. Her voice, he recalled, was sweet and the song she sang was a ballad on unrequitted love. One night, waking up during an air-raid signal that seemed to shake the valley of Setagaya-ku, he asked Isabel to turn on the light when the all-clear sounded. It was a dim lighted bulb encased in a green Japanese lantern, which he himself had fancied for no other reason than that the lighting made both of them look unreal, as though they were not themselves, but strangers, apparitions.

135

"You don't look like you," she would complain, turning away, always turning away every time he made love to her with the green light on. Or she would close her eyes as he talked, urging him to keep talking. "It's your voice, Sol, I can almost touch it in this terrible night. I love your voice. I can listen to you like this all my life," Isabel would say.

The green light continued to fascinate Sol. He felt an added thrill that the beautiful body lying beside his was not Isabel's. One night when he found out that she had removed the lantern with the green shade, he was furious, and contritely, she put back the Japanese lantern. That night, she cried softly, as in a dream or a nightmare, "I'm afraid, I'm afraid." Her voice was not like her own, but a child's, helpless with fear in the dark.

So that night of the air-raid when all was quiet in the valley again, he asked her to turn on the light, the green light. He had been feverish all day. Every fifteen or thirty minutes, she took his temperature and placed a hot bag under his feet, which he kicked away. She replaced it as often as he kicked it off the bed, saying, "Darling, you need this, your feet are cold."

She watched over him all night. Every now and then, he felt her palm touch his neck or press lightly against his cheek or nape. Although his fever remained high, he was not delirious. Much of his ailment must have been due to the constant fear he had of Tokyo being bombed and wiped off or some Japanese fanatics forcing their way into their house and torturing them to death. Suddenly, he felt a yearning for his mother's voice.

All the time while the air-raid siren shrilled in the night, Isabel was pressing her body to his. The coolness of her skin was like a gradual quenching, a slow immersion into a shady spring, as the heat of his body seemed to rush into the waiting pores of her skin to receive his fever, but after a while, the heat was still there. Instead of one burning body, now there were two.

"Move over," he protested, shaking her off. "I have a fever, don't you see? You're getting it now."

But she pressed him to her closer, whispering, "It doesn't matter, it doesn't matter," and pushing her lips on his burning flesh.

He wanted to stop her, but her lips were cool, yet the burning went on with a fiercer fire.

After a while, Isabel reached for the light by the bed and sat down beside him, holding his hand.

"Why did you turn on the light?" Sol asked.

"I just wanted to see you," she answered. "How do you feel now?" She began passing her fingers on the back of his palm.

"If I can only perspire, I'll be all right," he said softly, his voice hardly audible, but she heard him. He lay quiet and silent, looking up at her, then quickly added as if it were as important as what he was trying to say about himself getting well, "Now in this light, you look sick also."

"Shall I make you tea?" she asked.

"No," he answered. "Just sing to me."

She stared at him, saying nothing, as though suddenly, he was not real, his voice was not his own, that was not what he had meant, but something else. She pressed his hand on her heart, saying nothing.

"Sing to me, please," he repeated.

NOW ISABEL looked alarmed. She bent her head close to his till she could feel his hot breath on her face and whispered, "Sol, darling, why do you ask that? You know I can't sing. I don't know any song at all. You have never heard me sing. Because I don't know how."

"Just hum, hum any tune," he insisted.

Now she wished she could sing. Had she never sung really? Never knew how? She played the piano. Love songs mostly, ballads of unrequitted love, of despair and betrayal. Oh, but she used to sing. When was that? A long time ago.

Hesitantly at first, but after a while, more freely, Isabel began to hum, softly, soothingly. It was not any particular melody or song. She just wanted to please him. She would do anything to please him, even if, right now, she felt a tightening around her breast and she wanted to cry. Suddenly, she knew why she had never sung all these years.

Sol closed his eyes remembering other times: A nipa-thatched house beside the kangkong fields; sudden, loud, drunken talk in the dark streets of Palomar, curses and exclamations in a dialect he knew too well; a mansion with many rooms and many corners; the whistle of a train promising return; dust in his eyes and throat in a season of Lent — flagellants rolling on the earth, their naked bodies oozing with the blood of self-inflicted wounds, and a man dragging a huge cross, surrounded by the curious and the penitent, and gazing up at a sky that seemed not to know him, a deep loneliness in his face; the drone of a sewing machine, a gray head bent over the needle, withered hands fumbling with a thread under a dim light, and the kindliest of eyes, the sweetest voice. Like this, this cool, heavenly singing. Then there were tears on his cheeks, but not his tears. The humming had come to a sudden stop. Isabel had bent down to kiss him, sobbing softly.

In autumn during the third year of the war when the mist stayed longer in the valley, the somber darkness somehow seeming to lengthen the nights, Isabel began planting tree peonies.

She had bought the seeds from a stunted beggar who peddled them in an alley near the boulevard.

"Fair lady," the beggar had called after her. "Here are miraculous seeds for a hundred yen only!"

"Let me see?" Isabel was curious. She stopped to examine the seeds well. The alley was narrow and dark. "What miracle do they bring do you say?" she asked. She spoke Japanese well.

"Plant them and see them grow as your fortune grows," the beggar said, smiling toothily, her arms red and coarse, the rags on her body, too thin for the chilly air.

"Why don't you plant them yourself then?" Isabel asked. "Then watch them grow as your fortune grows." She used the girl's exact words, which seemed taken from a book.

"But lady, I have planted these seeds a hundred times, I had too many of them, in different places, and waited, but none have grown," the beggar explained, her voice sincere and whining. "That's why I'm poor, see? I'm a beggar girl." She smiled, watching Isabel's eyes, then looked down at her old, dirty rubber shoes.

"Then these seeds are no good," Isabel said.

"That's for you to find out," the beggar argued, looking up at her again. "That's for you to find out."

Perhaps she was only a girl, really, Isabel thought, but she will never grow.

"What a foolish thing to do," Isabel said.

"It's the truth, fair lady," the beggar girl insisted, "these are miraculous seeds. I can see from your eyes, these seeds will grow in your garden. For centuries, you know, they grew nowhere except within the palace gates. Now for one hundred yen, I'm giving them all to you, all these you see in these packets. I must hurry home. My father is sick and soon he's going to die." She smiled again.

It was the smile, not the foolish things the beggar said, that touched Isabel's heart.

"How do you know your father will die soon?" she asked.

"I told you," the beggar answered, "I have many of these seeds at home and they will not grow in our garden."

Isabel got them for seventy-five yen, and now, as she brought them to the room where Sol lay sick, she did not tell him what the beggar said because she herself did not believe in it. She told him only later when the peonies began sprouting, while the frost was still on the ground. She burst into the room, crying, "Sol, they're growing, the tree peonies are growing. You'll get well now. Thank God, you'll get well now. The war will soon be over!" Sol was baffled by her excitement. Then she told him how she had come to buy the tree peonies seeds. She had not believed at first in the peculiar logic of the beggar, but when they started growing, she felt, they were, indeed, miraculous. They had to be.

She was restless all day, visiting the garden at frequent intervals as though a matter of hours could make a visible difference in the growth of the wee sprouts shoving up the loosened earth. Isabel prayed hard against rain, and strangely, no rain fell.

ABOUT THE time April came around, the garden under their window was crowded with stunted woody bushes that looked like fat dwarfs with their heads beneath a hood of green, who had strayed into the garden the night before and had been petrified there, first by the sun, then by the moonlight.

Sol had to be content with what Isabel told him. She described what changes each day brought: today, it was a deeper green in the leaves bare to the sun, all shades of green, wet and sea-like; or on another day, the stems were turning red, the buds had appeared, soon they would burst into flowers; prepare, prepare for the unfolding of the color, for the heady scent like wine from these flowers shaped like goblets.

He didn't believe her at first, he wanted to see for himself, but he could not. Later on, he felt she was telling the truth, she could not have imagined it all, he was more eager than ever to see. There were times, however, when he could move only after much pain and effort. He was wasting away. True, his fever came at longer intervals and were of shorter duration, but there were times when he could not even sit up in bed. Although Isabel had always insisted that he use the chamber pot she had placed conveniently on the floor at the foot of the bed, Sol would drag himself to the bathroom, holding on to the furniture, leaning on the wall, or crawling on all fours. He felt all his joints had been unhinged. She scolded him about this, not quite understanding his delicacy, his over-concern for her, who, after all, was his wife, that made him go through the ordeal of trying to reach the bathroom. She was herself, tireless, uncomplaining. In difficult moments, she had to help him wash. Sol felt so useless, he could not help shedding tears.

It was not mere shame, really. He tried to find what she felt as she gazed on his young but wasted body. He could not detect any flicker of regret in her eyes or in her words and acts, that she should be tied down to a dying man — he believed he was dying —

139

much less disgust at the sight of the transparent, hairy skin showing above protruding ribs and bones. As much as his feebleness would allow, he would cover his body with a towel and push her hand or his body away every time her hand strayed between his thighs, while giving him a hot sponge bath.

"You don't deserve this kind of life, Isabel," Sol said.

"Stop talking and acting like a child," she chided him.

"You may leave me if you wish. You deserve to be happy. Not like this."

He was thinking then of a particular moment, one night, when he wanted to go to the bathroom. He tried to sleep and forget all about it just so he wouldn't have to move and wake up the woman beside him. But when he could not stand it any longer, he rose, very slowly and quietly. He didn't realize he was that weak. A dizzy spell came over him. Before he knew what had happened, there he was sprawled, face down on the floor, amid a lot of clatter. He had spilled the chamber pot. Isabel had turned on the light and tucked him back to bed, wiping his skin where he needed wiping. Then she knelt on the floor and mopped off the urine and the grime.

There were times when Sol could not help thinking that these hardships in their life, including the war, for much of this unpleasantness occurred because of the war, were their punishment for the evil they had done, running away the way they did, leaving behind a husband dying in the hospital and the little girl alone. The doctor's subsequent death. The anguish they had caused all around. This was their punishment for all these. Isabel's enduring patience must have arisen from a similar sense of guilt, and this, for her, a sort of expiation, a day to day sacrifice, a kind of atoning in installments.

Isabel had refused to sleep in another bed. She always slept close to him, whether he burned with fever or trembled with chill. In the rare times she could talk about her first husband, she confided to Sol that she had never shared the same bed with him. At least, she had no memory of waking up in the morning and finding him beside her. As a matter of fact, she did not remember anything about him at all.

Such forgetfulness, Sol thought, could be a part of the pattern the guilty conscience often wove in the subtle gesture of turning away, an escape.

"Try sleeping away from me," he told her once. "You'll feel better. You know I sometimes cannot sleep and I disturb you."

"No, you don't," she answered. "I want to be awake when you're awake."

"But how can you stand my fever?"

140

"That fever is also mine. I want all of it, as a matter of fact. Besides, you don't have fever any more."

"And I'm not so clean, darling, I smell, don't I?"

"Everybody smells. Besides, I love your smell. I love everything about you. Please, don't drive me away."

Whenever the talk reached a point like this, Sol did not pursue it further. In the beginning, he used to say, "Now, of course, you're right. Again, as usual, I'm wrong." Now he simply kept quiet or talked of other things: what were the signs about the possibility of the war ending soon? This was not a welcome topic, he thought. It brought sadness to both of them. Each thought of home, Villa Magdalena, Elisa, Doña Magdalena and her invalid sister Doña Asuncion, Don Magno, Nora — who had survived it all? Who were no longer living? Better talk of things happening around: What are they talking about in the boulevards and the alleys of Tokyo, how many of the young men from the valley had been heard from, who had recently left? Which of the vegetable crops have yielded the most fruit? Or talk about the peonies, they were ready to bloom any time now.

"I shall bring you the first flower," Isabel promised him. "We shall smell its fragrance together."

From day to day she reported whatever change there was, real or imagined. While they were waiting for the buds to open, Sol remembered a Japanese story he had just read about an invalid husband who watched his wife working in their vegetable garden outside beneath his window with the aid of two mirrors.

"Buy me two handmirrors," Sol requested her. "I shall watch you in the garden. Then you'll always be beside me. Then I could also see how lovely the tree peonies are."

To his surprise, Isabel did not appear enthusiastic.

"It's not too good for the sick to look at themselves in a mirror," she said.

"But I'm not going to look at myself. I know how hideous I am. I want to see the garden and you among all those flowers," he said.

She gave another excuse: it was too dangerous to go to town. Who knows, the next air-raid warning might bring a real one?

"Don't think I'm not aware of what I look like," Sol told her, believing that this was the chief reason why she didn't want to get him the mirrors he had suddenly wanted to have. "All I need to do is pass my hand over my face to know. And the way you look at me, Isabel. How you pity me, don't you? Please, don't."

Isabel protested that it was not pity but love, that she loved him no matter what happened to him. Of course, he believed her. In the beginning he used to think that this woman who had been false to

141

her husband, who had been in a much better position to give her everything she wanted, could also be false to him, who had nothing, but his looks and youth. For him their first years together were a sort of waiting, the first hint of regret in a casual word or act. But nothing of the sort happened. There had been men among their circle of friends, there could have been occasions. But Isabel proved true to him; and when times became difficult, especially during the war and the long period of his illness, Isabel was the stronger, the more steadfast in her love.

In the days she expected the peonies to blossom, she was often in the garden, but Sol, in his sick bed, showed indifference, even on the day she came running to his room, shouting, "They're blooming now! The buds have opened. Many of them."

One day, soon after, Isabel arrived from a trip to the city, carrying with her a big package. Sol showed no surprise when she opened it and gave him two handmirrors, one oval shaped and the other, rectangular. He had known she would not deny him his wish too long. She was that way. He thanked her with a smile. His first glimpse of his face after so long was not too ugly because he was smiling then. But afterwards, alone, he had bad moments. How changed he was! If Isabel had loved him only for his looks, she would have deserted him long ago.

TOGETHER, they placed the two mirrors in such positions as would allow a glimpse of the blooming peonies. The first time he looked into the mirrors, he felt dizzy straining to get a good view of the garden. He broke into a cold sweat and he put the mirrors away. He didn't tell Isabel about it. There was no need. The next time he tried to look, he felt nothing at all, although he looked longer into the mirrors and spent quite a time getting the proper angle of vision.

Somehow he felt good being able to share with Isabel the pleasure the peonies brought. Some of the flowers were huge, the size of apples. At night, their perfume reached their room and seemed to give Sol strength. When Isabel heard about this, she felt happy. Soon there was no need for the mirrors any more. He could stand and move about. He could look out of the window and talk to Isabel. Sometimes he teased her, saying, "Wait for me, I'm coming down to the garden, too." How they waited for the day when he could really do that. For a time the war was forgotten. The first time he was able to shave himself marked the beginning of another lease on life. He felt young again and strong. One day, he himself went to the garden and plucked a flower and brought it to Isabel who was resting in bed. The gesture meant a lot. She clasped his hand and pressed it hard against her cheek as she looked up at him, her eyes brimming.

Still, like foolish children, they would lie together in bed and quarrel over the mirrors, each claiming to have found the perfect angle for both of them to get the best glimpse of the garden below. Together they would look, pressing their cheeks together and this thrilled them unlike anything that had thrilled them before. But soon they tired of looking at the garden. They also looked at the sky through the mirrors and indulged in fantasies. They imagined the mirrors giving them not only sights of flowers and clouds but sounds, voices and words, of friends and strangers, voices from the past. With their mirrors they heard the terrible sounds of death in many places, far and near, the distant detonation of bombs. They saw burning cities as yet without names. Oddly, they waited for the same terrifying sounds over the nearby city, and when it came, it sounded familiar, it was not too terrible because they had known all about it from their mirrors, on which, it seemed, they had been able to breathe magic.

In the winter the peonies stood sad and bare, but Sol and Isabel had their own memories of color and shape and scent to last them a lifetime, and they were not too unhappy when winter came and laid their garden desolate.

I Mean To Live

Hirabayashi Taiko

OTOME WAS for the second time meeting a prospective husband. From noon I could hear women at the well cleaning rice for the next day. As the light of the western sun struck my pillow from the crack in the curtain, my dinner was brought in. The dull fiber bowl caught the sunlight, and bits of fish floating on the soup like so many rootless plants came to me almost as the symbol of a marriage at forty.

Otome went downstairs dressed in a kimono of Akashi silk — she had borrowed it from me. I looked at my husband, who was taking quilts from the closet, as if I were a child making sure that its mother was still with it.

Laughing a husky laugh, for no very good reason, I said: "This time I think she'll make it. I have a feeling she will."

Somehow the encounter made me think of a vaccination.

After Otome had met the man, there was a certain flush about her, a certain swelling of the soul, a faint mark as of the first tiny stirring of life. It was not love, or passion, or even lust. It was rather like a sort of spiritual pregnancy preceding physical pregnancy.

"Is it something to be proud of, being a virgin at forty?" he asked. "Or is it a disgrace?"

"In Otome's case it doesn't seem to be either."

The notion of virginity for a time lay between us like some receptacle. I did not like seeing my husband so interested in it. I thought that not himself having known the resistance of "virginity," he was quite missing the point. He was awed by the forty-year-old virgin. He seemed to think her an unbreachable wall.

Seeing the outcome thus fixed as the result of a single meeting, I had an impulse to ridicule the utter want of reason in relations between man and woman. Indeed, if I may be forgiven for speaking quite freely, I thought Otome much too reckless. The time had come, in any case, for a break in a dike kept mended forty years. I feared that these crises in the affairs of life and the flesh were not to be brought to terms by such weakened nerves as mine.

144

Behind my fretfulness lay bitter thoughts about myself, abandoned once again, so ravaged with illness that I was like some pale, bloodless fish.

Needing my husband to heat my gruel and wash my hair and tend to my bedpan, I reminded myself of a drowning person who clutches at the arms of his rescuer. I had succeeded in having him dismissed from his work because I had too frequently had him telephoned at the office to be told that my heart was suddenly worse. No doubt, running off white and worried every day, he had passed beyond sympathy and become for his colleagues an object of ridicule. I could not myself understand why it should be; but when I heard him fling open the door downstairs as if he were forcing open some ultimate barricade, my pulse, until then as irregular as a badly stitched seam, would suddenly begin to march smoothly forward.

Foolish couple though we were, we had a background of emotions only we could understand.

In the days when we had watched the flame of my life about to go out, yet still burning on, he had been in jail, a political prisoner. As he tried to grasp at what must go on evading his grasp, the desperate wish to exorcise the sleep-bringing demon had driven him to a sort of nihilism. He would ask the guard each day what the almanac said, whether the omens for the day were auspicious or not. He could only rely, whatever the evidence for it might be, upon the mystical individuality that the diviners had given the days.

"What is it today?"

Sorry for him, the guard would consult the almanac.

"So maybe it will happen today," he would say upon learning that the signs were unlucky. That night as he went to bed he would be almost sick with relief at having seen the day through with no emergency summons.

"What is it today?" he would ask again the next day.

This time the horoscope would be such as to make him think my life safe for the morning, but the gloom of the afternoon would more than balance the respite. If there are those who find such behavior on the part of a materialist laughable — well, let them laugh.

For some reason the days on which he had unexpected little pleasures often proved to be days on which he had bad news of me. The pleasures were, of course, no more than an extra dessert or a hot bath. One day there was a rather special one. To bring him out of his gloom, a sympathetic guard took him to a waiting-room and offered him a cup of tea. Or so it seemed; but the amber liquid that might have been taken for weak tea was in fact *saké*. This astonishing treat was such as to arouse his tongue and throat, dulled by disuse, to the point of ecstasy. Then he remembered, and it was as if he had been dealt a slap in the face.

He had been a man dying of thirst who had come upon a well; but immediately he was himself again. The balance of omens hung before him with sudden vividness. He knew that when it would be rising for him it would be falling for me.

"Oh, no!"

"What's the matter?" The guard looked at him curiously. His color had changed.

I was then in great pain from sores on my back.

One day, as I fell into a light doze, he appeared at my bedside.

"Have them put cotton where it hurts," he said, and disappeared. The daytime dream was over as swiftly as such dreams are.

Cotton had been forbidden because it was said to fever the sores. He had had no knowledge of illness, and for him to appear thus in a dream and display his ignorance was somehow very endearing. I wept silly tears as I told the nurse what had happened.

"Well, if that's what he recommends, suppose we try it for a while," she said. The alacrity of her acceptance was also most endearing.

Presently there came a change in our state of affairs.

My husband came back to me. From the day of his release he went to work, and found this shabby two-story house, once a rickshawman's lodgings, on the outskirts of the city, at a spot where a district of imposing residences gave way to mean hovels. He moved me here in a car and stretcher.

I was at the time like a great doll that had to be dressed and undressed and lifted by numbers of people. I could not support my own head, but had to have it held up. Once in a hospital, when I had not yet been ill for very long, a young man about to urinate in the next room looked calmly in my direction as he took out his organ. The end of his life was not far away, I said to myself, looking down. And now I had taken his place. One day a young apprentice nurse brought in a bedpan and laid it on the floor, and, as she rolled up my nightgown, she giggled, looked down, and turned scarlet at my want of shyness.

"Ah, blushing maiden, I myself was once like you."

The nerves that went out to her winsomeness had not yet been whittled away, but the nerves that should have pulled back at the sudden exposure to cold air were gone.

"It's cold. It's hot." I had become a lonely, difficult invalid, given to saying such things with a sort of pleading arrogance.

"Don't talk nonsense. What is it you want me to do?"

146

Even while reproving me for the state of my nerves, however, my husband would be reflecting upon these complicated sensations "hot-cold" and "cold-hot," trying to understand them.

In midsummer, drenched with sweat, I would say to him over and over again: "Close the window. Please. Close it." I was very insistent. "Don't you understand? There's cold in the heat. The hotter it is the colder it is. Don't you understand?"

Sweat dripping from the hair on his chest, he would sit by the closed window leafing through a dictionary, and occasionally dry himself with a towel.

"Don't think about anything," I would order myself, trying not to look at the papered-over holes in the ceiling or the broken lattice-work at the doors. Just as the road of art had stretched on and on, however diligently I had pursued it, so also the road of illness stretched endlessly into the distance. I was boldly traveling that road alone, under the two-colored banner of life and death. I had become a heroine in the ranks of illness.

Life and society had vanished from my sight. I remembered only something that a pro-German doctor had said at the time of the Flanders campaign: "They'll be landing in England one of these days."

I was so far beyond it all that at a time when the possibility no longer existed, I asked: "Have the Germans taken London yet?"

Once someone spoke of a certain geologist who, dying of cancer in the Imperial University hospital, dictated his remaining work. I laughed at the difference between the delirious and the rational passages.

"The happiness of being sick — that's enough for me. It has its own poetry and life and ideals and creations." They were words designed to grind down the hopes of my husband, wearing himself out as nurse and provider, wanting to see me raise myself even a little. And they were designed to provide a place for my willful ways, demanding ice cream and sending him around the city in search of it, and getting him up in the middle of the night to heat a hot-water bottle or take my pulse.

"Please turn down the light. Please," I would say. He had lost his job and was working at home.

He would drape a kerchief around the desk lamp and go on shuffling his papers. Even so the wan light would show the low ceiling and the faded mats.

"Turn it down lower. Please." As long as I could see light my heart would be a wild horse dashing over the moors.

"If I make it any darker I won't be able to write. Then how will we eat?" Finally he would lose his temper.

But the matter of darkness was not the worst. There were times when my nerves were unable to bear a moving object.

"Please. Can't you go outside for just a half-hour?"

"But what are you thinking of? I'm not doing this just for the fun of it. Don't you feel even a little sorry for me when you say things like that?"

"Not a bit." I spoke the words clearly, though as always in a voice that seemed about to fade away.

He looked at me in open astonishment. "No? Why not?"

"Well, maybe it's bad for you, but a sick person has a right to get well."

Tears like falling leaves played an accompaniment to the words. They had the power to throw him quite off balance. He would look at me in growing bewilderment, but then he would remember the cause he had dedicated himself to, and, calming his irritation, set about making the room yet darker. In a narrow slit of light such as a watch repairman might use, he would go on writing.

Because I was such a difficult patient, any number of nurses had left me. I was happy when the two of us were alone, however, and had no further wishes.

It was into this situation that Otome came. I do not remember which number she was in the line of nurses.

The weather was bitterly cold. The sliding doors had been taken out between the next room and mine, and the windows were open even in the middle of the night. Otome and my husband sat with a brazier between them, one of them sewing, the other writing. Occasionally one or the other would put out a hand to warm it over the brazier, or blow at a numb finger. I could see tiny needles of ice in the cup by my pillow.

"I can't stand much more of this. Let's close them." The two of them would finally get up and close the windows, but immediately I would protest.

"It's suffocating."

"Your nerves again. But why try to fight a sick person? Go open them again, Otome. God, but it's cold."

And so the windows would be opened again. It was as if I wished to make of my husband, already subdued by my illness, an invalid like myself, and I wished to sacrifice the newly-arrived Otome with him.

What my illness had done to him could be seen, for instance, in the workings of the rusty little bell with which I summoned him from downstairs — my voice would not reach that far. It seemed to trouble him even more than my voice, and when, out in the street, he would hear a noise similar to it, he would start up in alarm. Once as he was crossing an intersection there was a loud ringing from a traffic light. He froze in the middle of the street, and had to be shouted across by a policeman.

He had about him an awkwardness that made it impossible for people to work under him, but now, as if he had become a different person, he was wholly weak and unassertive.

One day, shortly after his release, he brought three pink dahlias and put them at my bedside.

"Aren't they beautiful," said the girl who was then taking care of me, a relative of my husband's. "I'd like one of them too."

While the two of us watched in astonishment she brought another vase, put water in it, and took one of the dahlias to her desk. Her flower vase looked strange, but mine looked even stranger. There seemed no way of bringing the two flowers together. They insisted on going their separate ways.

"Is it possible to make an arrangement out of just two flowers?" The words were mild enough, but mentally I was clenching my fists and stamping my useless feet — not unreasonably, I think. The girl had somehow acquired mistaken notions of equality, and she was under the impression that in this house she could have her way. She declared it an injustice, this pampering of an invalid. When I had meat she had to have meat, when I had eggs she had to have almost as many eggs; and from beneath her skin, muddy and lusterless when she had come, a white glow began to appear, as if polished to the surface. Partly out of deference to the family, my husband said only that she was a bit too much of an expense.

And when he saw the ridiculous arrangement in my vase, all he said to the girl was: "She wonders if it's possible to make an arrangement out of just two flowers."

He was compelled to change, however, when Otome came.

Noting on one occasion that my soup was salty, he thereafter was careful to taste all my meals. "Too salty. She's weak, and should have very little salt." He also had to test the water with which I took medicine. "That will do — you can give it to her now. She chokes on it when it's lukewarm. It's better hot, or colder like this."

And he urged Otome to cut down drastically on food for the two of them.

At the time I was getting a quart of meat broth every day. It was he who had suggested the new diet, but, since it would add to our expenses, the project was not one to be undertaken lightly. I felt that he was waiting expectantly for an answer, hoping a little to hear me say that the broth would be hard to down.

149

But I was not one to refuse. I had not once had meat broth, and heard that it was, in fact, somewhat trying. All the same my answer was almost eager: "They say it's not easy to take, but I'll try it, to keep myself alive." Thus did I walk over his finer feelings.

With a solemn, thoughtful expression on his face, he went out to negotiate with the butcher. The broth came everyday in one of the bottles in which sauce was carried in the days before Occidental restaurants had to stop deliveries. The boiled shreds of meat would come with it, wrapped in a bamboo leaf.

It was natural that the other two should cut down on their own rations. The meat shreds, with rice, became their main food.

"Horrible stuff. Just like eating shoe leather," he would say, picking his teeth, as he came upstairs after a meal. He did not seem especially unhappy, however. Indeed the remark carried a suggestion that eating tasteless things for my sake gave him a certain pleasure.

But I paid no attention. I looked at the ceiling every day, and at the blue sky outside, and even the blue sky, uninterrupted for a few days, would come to seem loathsome.

"The sky is an umbrella people can't get out from under. One they have no choice about." And I would go on irrelevantly: "Toller once said that a person without dreams has no right to live. A nice idea — but it makes you wonder, when you think that Toller committed suicide."

Sensing that I was in a good mood, he decided to go out.

"Don't go out today. I can feel breaks in my pulse."

Pinned down by my wish to have him go out as little as possible, he sat down at his desk. But even so he did not lack exercise. Like bullets from a machine-gun I would fire orders at him, the whole series at least once every hour. "Close the window." "Open the window." "Wipe away the sweat." "The quilt is too heavy." And so on.

It was at about this time that Otome began complaining of a kidney ailment.

"Does your face swell up?" asked my husband.

"Not particularly. But I have palpitations, and I feel sluggish."

"Well, don't overdo it, and have another bottle of milk every day."

The real trouble was malnutrition.

Finishing dinner early, Otome went to consult with relatives. The way nurses had of finishing their evening work early and going out suggested something to us, for we had seen many nurses.

150

"Otome wants to quit this sort of work and find herself a husband," I said. My judgment in these matters was a thousand times keener than a healthy person's.

Because of a childhood accident, Otome had two front teeth, white as moonflowers, that projected at right angles to her lip. She had gone to work as a housekeeper and nurse because she had decided that she could never marry. Small children at places where she worked would put out their fingers to feel the teeth. The pain, now that she was forty, made her want to hurl stones down upon the path known as matrimony. It was a path reserved for others. Since she had stopped going out on odd jobs, however, and had come to live with us, she had been able to put aside a little money. From the thought of using the money on her teeth it was but a step to the thought of using her new teeth to attract a husband.

It was quite as I had imagined. Dressed in my kimono, she went out to review the possibilities. She rejected the first man. Arrangements were made for her to meet a second.

Late in the evening the front gate slid open and Otome was back. The next morning there was a messenger from the other party, and there were secret consultations downstairs, and the talks came to rest where it had been hoped that they would.

The moment Otome had left, all the little chores fell on my husband.

I said only: " 'Every Jack has his Jill' — I wonder who thought that up."

A "day of great peace" was chosen from the almanac for Otome's wedding. On the same day a bride came to the son of the tinsmith who had the other half of our duplex. My room shook from morning till night as people trailed up and downstairs. I did not mind, however — I was spared that metallic screeching.

" 'Great peace' — so that's the day for weddings." He sat by the window and looked down at the alley with narrow, bloodshot eyes. He was not looking at the alley but at memories far beyond it. Mention of "great peace" was enough to bring back harsh memories of the days in jail, so thickly laid over with apprehension.

In that granite jail, an almanac containing omens for all the days, lucky and unlucky, had hung from a pillar behind the guard.

"I didn't know 'great peace' was the day for weddings." He said it over and over again. Otome left, and scarcely was she gone when an automobile pulled up and the tinsmith's half of the house came to life. Our second floor rocked and shook.

In the evening, my husband went from one corner of the room to another, tightening the slack green mosquito-net. The humming of mosquitoes was like a sad ballad.

151

"And so you have to put up the net again." Spiritless tears came to my eyes, as if welling up from my whole body.

Through the cracks in the ceiling, I saw a flash from next-door, where pictures of the wedding reception were being taken. When the house had been made into a duplex, the partition had not been extended to the paper-covered ceiling.

"So she got married because of a couple of teeth." It was to such remarks that the excitement had brought me.

As a sort of sedative, something to put me to sleep, my husband would bring a bedpan up from below. Pushing the tin, shoe-shaped object in under my hips, and waiting for me to finish, he would apply soft paper, the last stage in the process, and go back downstairs. It was a process we had been through hundreds of times before. Like a baby, I would bare my body to him, and accept his ministrations calmly.

But tonight as I watched him raise the mosquito-net and crawl inside, I was somehow apprehensive.

However much I hated having him away from me, beyond the wall of the great city for even a day or even half a day, however much I sought, like a powerful magnet, to draw him to me, I would yet break into cold beads of sweat when his face or his body approached nearer than a certain fixed distance. A kiss was as difficult for me as the time a diving woman must stay under water.

"Suppose we cuddle a bit," he would say.

Even though I knew it was a joke, I would ward him off fiercely. For I was a middle-aged woman of considerable experience, and I knew too that the joke might possibly not be a joke.

"Let me do it by myself tonight," I said, all the harshness of that moment of fear in my voice. But I was too late. The cold metal was already at my hips.

In the dim light from the next room, the sagging flesh of my legs showed faintly white.

Even when I had finished, he did not take the bedpan away. He was gazing at the point where the white gave way to a dark valley. There was a bitter silence, such as I had known a number of times before.

I should have offered him soft words of consolation. I should have stroked his back.

Instead I called out sharply, with the roughness of the undergrowth I still kept alive within me: "Take it away! It hurts!"

The instant collapsed like a wall. His manner making it evident that his blood still ran high, he deliberately made his way from the net, the bedpan shaking as he went.

152

"Please," I called after the dejected figure. "Put up a separate net for yourself tonight. The way you always do."

Bedpan in hand, he looked at me through the blur of the netting.

"I'm not a saint, after all, you know. Would you mind telling me what you think I ought to do?"

"I don't know about you," I said, in tears, "but I mean to go on living."

The new phase was off to a bad start; but it was life with the two of us alone that I liked best.

I felt as if illness had taken away all the old leaves from the plant that was I, and given me fresh, new leaves in their place. My tired old blood had been quietly drunk away, and, whether I wished it or not, I was being given new blood in return.

He ate the meat shreds as usual, and as usual came upstairs saying how bad they had been.

The time he spent over my meals and bedpan had to be made up for at night. He stayed up later and later.

"Turn down the light. Please." I repeated it over and over, as always, but it had become a way to prevent the late-night work that was so bad for him.

One night, stooped over a dictionary with a magnifying glass, he looked up.

"Isn't there something funny about the light?"

"None that I can see."

"But there is something funny. There's no light at the center of it."

"Oh?"

No more was said that night; but the next day when he came home from shopping he was worried. "There's something wrong with me. I have spells of not being able to see. And how will we eat if this goes on?"

"But I can't see anything wrong." I was already in tears. "What do you suppose it might be?"

He went to a doctor and had numerous blood tests made, and was told the up-to-date name of some eye ailment. The cause was unknown, but matters having to do with the eyes suggested malnutrition.

"He said if I went on working I'd go blind. So what am I to do?"

He could not stop the piecework he was doing. He was paid by the page.

Yet another cold winter came, and, blowing on his fingers by the window, he would thumb his dictionary.

"Well, something will come along." Thus we managed in a vague way to comfort each other.

Meanwhile his case was progressing in court, and all sorts of documents would come by registered mail.

Hearing the postman's voice, the man next door, father of many children, would complain: "Look at the money they keep getting in the mail. And not a thing for us. Can't we expect a damned thing from your family?"

And so there would be quarrels, and the two of us would smile. While the misfortune of others was not our good fortune, still to be companions in poverty brought a certain comfort.

"I can't see at all. I'm going to have to stop for a while."

One night, he laid down his pen and climbed hopelessly into bed. He straightened my bedclothes as if he were ministering to a baby.

"And so we've come to this. Well, I'll keep you alive. Do you want to live? You who make a specialty of wanting to live?"

I nodded. There were tears in my eyes.

(Translated by Edward Seidensticker)

My East Bengal

Syed Ali Ahsan

What an amazingly cool river
        is my East Bengal
How quiet and again how gay
        in sudden overflowing abandon
Once loud and noisy, many a time
        sleepy and lethargic
At other times
        a continuous flood of subdued voices

How often cranes and river-snipes
A kingfisher or two
Some chattering crows
Cluster of Kash-thickets singing in the wind
A river of words rich with waves
A tiny island of earth
With a few trees and some cottages
Thatched with sun-dried cocoanut leaves

You are bottomless
        in the overflowing waters of the monsoon
A heaven of generous heart
A wide expanse of life
        stretching beyond the horizon
A greeting like the boat
        swimming onward with the sweeping current
Like the full-throated song of the boatman
        singing with abandon
From his seat perched way up at the projecting front.

What astonishing wealth of life

155

How many times in how many strange lands
        have I seen
Numberless trees, hills and smoke
The richness of many seas
        dark thick blue, gray like the fog,
        Or black,
Seen the sun in the sky of many countries
Right and left, touching the horizon
Or glittering on the ice
        red, blue, or crystal white
And in the generous width of the woodlands
        of Western Bavaria

The air the light of the sun
        and every moment then had
Seemed to envelop me in some
        soft green languor.

But the generous profusion of green
        in all its wild splendour
Now suddenly comes back to me
        new and fresh
Here my world is much more glamorous
Here is a land like a river
Quiet, overflowing, full of music,
Myriad-faced, a line-sketch of many colours

This is my East Bengal
Whose likeness is a cool quiet river.

My East Bengal is a smooth dark cluster
        of Tamal trees
A bower heavy with the intimacy
        of many leaves
Like the blossoming of the dusk
Like the bottomless depth of the lake
Like the gathering of the black-haired clouds
The intoxicating peace wiping out the pain.
My East Bengal is the love
        of the darkness of the rains
The wet blue sari touching the deep corners
        of the heart

The precious moment of looking at the sky
      with hair dishevelled and awry
From the bower of the Tamal trees
      surrounded by golden creepers
An abundance of gaiety
      rich with boundless feelings
Once many feathers of clouds
      screening the sun
A strange benumbling smell
      of sheaves of paddy and earth and water
Many moods of the love-lorn-one two three
      and ten
Here is eternal journey towards and the lover's abode
      in frightened haste
Home and abroad and one's own courtyard
      all one in overwhelming passion

A branch of the Kadamba tree
      with three flowers and many leaves
Bends low touching the ground
Many more trees leaves creepers
Blue yellow violet or white
An endless flood of million flowers
Peace like the softly closing eyes
      in the laziness of sleep

Loosening the hair black like the eyes
      of the crow,
Planting the feet in water –
      whose image is the red lotus
Skirting the body with the wet blue sari
      that touches the deep corners of the heart
The likeness of which body is the smooth Tamal
You are my East Bengal
      A tower rich with joyous profusion.

Translated by Kali Chowdhury

A Tale For Dien Tamaela

Chairil Anwar

I am Pattiradjawane
Whom the gods watch over
I alone.

I am Pattiradjawane
Foam of the sea.
The sea is my blood.

I am Pattiradjawane
When I was born
The gods brought me an ear.

I am Pattiradjawane, guarding the nutmeg groves.
I am fire on the shore, Whoever comes near
Must call my name three times.

In the night-time quiet, seaweed dances
To the sound of my drum,
Nutmeg trees become maidens' bodies
And live till dawn.

Dance!
Be happy!
Forget everything!

But take care not to make me angry
I'll kill the nut trees, stiffen the maidens
I'll bring down the gods!

I'm in the night, in the day,
In the rhythm of the seaweed and in the fire that roasts
    the island...

I am Pattiradjawane
Whom the gods watch over
I alone.

Translated by Burton Raffel and Nurdin Salam

Meeting (*Bertemu*)

S. Takdir Alisjahbana

Standing beside the grave
With the morning sun glistening pink on the earth,
My soul bends down
Seeking your face,
And my senses swell and flood.

Confronting you,
Piercing the thick ground,
I let my eyes wander
To the rows of graves, hundreds of stones
In red earth, in thick grass,
Mossy wood and singing marble,

And like lightning it flashed in my heart:
So many sorrows well up,
So often sadness slices tears
Onto the earth.
Oh, loved one in white,
You're not alone in the ground!

And my poor soul bends
To God's feet:
Before you my sorrows are the sorrows of the world,
Misery clings to my heart
I am dust in the air,
Blown by the wind.
A cool dew drops on my soul
And shines brightly in my eyes.

Translated by Burton Raffel and Nurdin Salam

Cathedrale de Chartres
(*Chartres Cathedral*)

Sitor Situmorang

Will He speak in the quiet night
If snow falls and the birds are white?
Sometimes the heart wants to give itself
Into the keeping of pure prayer.

Oh, God, we will never meet again
In the Communal prayer.
Here I bring love in the sad eye of my love —
Life is not separate from dissolution.

On Easter's day she sobbed, crying wildly
As we made our pilgrimage to Chartres Cathedral.
Her prayer lay sad on the wet stained glass colours.
Jesus is crucified and man has words no more.

The night before the cock crowed
And the people of Chartres left the fair,
He sobbed through the lateness of night,
In the drizzle his memory wandered.

To his mother, his wife, his children, to Jesus.
Adultery and faithfulness fought for his heart —
My love is one, God is one,
Life becomes one with dissolution.

This was the tale of our love
Which began near to Notre Dame,
At dawn in the flower market,
When the springtime sun was still misted.

This was the story of Easter's day
When the world was pursued by anxious unrest,
But lust and adultery, love and the city,
Because of her, and me and my faithful wife.

And during that night in the place of rest,
In the pure atmosphere of the church music,
The curse of desire and the grace of God were united.
The salute of the wife, the embrace of the mistress were one.

This was the Easter's day story
When the earth gathered wetness
And tears were uneasy
And the flowers held open their petals
In the land of France,
In the sweet land
Where Christ was crucified.

Translated by S. Thornton

To A Friend

Chairil Anwar

Before emptiness draws closer
And the final treachery leaps at us from behind,
While blood runs and feeling beats
And despair has not bloomed and there is no fear
Remember the evening fades, without warning,
A red sail dipping into darkness,
And, friend, let's part now, here;
The emptiness that pulls at us also strangles itself,
So
Empty the glass,
Pierce, traverse, invert the world,
Love women, but leave the flatterers,
Rope the wildest horse, spur him swiftly,
Tie him to neither noon nor night
And
Undo what you've done,
End without heir, without relation,
Without requesting forgiveness,
Without granting it.
So
Again let us part:
The final agony will draw us into an empty sky.
Once more, friend, one line more:
Shove your sword to the hilt
Into those who've diluted the pureness of honey!

Translated by Burton Raffel and Nurdin Salam

Traveler First Class
(*Penumpan Kelas I*)

E. Tatengkeng

Before I was thirty
I was never more than a deck passenger.
Thanks to the efforts of my friend
And the transfer of sovereignty
I'm now a traveler first class.

I'm one of the army
of inspection officials
Wandering
From island to island
Building up the country.

Every evening I play bridge in the salon
And drink my beer
And rage at the waiter.

I've never written a report.

I disembark
And give half a rupiah
For the workers on the first of May.

Translated by James S. Holmes

In Praise of You
(*Mumudji Dikau*)

Amir Hamzah

When I praise You, with closed lips, my eyes shut,
I bow down on my knees, my head on the ground, deep in silence,
    in the darkness of Supreme Love.
Your beloved comes to me, finds me sitting alone, lonely
    and quiet.
She kisses my lips, clings to my shoulders, hangs on my neck,
    desiring only the sound of love.
While my heart sings, and my whole body bends in prayer, she
    presses my thighs, drinking my voice...

And
She floats back to her home,
Pure light,
A tongue of fire wrapped in glass,
Ascending toward grace, and the blessing of peace.

Translated by Burton Raffel and Nurdin Salam

Ballad of the Men of Limestone Soil

W. S. Rendra

The men have gone into the street
Their swords tipped with lighting
And the horses of the robbers
Can be seen in the yellow hilltop
Blood is the speech now

Behind barricaded doors
Weep children, pray women

Without victory there is no word "home"
The coward will lie in the courtyard
And his wife will not open the door

The beat of hooves draws near
And the wind begins to sing
"I shall tap the blood of men
From the steel jar of their breasts
Like generous dealers in wine
The men will lie in the street
Opened by howling wolves

O thriving down of the breasts
Garden of sweet vines!

Half way round the stockade
Spreads the beat of the hooves
Then the cry of combat
Men drawing life from their swords
The spread of a stinking liquid
Mouths foaming and dust in wounds

At the third cry of the cockerel
And the first blue light in the sky
The men go back to the village

Erect with their wounds flowering
Red gashes and open breasts

The door is marked with sweat

Who knocks

Your man has come home, faithful women

The women stream from the doors
To lick the wounds of their men
The girls chant in the windows

The headman of Kudo Seto
Like a flower famed for its sap
Slowly runs his hand
Over his red body

And at the door of the hut
His wife clings to his feet
While to his son he says
"Only child of mine,
I hung the sword of the lord of robbers to give to you
Store it in the flesh of your right breasts!"

Translated by Derwent May

Gauri

Gopi Gauba

SATYADEVI, wife of the village priest helped her husband, Gurudev, by teaching the children and attending to births, deaths and the religious rites that were performed at various festivals. Together they worked for the good of the community and were generally loved for their charity and goodwill.

They did not mind their poverty; when there was no wheat in the house, and the remains of the previous night's vegetables had been given to the hungry sweeper, they ate fruit and drank sweetened milk But if there was no fruit and the cow went dry, they looked up the almanac and usually found that it was a day for fasting.

They were attached to each other and had a secret joke about their lack of children. The almanac said that one fine day a daughter would be born to them. With happy impatience they waited for the female child and at night as they rested when the breeze was fragant and cool and the sky seemed full of a smiling peace, they asked each other when it would be.

Gurudev was kind, gentle of soul, and the reading of scriptures had expanded his already generous mind. But Satya, his good wife, knowing his secret hankering, worried that she could give him no child.

One early morning, before the first rays of the sun could touch the earth and the dew of spring still lay wet on the terrace near the room where Satya worked on the grinding of wheat in their stone-mill during her morning prayers, Gurudev came running towards her. He was inarticulate with joy. He dragged her to the centre of the compound.

"There was no rain," they whispered to each other.

They sat on their haunches, watching in silent wonder and delight the green plant that had sprung out of the arid, dried-up earth. The auspicious day of the almanac! Both knew it and they did not question the form and manner of what they considered was their miracle child.

"Our Gauri, Incarnation of Parvati, Consor of Shiva" they said in unison.

The joking was over. Instead an earnestness took its place. They worried as only fond parents did; their interest and pleasure became concentrated in this little plant growing taller each day.

Every morning Satya brought a pail of water from the village well and saved it diligently from their daily quota. Carefully she watered the plant, taking care to open out the earth at the roots for fresh air. Every evening she washed the leaves and the young branches, one by one, of their day's dust, as a mother might lovingly wash the limbs of a child who had played in the mud. She sang while she thus washed the tree and the words that she used were the meaningless words mothers used when they crooned to their young. At night she whispered lullabys, a nameless ache within her to carry her beautiful Gauri in her arms and rock her to sleep.

Gurudev watched the sun growing hotter each day. Afraid that his Gauri might suffer from the heat, he gathered bamboos and strips of cane and built for it a shade through which the sun filtered gently. At the approach of cool weather, when they could no longer sleep out on the terrace, again this particular fear entered into him and he covered up the awning with gunny bags which Satya sewed together. And, when frost hit the ground and real danger hovered in the winter wind from the north, he brought out their blankets with all the unquestioning care of blood parents and folded their Gauri in their warmth.

One evening as Satya washed the leaves, though by now the tree had grown too tall for her, she suddenly stopped. She blushed and a wave of pleasure flashed deep down into her. She took the slim branch in her hand, intent on what she saw. Gurudev, who sat on a straw mat grinding herbs for the preparation of a certain ointment was always secretly delighted listening to her nightly monologue.

"Seen something?" he asked.

"Come! Come!" she replied holding the branches in her open palms.

The berries were hard and green and very tiny. But they were perfect in shape. During their evening meal the old couple watched the tree as it swayed in the breeze, tall, slim, elegant. To them it was their daugther, the beautiful Gauri, grown into a happy young woman. It was early spring and the night was chilly, but these two brought out their available covering to sleep in the open, to listen to Gauri's whispering and singing as she danced with the night wind. This was their happiest day, comparable only to another time when the berries stood out lusciously red, round and glowing like jewels. There was no doubt that the berries would also be deliciously sweet.

"Sweeter than all the sugar in the milk of white cows, sweeter than syrup made out of the attar of red roses, sweeter than golden honey brought by mountain bee..." sang Satya beside herself with joy. Gurudev understood his wife well, for he too shared her poetic fancy in his own silent way.

When the berrries were fully ripe, Satya brought a basket and covered its bottom with moist palm leaves, and one by one she placed the berries in neat rows, as Gurudev gently plucked them, counting each one and leaving ten berries on the branches for their evening meal.

"Our daughter" they said to each other "is a bride today and the village will have a feast." Then with a proud smile Satya set forth, the basket in the crook of her arm, to distribute the precious berries to friends and parents of pupils and donors of fruits and sweets.

Gurudev stayed behind to finish the day's work. The news spread like quick fire. The cool of the evening had hardly set when the good neighbours came to compliment him on the sweetness and magic beauty of the berries. They described the colour, smacking their lips as they compared the taste with nothing they knew that existed similar to it on this earth. And Gurudev, brimming with pride and happiness, showed them the tree as it waved its shining leaves with delight over the songs of praise. And such was this overwhelming feeling in him that he plucked two out of the ten berries still on the branches and gave them to his friends. More admirers arrived and he plucked some more for them.

There were now only two berries left. He plucked them, wrapped them quickly in a palm leaf, and hid them. Darkness had come and Satya had not returned. He was beginning to get impatient, but he would not eat without her. He said his evening prayers and sat on the terrace watching Gauri, marvelling at the way the leaves took up the silver and gold from the rising moon.

The Zamindar of the village arrived and Gurudev felt immensely flattered. The Zamindar lived at the outskirts of the village, in a big brick house. He had many cows and buffaloes and owned most of the land around. However, he had no children, and recently his second wife had died. But the rumour was that he would marry again only this time he would make no mistake about the stock he would choose from. He had a vicious temper and was vain of his wealth and it seemed altogether flattering that he had ridden all the way up the dusty road to compliment Gurudev on the berries.

When Gurudev related this incident to Satya, she felt no rancour that he had given the last two berries to the Zamindar. She knew that she would have done the same. She was only disappointed that they would have to wait another long year to taste the berries.

It was a dust-filled summer, followed by a tedious waiting for the rains to cease, and then an equally depressing muggy autumn when the very air became limp and tired, and finally the bitter cold winter that almost froze the earth. When spring finally came and the beloved tree smiled and spewed forth green berries old Gurudev was dead.

Satya removed the vermillion from her forehead and cast off her meagre jewels and coloured clothes to follow the rigid mourning custom of her country. She resigned herself to the white cotton of the Hindu widow and spoke of her loneliness and grief only to their "child" which stood in mute sympathy as if she understood. When the berries were red enough to be plucked, Satya brought out her basket and filled it up and set out for the house of her neighbours. Her husband, who waited patiently for this season, had died without tasting the berries. She found it unthinkable to eat them.

Many summers and winters passed and many springs came, and Satya went about with her lot contentedly. Some of the neighbours begged her to stay with them, but she could not leave her Gauri behind. It had grown to be even more beautiful and she took care of it day and night, in the cold and the heat and the rain. She continued to teach the village children and to read her scriptures, and spent long hours attending to the sick. But she always hurried back with an inner gladness to her beautiful Gauri.

One fine morning as she walked along the dusty lanes of the village she met the Zamindar. He rode on a horse and he looked even more frustrated and restless as he still had no child of his own. He called loudly at Satya. She arranged the cloth on her head and waited for him to speak.

"Why have you not sent the berries to us?" he demanded.

Satya was surprised but she tried to smile. "You have been away so long" she said gently.

"Well now I am here" he retorted.

"I shall bring the berries next spring, I promise" she replied.

"Next spring!" he cried out "are the berries this season finished so quickly? What right have you to give away my share!"

Satya tried to placate the man. "Forgive me" she said "I have been to your house and every time it was closed, and your place is so far I can no longer walk as I used to."

"Those are silly excuses!" shouted the Zamindar.

Satya could stand his rudeness no longer. People had gathered and the dust under their feet was beginning to rise in the air.

"It is my tree, is it not?" she said in a loud voice. "I can give my berries to whomever I wish to. And you could get off that horse when you speak to an old woman."

Now, no one had ever spoken in such a manner to the Zamindar, particularly an old woman and in front of a crowd at that!

"I am the landlord here" he screamed at her "and that tree of yours, and every other tree in this place belongs to me. To me! You are a Brahmin widow, you have no right to possess anything." And then as his horse pranced he added even more viciously "I will teach you a lesson for daring to speak to me like that!"

Poor Satya was upset and had to rest in a kind neighbour's house, before she could walk back home. It took her sometime to reach her cottage, but as she approached it, she halted in her tracks. A crowd gathered in front of the terrace and the Zamindar could be seen bobbing up and down on his horse. As she rushed towards her beloved tree she already knew what had been done to it. She knew with the instinct of a mother that her child lay on the ground, bruised and brutally mangled with an axe. It was uprooted and torn out of the warm embrace of the earth, like the upturned helpless feet of a dead child. The branches lay inert and lifeless on the ground and the breeze that rustled through the leaves seemed to know that it passed through the tresses of a dead girl.

The crowd made way for her and silently she stood in their midst, staring at what she saw. A great sorrow filled her, unutterable because to others it was only a tree.

She sank down, her knees under her, and as she loosened her hair as in mourning, she began to weep as one weeps for one's beloved. She wept quietly and intensely, and as each of her tears fell she spoke to the dead tree. Only then did people perceive that Gauri was her child, born out of her womb and Gurudev was the father. In awe they listened to the dirge of a heartbroken mother who would never again see her daughter sing in the rain and laugh at dawn and dance with the stars. A great hush fell and the crowd hung back.

Then Satya talked of the berries, berries that would never ripen, berries she herself had never tasted. And the sorrow that she had lain by at the death of Gurudev came out again. It broke the very walls of her heart as it burst forth in great torrents and the evening took it up and it swirled out into the darkening sky, shutting out everything else. When at last it was over, she sat in silence, a grief-stricken lonely old woman.

Some of the women in the crowd whispered together and decided to take her forcibly to themselves. But they stood helplessly, afraid to intrude. Presently Satya got up and went inside her house. She brought what she could to make a decent funeral pyre. She had a small tin of clarified butter; there were flowers for the evening prayers and a little sandalwood paste. She opened her tin box and brought out her old red silk shawl and in a gesture of tender farewell she covered the fallen tree with it. And as she set fire to it she whispered "go now my Gauri to thy father where he is gone."

Someone in the crowd suddenly shouted the name of the Zamindar, who had brought such sorrow to this worthy woman and deprived the village of the berries. And the young, with their passion roused to a frenzy, darted in all directions to find the Zamindar. The wily fellow, however, had long disappeared on his horse.

While this commotion went on, a vast futility and emptiness filled Satya, seen clearly on her face as she stared at the fire soaring golden into the dark sky, exuding white heat while the red of the silk shawl shimmered like brocade. The decision must have come suddenly to her, in one blinding flash, as most decisions do. Before reason could come to her rescue, she jumped into the middle of the burning tree. As she sat crouched, her hair spread out, hiding her face as though behind a screen, and Gauri stretched out her many arms to fold her in an embrace. Almost immediately the two were united in one big blaze.

All this happened far too swiftly for anyone to do anything except gape in shock and wonder. The next day they found that even their ashes had mingled, which the wind took and scattered into the surrounding fields. The good neighbours picked up the bones and the remains of the ashes and cast them into the sacred river, as is the Hindu custom. Where the tree had stood they built a shrine.

The village folk gather daily at this shrine and the cottage is a school where the children come to play, to learn and to sing; and one of the songs they sing is the story of Satyadevi, mother of Gauri the beautiful berry tree.

Van Buren and the Village Girl

Achdiat K. Mihardja

It happened in Amsterdam, one windy evening in autumn. I lost my way and had to ask how to get to Valerius Street, I was rather startled that the man I asked should answer in Indonesian and said 'Merdeka' in response to my greeting 'goeden avond.'

"This way, saudara." He was good enough to accompany me sociably to the street I was looking for. It turned out to be only a couple of turns from the place where we met.

The man was rather small for a Dutchman. From time to time his hands went to his hat to hold it down against the wind. Like the hat his overcoat was worn out and sloppy. Although I couldn't see his face clearly, his calm manner of speaking and soft voice gave me the impression that he was a likeable man.

As we walked, he told me that he had been in Indonesia at the time of the revolution. And he was kind enough to invite me to visit his house. We fixed the time right then.

One afternoon three days later, at the time we had settled, I rang his doorbell. He opened the door himself, and straightaway we climbed the gloomy stairs to the third floor, where he lived in such a room as would suffice for a simple and solitary life. And indeed, the room was very simple, one would almost say impoverished — no more than three chairs, a table, a dresser, and a divan which seemed to do double duty as a bed, all of them very old. Everything was disorderly — books here and there, chess-men on the table not yet cleared away from the last game, and near the window an unfinished painting on an easel, with brushes and tubes of paint scattered on the floor beneath it.

"So you paint?" I asked.

"Just a hobby to pass the time." He pulled a chair from the corner and asked me to sit down. Now, in the light of his room, all the impressions I had of him on the evening when we met, were confirmed — my host was indeed a friendly yet unconventional individual.

He busied himself with showing me some of his finished works, which he took one by one from a pile leaning against the side of the easel. They showed a variety of styles. It seemed that he was still searching, experimenting a great deal without having found yet the right means of expressing his personality. The unfinished work on the easel was a landscape of rice-terraces on the slopes of a mountain.

"The Priangan country," he said, picking up a tube of paint which he had almost trodden on. And with longing in his voice he explained how often he recalled that mountainous countryside of West Java.

"Can I hope to visit it again some time in the future? To wander again among the tea-shrubs that cover the slopes of the blue and towering Gedeh-mountain? To listen again to the gay songs and laughter of the pretty and simple village-women dressed in colourful *kebayas* and *batik sarongs,* while they pluck the tea-leaves? And breathe again the fresh and cool air of the jungles...?"

Evidently he was drowned in a sentimental mood, heavy with a mixture of vivid recollections and strong longing.

"Why not? You never can tell."

He sat a little sad with his legs crossed.

"I love this beautiful country-side as if it were my own birth place. Strange perhaps, but I can understand it."

"How is that?" I asked.

"It's not simply that its mountain ranges are so magnificent — because you yourself may know how extraordinarily beautiful the Swiss Alps are — yet they are not as lovely as the Priangan country to me."

I smiled, suspecting that he was merely humouring me.

"I believe," he went on, "it is rather my love for its inhabitants, its people, the simple and friendly countryfolk. This is a feeling that give everything beauty. Think of the desert, for example. Isn't it true that those barren and monotonous areas can become vistas of beauty for a man stirred by love?"

He uncrossed his feet and continued his story, telling me how at the time of the revolution he had been a sergeant in the Dutch Imperial Army, and how he was later sentenced to a term of imprisonment and eventually returned to his own country, because, as he said, he refused to continue shooting people whose only crime was the desire to live in freedom.

"Have a cigarette," he said interrupting his narrative. "I don't smoke them myself. I just indulge in this," he said, taking a pipe from the back pocket of his trousers. He went over to the dresser to get an ashtray, and continued: "I couldn't stand it any longer; it was revolting. One evening in Dago Street, Bandung, I saw some soldiers stop a young boy who happened to be passing on his bicycle. For no reason at all, the youngster was seized, dragged roughly to the edge of the road and ordered to stand erect against an electric light post. Then without any warning, one of the soldiers drew his sword and cut through the boy's body with such violence that it clanged against and struck sparks from the iron post. Just think, all this took place for no reason whatsoever, except that that poor boy belonged to a people who wanted to be free. In just a few minutes his soul had fled, and no account taken of it."

Van Buren (for that was his name) told his story with great distaste, but calmly. From time to time he shook the saliva from his pine onto the floor. Then the bell rang. He immediately hurried to the door, and a moment later a newcomer entered. He was an Indonesian, dressed neatly in a dark-blue suit. He was short in stature, with a small nose and slit-eyes that seemed to be constantly moving restlessly. His head was half bald, which gave his wide forehead an appearance of unusual heights; and his movements were nervous and unnatural as though he were trying to shield himself from suspicion by acting rather haugthily. He whispered something to Van Buren, and then went away again just as he had come — without greeting me.

"An old acquaintance," said Van Buren, asking me to sit down again. "He just came from Indonesia, two days ago. Actually I don't like him much."

From that time on I saw him at Van Buren's house on several occasions. I always wondered why his attitude was always so strange and secretive. He showed no sign of friendliness.

One afternoon Van Buren asked me to come again to his house.

"The picture of the paddy fields is finished. You must see it. And I've got a bottle of the sweet sherry you like so much."

The painting was quite good, although it was clearly an imitation of Van Gogh.

"You know the region?" He filled our glasses with the sherry.

"Of course," I answered. "That's the Tjipanas district with the mighty volcane Gedeh behind it."

"Yes, I know it very well too. Your health, prosit!" He held up his glass.

"Yours, prosit!" I answered. We drank.

"You know the inhabitants too, naturally?"

"No. I only like to pass through when I go to Bandung by car or by bus. It's possible that you know them better than I do.

"How is life treating them now, after independence?"

"Quite well," I answered.

"Thank God for that." But after a moment's thought he asked again: "What exactly do you mean by 'well'?"

I didn't answer immediately, and he continued:

"I know some of the people there — peasant cultivators, and a few plantation workers; and tea-pluckers too. What do you think, would the earnings of a plantation worker be sufficient for their livelihood now? I hear that many of them are suffering from malnutrition. This sort of news is very disquieting, you know."

I had no opportunity to answer, because the sound of the door-bell interrupted us.

"Ah, who on earth is that," said Van Buren rather annoyed. He opened the door, but no one was invited in, although he himself disappeared behind it. Then I heard his footsteps rapidly descending the staircase, and shortly afterwards, following a brief silence, acrimonious voices from under the stairs.

I was astounded. "What could be the matter?"

"He's quite shameless." Van Buren continued his tirade, as he reentered the room. "A man without morals, without character, without any principle at all."

I let him expostulate. It became clear that the man he was referring to was his neatly-dressed secretive Indonesian acquaintance.

"Listen, what would you say of a man like him. I got to know him in the South Banten district shortly after the so-called 'first police-action' of the Dutch against the Indonesian Republic in 1947. Exactly one week — I haven't forgotten it — exactly one week before I was thrown into prison, he came to tell me of a 'service' that he had done for his people."

It was only when he finished his story that I realised he was using the word 'service' rather sarcastically.

"A whole village was reduced to ashes. And all the fifteen Indonesian guerrilla fighters, already as exhausted as tired cart-horses after a long march, were annihilated by the Dutch army. The encirclement was perfect and the attack absolutely unexpected. No one could escape. All of them died in vain. That was the man's 'service'," he concluded.

As he talked Van Buren was unable to sit still, striding to the window and knocking his pipe against its sill, coming back to the dresser to refill our glasses with the sherry, and stepping back to his chair and standing with his right foot resting on the seat.

"And do you know," he said after a pause, "on another occasion he came again to tell me that as a reward for his 'service' he had been promised a high position. I didn't feel disposed to believe all that he told me; but his stories sickened me." And with these words Van Buren violently sucked on his pipe, that, during his talk, had rarely touched his lips.

I asked what had just happened. He answered: "Yesterday I chanced to meet him in a small cafe near Leidse Plein. As usual he bored me with his gossips about his own doings, especially about his adventures with women. I was so fed up that I said quite frankly that he wasn't worth a penny in my estimation. Apparently he felt quite offended. It seemed that he came to the house just now with the intention of showing me that although I had such a low opinion of him, other people considered him worthy of honour and esteem. For this purpose he showed me a telegram he'd just received from Djakarta. O how sickening! He showed it to me with such triumph, such pride and conceit, that I was rude enough to show him the door before he came inside."

"What was he proud of?" I asked inquiringly, half amused.

"He was proud because of the telegram he received."

"But why?"

"You won't believe it — the telegram was sent by his political party to inform him that he'd been nominated as a candidate for a parliamentary seat in the coming elections."

"Oh!"

"Can you believe it?"

I shook my head in amazement. After sitting lost in thought for a while, Van Buren said finally: "It is to be hoped that your country will be preserved from all the disasters such men can cause. For the sake of your people's happiness... And," he added, after having again fallen thoughtful, "especially for my little boy's."

"Your little boy's? What do you mean?" I was startled.

"Yes, my little boy's, my child's."

"You mean you're a father?"

"Yes." I'm my little Joseph's father. Yusup as they called him there. Let's hope he's still alive." And, as he went to fill glasses again at the dresser, I was still surprised. He went on: "The mother was Siti, a sweet village girl, simple and gentle in her devotion and gay in her innocence as illiterate young women from the mountains so often are. She plucked tea for a living. But unfortunately, while I was lying in a Dutch prison, she was killed by a mob.

"Killed?"

"Yes, killed like a dog. They vilified her as an informant and an accomplice of the enemy." Van Buren finished his glass and fell thoughtful again for some moments, half lost probably in a mixture of sweet and bitter memories.

"But really," his voice was moved and at the same time cynical again, "what did this village woman know about politics or revolutions? She was too simple to be an 'accomplice.' She was no candidate for parliament, was she? But yes, I forgot, I always forget, she did have a child, and that was my child, an enemy's child..."

When the Iris Bloomed

Shon So-Hee

I DON'T KNOW how long it had been. Going far up the stream in the back of the house I had turned over dozens of rocks and searched the gaps for dozens more, but I wasn't able to find any crayfish. I was quite vexed, my feet ached and I was hungry, so I washed my hands and went back to the rock where I had left my school bag and shoes. From a distance I could see someone sitting on the rock. Wondering if my mother had sent my Sister after me, I whistled deliberately on my way back to the rock. There was a strange girl, slightly younger than my Sister, sitting on the rock.

I looked at her wondering who she might be as I got my school bag and shoes which were just where I had left them, right next to her. I stared at her blankly. Her mysterious eyes on a face even smoother and whiter than the lovely white hands that lay on the rock grew even more mysterious as they followed me. I was bewildered, and with a reeling head I hurried home. I met no one along the way. But even so I felt uneasy. It was partly because my light school uniform was covered with mud, but even more, I was ashamed of having stared at a strange girl for so long. Somehow, when I thought about it, there seemed to have been a smile hovering about her lips. Looking at my clothes again, I said to myself, "What's wrong with them?" After I had taken a good look at my cuffs and shirt front all stained with grass and mud, I kicked a stone that was on the road. And again I muttered, "what a mess, just like a beggar." I kicked at anything that happened to be in the way. As I came near my aunt's house kicking at things as I went, I couldn't keep from turning around for another look at the girl. She was still sitting on the rock.

I kept thinking of how beautiful she was all through supper. When I came out after supper, the multi-colored clouds in the west were reflecting the sunset. I was somehow excited as I went to see Tong-su at my aunt's as usual.

"Haven't you gone home yet?" asked my aunt as she put her sewing aside and turned to me. "Tell your sister to come over and play, too. We've a friend for her." She went back to her work.

"What friend?" I asked as I sat on the edge of the porch stamping my feet on the stone step.

"She's a cousin of Tong-su's. She came to the hospital here after she had to leave school."

My aunt's soft voice had hardly finished when the picket gate opened and a strange girl came into the yard. I glanced up at her unconcernedly, but I was stunned. I got up and stepped down into the yard. It was the same girl who had been sitting on the rock.

"Is that Tong-su?" my aunt asked, not aware that I had left the porch.

"No, it's me," the girl answered. Then I knew she must be Tong-su's cousin.

"Is Kyong-ho there?"

"Yes." I watched her slim figure through the corner of my eye.

"She's Tong-su's cousin. Why don't you introduce yourself before you go? She's almost a member of the family."

I rushed out without answering and went looking for Tong-su as if I just had to find him.

Tong-su was my aunt's only son. He was a year behind me in school. My uncle had been dead for some time, and my aunt supported herself and the family by doing needlework and taking in occasional lodgers. My sister and I often went to my aunt's to play cards and other games. We could never think of playing at home. Our elder brother hated all games. He thought they were a sheer waste of time, and so my sister and I would sneak out of the house and go over to our aunt's where we were free to play.

"You're no good for anything but games," my sister would sometimes complain, as she rubbed her red and swollen wrist where she had taken the two-finger slaps that were her due as a loser. But still she seemed to like the games and we continued to sneak away from our big brother to go to our aunt's. Sometimes when we would be playing cards at our aunt, my sister would start complaining about our brother.

"I don't think Brother will ever get married — he's so choosy that no girl will ever be able to satisfy him."

"Why don't you get married first?" I broke into the conversation with a face and made them both laugh.

The next morning, I asked my mother for some clean clothes. She seemed a little surprised, and as she gave them to me she said, "Well, what's happened to our little crayfish hunter that he wants clean clothes?"

180

I went to school feeling that I was perfectly dressed. But I spent more time thinking about going crayfish hunting with Tong-su in the stream than on my school work.

The spring that fed the stream was in a valley behind our house. The stream ran down a rocky course. It was not very large. On a lucky day, we never had much trouble in catching four or five crayfish.

But what made me even more eager to go crayfish hunting was that both Tong-su's and my house were along the upper stream. That day, it was because of his cousin that I called Tong-su out to go crayfish hunting. She might be sitting on the same rock again and it woud be awkward for me to greet her, and just as awkward not to greet her, or, if she didn't happen to be there, there would be little reason for me to stop by Tong-su's house — in any case, I had to hide behind Tong-su to see his cousin.

With all these in mind I just took Tong-su by the arm and led him to the river. His cousin was not there. I felt a little better. I put my schoolbag, shirt, and shoes on the rock as I had the day before. Tong-su did the same. He went whistling up the stream turning the rocks on his way. I went down the stream looking in the gaps between the rocks. That was why I was able to take a quick look at the rocks now and then. After hunting up and down the stream for half an hour, Tong-su had caught three crayfish and I got one. He said he was hungry and wanted to go home. I knew he'd probably suggest going to his house to broil the crayfish and eat them, but I was afraid he might not. For some reasons or other he didn't say a thing about going to his house until we were almost at the gate. Rather puzzled, I was about to go right on when he said, "Why don't you come on in?" and pulled out two crayfish to show off, laughing freely. I could see that he had taken it for granted that I would stop by his house. I followed him in. Tong-su's house with its wooden gate, its low roof, was as familiar as my own to me, but that day I could not go in without a painful hesitation.

When we came into the house from the flowered porch, Tong-su's cousin looked up from her magazine and said laughing, "What a lot of dirt on your legs." Then she frowned. I looked down at my feet without thinking and felt a blush rising. Tong-su wiped his legs with a rag and went over to the basin. The iron was hot and he broiled his crayfish over the charcoal while he bragged about catching three of them. He claimed it was because he had gone upstream while I had gone down. My heart began to beat fast for I was afraid she might guess what I had been thinking about when I decided to go downstream. I smiled with difficulty and said, "It's only because I went up the stream yesterday."

181

"Then you ate them all by yourself?" Tong-su said, laughing to his cousin. I felt myself blushing again for no reason, and I looked at Tong-su's cousin as if I expected her to explain that I hadn't caught any crayfish at all the day before. But as soon as our eyes met, she looked away. Her face, pale as a sheet, colored slightly. I found myself blushing with her for no real reason, and again I thought that she was really strange. We had not only met by the rock the day before, my aunt had even introduced us, but still she continued to ignore me. Did I make her bashful? That couldn't be it. She was such a beautiful girl, and so much older than I. Why then should I, a sixth grader, be bashful in front of her? Was it because of her beauty, or was it because she knew much more than I did? I knew it was neither. I felt sure I knew the real reason when she ignored me and why she blushed when she saw me, and again I felt my face turn crimson. I rose and pretended to be getting a drink of water while my face cooled down.

"Now this is for you," said Tong-su, giving her a well-cooked crayfish.

"How can I eat that fish when I'm taking medicine?" It was like a stone falling among fish playing in the water. Again, I was troubled by her words.

"Should we play cards until mother comes?" Tong-su asked her.

"I guess so."

"The loser has to sing."

"No, let's just play."

"No — then we'll slap wrists."

"You mean like this?"

Smiling a little, she took the cards from my hands. But she never once looked into my face, and it was obvious that she was deliberately avoiding my eyes. And while we were playing, though she would answer Tong-su with a yes or a no, she never said a word to me. I couldn't say anything either; my tongue was frozen. But I had to keep looking at her. I nearly forgot my manners as I studied her face, her eyes, her nose, her forehead — all with great admiration. It wasn't as though I were looking at a madman or an invalid; it was all because she was beautiful. Yet that beauty might have been only in my eyes.

Probably because I was staring at her so intently all the time, I lost the first hand to Tong-su. He slapped my wrists with his two fingers until I had big welts. The second hand, I lost to his cousin. She looked at me once out of the corner of her eye, then took the wrist that had no welt on it in her hand, blew on her two fingers with a a smile so mischievously put, and gave a sharp slap on the wrist. At the moment, I felt something, but when I looked at her she just went on shuffling the cards, her eyes cast down. From the next hand on I tried hard to win, but somehow I lost again and again to Tong-su. If my aunt hadn't come home from her shopping, I don't know how long the card game would have gone on.

From then on I played cards at Tong-su's every afternoon. Sometimes the games went on until late in the evening. This gave me quite a few chances to make red welts on her white wrist where the blue veins showed through. But the strange thing was that she seldom laughed, and even when she laughed, it was only a thin smile.

It was a Sunday, about a month after her arrival. I had just finished my homework and was coming out of my room. Tong-su's cousin was in my sister's room. I was surprised and shied back. The shirt which I was supposed to change that day was filthy, and my feet were even worse. Without even taking time to say hello, I went into the room where the wardrobe was, and rummaging through the drawers, I found a change of clothes and socks. I turned to the mirror, straightening out the starched front of my school uniform shirt. My big brother, who was combing his hair, stopped and looked at me. "What's up?"

I didn't know how long he had been watching the way I had been fussing around my get-up. He disapproved of the whole thing; his eyes were glaring. I gave up the idea of looking in the mirror, and it was only after he had left the room that I said resentfully, "I only changed my clothes."

All the pleasant thoughts and anticipation suddenly left me. Somehow my big brother had seen through me, and I started to brood. Very close to tears, the next thing I knew I was on my way to Tong-su's. He was sitting humming on top of a pile of wood and told me to crawl up. I said that my sister and her company looked like they were going somewhere and maybe we should tag along. We almost ran back to my house. But when we got to my sister's room, we had to stop short. My brother was in the room with Tong-su's cousin His face was unusually aglow that morning. I didn't know whether it was his fresh shave or the pale blue tie against his white shirt. My face screwed up, and before I knew what I was going to ask for, I called my sister in a choking voice. Maybe I wanted to ask her to kick my brother out of the room. My sister stood there, surprised to see me so close to crying. But I had nothing to say once she got there. So I said, "Let's go to Tong-su's and play cards."

She put a finger to her lips and then turned to our brother and asked, "Why don't you give them some pocket money?"

Without a word, my brother took out twenty *chon* and gave it to my sister, but Tong-su held out his hand.

183

"We're going to the movies today, why don't you go crayfish hunting?" My sister thought I was holding out for more money and took another twenty *chon* out of her handbag and gave it to me. Tong-su was pleased at this unexpected take, grinned and took me by the arm. As he was leading me out, I glanced back at my sister's room. Tong-su's cousin was sitting in a corner with her eyes cast down, like a picture. I made believe I was looking at the sky, but my eyes were full of tears. I shook Tong-su's hands off, told him I had a bug in my eye and had to wash it out, and so I went to his house again. I thought his cousin might come by for some medicine before she went anywhere else. I waited for a long time; she did not show up to take the medicine. We had to go hunting crayfish.

My sister and her company got back very late that night so I didn't have a chance to see Tong-su's cousin. The next morning, I stopped by his place, pretending that I wanted to see him. She came out on the porch with him. In her pale blue spring blouse and light yellow skirt, she was more beautiful than ever. She was so beautiful that morning that anyone would have been happy just to look at her. I watched open mouthed as she put her shoes on.

"Did you catch any crayfish yesterday?" she asked as she stepped down from the porch. I began to blush, and not knowing what to do with my red face, I stepped down from the porch too and answered bluntly, "No, not a single one."

We had been seeing each other for more than a month and played cards together, and still we never spoke lengthily to each other.

"What's the matter?" Tong-su asked, thinking that somehow what his cousin said was making me feel bad so that I walked silently, looking down at the road. But I felt exactly the opposite.

I went straight home from school that afternoon, threw my school-bag down, and ran to Tong-su's. My sister was there too. She and Tong-su's cousin were talking about something in whispers. Tong-su's cousin seemed worried. Then my sister shook her head and seemed to be trying to talk her into something. I watched them from a distance. I waited for them to be through, like a dog waiting for his master to give him a bone. But as soon as they were done, Tong-su's cousin was getting ready to change her clothes and go out somewhere with my sister. Before I knew what I was up to, I asked, "Are you going to the movies again? Let me tag along."

My sister smiled and said, "How could we go to the movies this early?"

"Then where are you going? You can't get rid of me."

"Brother asked us to come," said my sister. Then I knew that my brother was going to treat Tong-su's cousin again.

She seemed a little upset by this and said, "I've got a little head-ache, I think I'd better stay at home."

This answer made me happy, and I clapped my hands in my mind.

"What'll I do then?" My sister stamped her feet and was piqued, but Tong-su's cousin didn't pay any attention to her. She suggested we played cards. My sister said she'd be back in a minute, but she went out and did not come back. "Tong-su seems to be late. Shall we play later?"

I could see that she was tired and wanted to lie down so I went on home. I was surprised to find my brother home already, sitting at his desk, writing. He said angrily, "What are you hanging around aunt's house all the time for? You'd better not be going over there any-more. A little kid like you, not studying at all, just fooling around."

I said to myself, "Yes, and you, a high school teacher, running around trying to make-out with a nice girl."

I had to study all evening under my brother's supervision. When I finished my work, my sister came in, and my brother began whispering something.

I went to bed and thought about Tong-su's cousin. I knew how young I was, but I made up my mind that my brother would never marry her. I made up my mind not to go to Tong-su's for a while, for that was the only way to let her know how I really felt. And so for two days, I never went over.

It was the third day. Tong-su came to my house on his way home from school. He asked, "Why don't you come over and play at my house? My cousin would like to have you come over and play cards."

"No, I don't want to. Let's go back to the stream and see if we can get some crayfish," I said and took his arm, hoping I would see Tong-su's cousin on the rock.

But she was not there. I sat on the rock exactly the same way she had sat. A vague sort of sorrow seemed to settle down on me from somewhere. As if to seek out the sorrow, I asked Tong-su to go up the valley to pick some flowers with me.

In the valley were a lot of tiger lilies, silver bells, iris and bell flowers. We picked flowers until our hands were sore and went back to Tong-su's.

Tong-su's cousin was reading a letter when we came in. She hid it quickly and said, "It's been a long time since I saw you. Why haven't you been coming over?" She looked at me and blushed. Then Tong-su broke in, "Look at these flowers." He held the flowers out like a child.

"Beautiful. Where are we going to put them? Take your flowers home and give them to your sister." She looked at me with sparkling eyes. I stooped, picked up my flowers, stared at them for a moment, and went out. As soon as I was out of the yard, I threw the bundle of flowers away and walked on home.

My sister was on her way to our aunt's. She asked, "Aren't you well?"

"Why?"

"You look sick."

"Are you playing postman again?" I asked, meaning my sister was going to deliver a letter for our big brother.

"None of your business."

"You were on my side once."

My sister didn't answer. She glared at me and went on. A little later when she had returned from Tong-su's, she asked me what I had done with the flowers. I said I dropped them on the ground and kicked them away. She asked me to pick some for her the next day. Even though I said yes, I didn't really feel like doing it. That night I worked under my big brother's eye again, but as soon as the work was over, I slipped out like an eel and went to Tong-su's. My aunt was out for an evening stroll round the village and Tong-su was asleep. Tong-su's cousin was reading something that looked like a letter.

She smiled warmly and asked, "Did you come all alone?"

There seemed to be a steel band around my throat. I couldn't answer right away. Then without thinking I asked, "You went out with my big brother the other day, didn't you?"

I already knew it from my sister and Tong-su, but I wanted to reproach her. She didn't answer and asked, "The day I came here you went crayfish hunting all alone, didn't you?"

"Yes." I answered softly, watching her face.

"Did you catch any that day?"

"No."

"So, that's why you were so sullen."

"No."

"Well, maybe I'm wrong."

"No, you aren't."

I blushed until the muscles of my face began to hurt, and it felt as if my eyes were blushing too. Looking down, I swallowed painfully and began to gather the cards. She said in a soft, tender voice, "Shall we play? If you lose, you sing, and if I lose, I'll buy candy."

We began to play cards. Even though I was sure I would win, I lost. So I sang the first verse of one of the children's songs I remembered.

"You're a good singer," she said, and we played again.

Just then my brother came asking for my aunt. My sister was right behind him. Without a word, he grabbed me by my shirt, shook me and dragged me out of the room. Then he slapped me a couple of times. If my sister hadn't pushed us apart, I would really have received a beating.

After that, I didn't go to Tong-su's at all for several days. It was partly because I couldn't get away from my brother and partly out of shame at having been dragged out in front of her. But almost everyday, I went to the stream at the back of the houses. I knew Tong-su's cousin would not be there, and just then, there weren't many crayfish, nevertheless. I turned one stone after another with a vengeance — as if I were building a castle.

A few days later, it was a half-holiday so I went to the stream much earlier than usual. As I brooded along the stream I began to miss Tong-su's cousin so much I just couldn't stay there, and so I sat down on the rock waiting to see if she might show up. I waited for a long time, but no one came by. I didn't know what to do, but finally I made up my mind to go up the stream to the valley and pick an armful of flowers to bring back to her. There were lots of flowers in the valley. I picked the same flowers I picked the last time. While I was picking the flowers, I remembered that the spring festival, when all the girls dressed up and went swinging, was not far off. I decided to pull out a whole clump of iris for her to wear on her lovely hair. I dug at the earth around the iris with the end of an old branch. Just then I heard a man and a woman singing quietly, but very well, together, somewhere near. I was curious as to who it might be and started up towards the sound. As I went up, the pine forest became thicker, and it was hard to spot the singing couple. Finally, I saw a man and a woman sitting under a spreading tree, singing softly. I leaned closer against a pine tree and did not move for some time.

Ever since my brother beat me I suspected that he and Tong-su's cousin might get married, but the sight of the two sitting alone ripped up my heart. Instead of crying, I turned around and picked up a rock. I hid behind the tree and threw it at them. The stone went on past and hit a tree. I threw another one. I wasn't really aiming at all, but I thought I was aiming at my brother. I did not expect to hit Tong-su's cousin, but the stone struck her on the back. She doubled up from the shock or the pain. My brother quickly put his arm out to protect her, then turned and shouted, "Who did that?"

I hid myself as I ran back to the flowers then to the rock. I put the flowers in the water and sat there for a long time. I didn't know how long I sat there. The sun began to set. Finally, I picked up the flowers, and regretting that I had not brought the iris, I sneaked into Tong-su's yard like a thief. As soon as I got in the yard, I could guess everything. And I made up my mind not to go crayfish hunting until

187

Tong-su's cousin recovered. A doctor and a nurse in white gowns were coming out of the house. My sister and my brother were sitting glumly on the porch. When he saw me with the flowers, my brother asked, "Have you been back on the hill?"

"Yes."

"When?" my brother snapped. I just stared at him blankly.

"Just now." I had to lie.

He turned his head and asked, "Whom are the flowers for?"

I answered, "Sister asked me to pick some flowers, so I did."

When I saw Tong-su's cousin's face, it was pale as the new moon. Tong-su told me that night that when she came back from the hill, she vomited blood. He said that the bleeding was caused by the shock. She was shocked by the rock that hit her back and the shock caused her to bleed. He said that was what the doctor said.

It was the rock I threw. I clenched my fists and sat hunched, writhing all over. Again and again, I had to wipe away my tears with my trembling fists. I fought against an impulse to go to Tong-su's cousin and beg her forgiveness.

After about ten days, Tong-su's cousin left my aunt's to go to the hospital in Seoul. My brother went along a good part of the way. I came home from school one day to learn that Tong-su's cousin died.

I slipped out of the house as soon as I could and followed the stream to the upper part of the valley. The clum of iris was lying there, part of its roots exposed, the flowers already withered. I went to the spot where my brother and Tong-su's cousin sat, but I could not find the rock that I threw. I did find, however two or three that looked like it. They were not even half the size of my fist. Holding them all in one hand, I carried two larger stones to the place where she had sat. I began to crush the stones as if I were grinding the bones of an enemy, as if I were crushing my own body together with my mind and all the feelings in it. They were crushed down to the size of beans, then the size of a grain of rice, until they were reduced to powder. I kept on pounding them. Finally, one finger on my left hand was cut and bleeding. Both the larger rocks broke to pieces. I looked at my bleeding finger wishing that more blood would gush out. After a while I scooped up the powdered rocks in my shirt tail and went back to the rock. I scattered it around the rock and stomped on it. My eyes were sore with crying.

Repenting what I had done and causing what had happened it seemed as though I would spend the rest of my life stomping around the rock.

The next day I hunted crayfish as before, but the few that I caught I returned to the water.

Translated by Choe Ikhwan and S. E. Solberg

Rising Flood

"Riem-Eng" (*Malai Chupinij*)

The flood from the north had risen by almost a foot during the night, making the Me Ping river, which curved past Pak Aow Monastery, flow over its banks looking vast and deep like the sea. Although the water rushed swiftly and ceaselessly carrying with it bushes and clumps of water plants, a youth insisted to get across to the plantation village on the other bank in his narrow "piggy boat."

The boat caught a bamboo bush that was floating downstream and it seemed that he would be carried away by the current. For a moment he thought of giving up the attempt to cross the river and bring the boat back to the landing. But like a fighting fish, the young man braved the river, enjoying strangely the danger of being tossed about in the foaming flood amidst the floating objects. He jumped on to the bush, tugged his little boat that got caught in its branches, and pulled it free. Then he paddled against the current as though he was trying to flee from a fierce animal or reaching for the winning post in a race. In a short while the boat reached the opposite bank, which was a few "sen" lower than the landing of the plantation.

"What a dangerous risk to take even if he could swim!" my wife tried to sound normal, although she paled visibly.

"When I was young, I used to swim out to catch teak logs and hold them for bidding. It was much more dangerous than this," I boasted. "Some of my school mates, who were born and bred on the sea, could not swim against me!"

"That cannot be compared to this" she insisted. "To be naughty is a childish prank. A child does not have to think. He does not have to reason, but merely acts according to whim. He realizes what he has aimed at. Take a child playing with fire—he would not know that it burns until he learns from burnt fingers."

"How can you definitely know if that young man crossed the river because of his youth or because of his courage to brave dangers?" I said. I do not believe he did it because of his instincts. What do you say, Nai Chune?" I turned to the pilot who sat on the stern.

---

¹ sen: A distance of 40 Meters.

The old man, from whom I hired the boat in Pak Nam Po to take us North, smiled politely while he made a slow reply.

"It may have been for either reason. The lady may be right, and so could you." He paused with his eyes fixed on the stern of the little boat, now almost hidden by the foam and the turbulent flood. That boy makes me think of another child thirty years ago. That other child was a girl who also tried to cross the flood at this very place but it was much more dangerous then since it was on a moonless night."

"A girl?" queried my wife with knitted eyebrows. Harsa's tone indicated that she was highly interested. "Whatever made her cross the river?"

"She did not cross over to the plantation village," the pilot said. "She came over to this side, to the monastery. But her boat capsized and she disappeared."

"Was she alone?"

"Yes, alone."

"She deserved it," I said. "What made it so necessary for her to risk her life in such dangers — crossing the river in such a condition? It's terrifying enough doing it in the day time!"

The pilot was silent for a while. His eyelids flickered over his clouded eyes, the color of rice-cream, as though he was deep in thought. Finally he spoke slowly, politely as usual, in a low tone.

"No, it was not at all necessary. As a matter of fact, nobody thought that she would have the courage to do what she had done. The man who made the appointment to meet her at this monastery did not think so either, or else he would not have asked her to come, and an innocent young life would have been spared from falling prey to the Mother of waters." He paused again and went on: "But human nature is a complicated thing. What we think is a small matter for one person may be a matter of life and death to another. Sometimes meaningless words pour forth from our lips which we think are of no real importance — but may be taken seriously by others."

Harsa was gazing at the old man's face, puzzled. Her eyes showed that she did not understand.

"Of whom are you speaking, Nai Chune?"

"Chome — that girl, of course. The girl who was drowned, because she took the meaningless words of the man she loved seriously." He looked deeply concerned. "The pity of it was the man who spoke those words was a monk in Holy Orders!"

"A monk!" Harsa and I exclaimed almost at the same time. "That girl and a monk?"

The old pilot smiled sadly and shook his head.

"Yes, a monk. But it is not what you are thinking. It did not happen because of the affair between Chome and that monk. There was no breaking of the Holy Discipline, none of any good custom for that matter. It was all due to the girl who let herself be concerned by her own heart or to put it more correctly, it was due to the foolishness of a man, who did not understand the nature of a woman."

Harsa may have kept silent throughout, but her questioning eyes seemed to tell the old man that she wanted to know all the details of the story.

These details, let me now put them together anew, in the way I have been accustomed to do with the stories from life, told by other people.

From the account given by the old man, whom I met first when we embarked at Pak Nam Po, I drew a picture of Chome, the peasant girl. Somewhat vaguely at first, then becoming clearer eventually. I could see her as though she were standing before me — the daughter of an ordinary country farmer. Chome at sixteen might have looked physically mature, but in her heart, — who knows? Her heart had grown up among natural surroundings; her mind was pure and simple, merry as a child, or as a little bird singing freely in the wilderness. She would have gone on living such a life, proud and satisfied with her conditions and surroundings until later perhaps, when a young man from the same neighborhood would step into her life to marry her and they would live happily together, according to custom. They would have a house full of many, many children just like the other happy families in the village.

I knew not whether it was a god or some stars that influence human destiny, who altered Chome's life from its course. Her story, which sounded more like a fairy tale than what could actually happen in real life, began at the annual preaching festival at Pak Aow Monastery, during which the Great Birth Story of the God Buddha was told. It was then that Chome had her first love which was with a monk preacher, who came to stay at the monastery. Nobody knew where he came from.

One can never tell the deciding factor that makes a person fall in love. It's true that in most cases love is due to one's youth, with its fleeting, flaming passions, or to the beauty of the face and form of the beloved.

But in the case of Chome, she fell in love with the voice of the monk, whose age was two full cycles of years more than hers. He was less handsome than the young men of the village who courted her. Chome was the prettiest in the neighborhood, and she could easily have attracted any of those men with a smile.

"I could not really see why she was so deeply in love with that monk," Nai Chune said. "Some said that she fell under a magic spell; but knowing that monk, I can guarantee that such stories were false. It is true that people of my own age believe in love magic spells, but then there must be someone to cast the love spell on another person to make that person love him in return. It was not possible in the case of Chome, for the monk was not attracted by her, nor wanted her. He was not even interested in her. She was, on the contrary, infatuated — so infatuated that she was without shame. She would paddle across the river from the plantation to bring food to his cell everyday, for the sole purpose of seeing his face and listening to his voice and being near him. Her conduct became the subject of widespread gossips in the neighborhood.

Seeing that the affair would cast a shadow over the good name of the Buddhist Religion, the old monk who also wanted to put sense into her head, told to her, one day, when she came to offer him the midday meal:

"My good sister, I think it best for you to stop coming to the monastery at least for a while, or else the unfounded gossip will be believed by some people. That will be bad for your good reputation and mine and it will destroy the good name of the monastery."

But the good preacher was speechless when Chome cried uncontrolled after she heard his well-intended, kind warning. She looked down, between tearful sobs, she confessed her love for him and told him that she could not possibly remain alive in this world if she could no longer come to the monastery to look upon his face, to hear his voice and to be near him. She told him that life would be worthless without him. Because of the great love, or infatuation that was gripping her heart, she begged him to forsake the yellow robes and to re-enter the world, to spend the rest of his life with her.

The representative of human goodness and purity in the world remained for a long time in disturbed silence. When he gave her his answer, his voice was without emotion. He was direct and firm:

"Good sister, you do not know what you are saying. But I will not hold it against you, since you are still very young and without sufficient knowledge of the world. I want to help raise the dark veil that now dims your real vision and bring you out into the light. What you now regard as happiness is but a chimera formed by an emotion that is based upon the senses. When the emotion has passed you will acquire a sense of morality, which is the true substance of one's self. Go home now, sister, I beg of you, and keep yourself in a quiet place, so that you can meditate upon this thing which you call love and which you have for me and try to find out by good reason what really caused

192

it. I do not think that i is my physical appearance that attracts you since, I am old and I know full well that I have nothing to inspire physical love. Think well, my sister, and you will clearly see in the end that your love for me is but a trick played upon you by your own mind, which makes you see me not as I really am."

I could guess the feelings of Chome at that time and realized how much she must have suffered. There is no misunderstanding greater than the expression of a seasoned and disciplined mind to a mind that is enveloped by emotions, especially to the mind of a country girl deeply in love like that of Chome.

She disappeared from the monastery for so many days, that the Abbot and other monks thought with relief that the gossips on both banks of the river would at last come to an end. But Chome's silence on that occasion proved to be but a quiet period usual before a great storm. On one moonlit night, she paddled her boat across the river from her home to the monastery to see the monk.

The celibate one was greatly moved when he saw the change that had taken place in Chome. During the few months that he had not seen her, she had lost all her quick, youthful movements. Her bright cheerful face had changed to something pale and haggard. Her body had become so thin. But none of these was as moving as that of the girl's pair of eyes — so deep and vague — eyes that told of great sufferings — eyes that showed clearly the hopelessness and the complete loss of interest in life.

"If it had not been against the Holy Discipline," said the old pilot, "the monk would have rushed forward to hold her in his arms and to whisper words of endearment to her, so that she would be freed of her sorrow ... no, not with the feelings of a man towards the woman he loved, but with the feelings of a father towards his child, or those of a nun to the little birds without home nor help from anybody.

Chome was ill. Her voice that revealed her sufferings all that time could hardly be heard like that of a man suffering from consumption of the lung during his last days. It was no use for the monk to give her any kind of admonition; Chome had definitely decided that there were only two ways left for her to choose from: either to live on with the man she loved or to take leave of this life.

"Do you mean to be adamant about it?" asked the monk.

In reply, Chome slowly nodded her head.

"Nothing in this world can ever change my decision," she finally spoke.

The monk fixed his eyes on the Me Ping River, whose banks were disappearing under the flood from the North. He knew very well that soon the shallow waterway would become a turbulent sea. He also knew that from that time onward, the swift current, the foam and all the floating objects would flow cluttering down from the North: even the streamers that piled for passengers between Pak Nam Po, Kambaengbejra and Tak would have to stop sailing during the night. There were too many dangers in the Me Ping River during the flood season to risk the lives of passengers. The boatmen feared its temper. The monk was silent for a while, then he said.

"Can you promise me one thing, sister?"

"I can promise you anything," Chome spoke quickly, her cheeks reddened. "If you would only leave your Holy Order and this monastery, I would follow you to the very end of the earth. I am a woman of one word and one desire, please believe me. If I should ever fail in my promise, I would never annoy you with my face nor my presence again."

"I cannot give you my decision now. I need a little more time. Come back again on the night of the fifteenth day of the waning moon. In the meanwhile, look after yourself well. Do not forget that I will tell you of my decision on that night. If my conscience tells me I must part with Religion, I would forsake my yellow robes and go away with you at once."

I am not quite sure whether the actual words of the monk correspond with what I am trying to put down according to what has been related to me by the old pilot, but he must have said something to that effect.

One thing I knew for sure and could not be mistaken about was that Chome was extremely happy. It was as though she had been helped from a bad fall, or she had been restored to life from a hopeless illness. When the young fall ill with love, they grow worse quickly, but they recover as quickly too. From what the pilot said I could see a new Chome while she was waiting for the date fixed by the monk — a Chome that was happy, healthy and bright and full of expectations. Everything that she had been dreaming of all these sixteen years of her life would be fully realized within twenty days time. Either by some instinct or imagination of her own, she felt sure that her dreams would come true in every detail.

At last came the fifteenth day of the waning moon, the most important day in the life of Chome. The North Wind had blown hard the whole day beating against the leafless branches, filling the whole area severely with cold. A heavy fog hid the river. Nothing could be seen within the distance of a few yards. In early noon the fog cleared out and in the evening only ribbons of light were seen floating across the water.

The young girl braved the cold wind and went down to the landing to wait for the appointed time. Her eyes seemed to penetrate the cloudy darkness of dusk to fix themselves upon the landing of the monastery on the opposite bank. She had made up her mind to go despite the coldness of the wind, nor the darkness which was upon the water. She had no fear of the dangers that were facing her. Her eyes were fixed and her heart was ceaselessly calling out the name of the one she loved. As soon as it was dark, she stepped into her piggy boat and pushed it from the bank.

"It was the maddest decision that I have ever come across," commented the old pilot. "Nobody would dare risk his life like that, no matter how well he could swim. The worst thing, you see, was that Chome could not swim at all."

"The Lord preserve us!" my wife, who had long been silent, said in a whisper. Her face paled at the thought of the young man balancing himself on the boat in the middle of the river a few moments ago, and her hand began to tremble.

Try to picture a young girl, who could not swim, sitting on a flimsy boat which was difficult to keep afloat, her small hand closed tight around the handle of the paddle, with which she was trying to take her boat across the swift current. Water plants and logs, scattered, and she is all alone on the wide expanse of water, covered by total darkness. One may think that Chome's action was madness itself, if love can be called madness. But isn't love indeed, a madness of another form?

I did not get from Nai Chune's account what exactly caused Chome's death. Her boat may have capsized because of the strong current or collided with the floating objects and logs. Unable to swim, she was probably too frightened to have sense enough to hold on to the boat or to a log and call out for help as one should have done. No one living on the river banks heard anything extraordinary that night. The next morning, Chome's empty little boat was found washed up on an islet called Ko Khi Lek, a few bends down the river.

I can still see Chome struggling in the current. Her head would go in and out of the water gasping for air, only to disappear again, leaving above the surface hands that waved desperately with all their might. Then they would weaken and succumb to the pull of the water until they too disappeared and sank.

"In all my seventy years of life, I have never been as deeply moved as the account of death," said Nai Chune finally. "No one in this village has been so hated by the people as that preacher monk — I can't say whether it was just of people to feel that way against him. But, when you come to think of it, if he made a mistake; it was without intention. He had been a monk through many rains and his disciplinary conduct was beyond reproach. In my opinion he made an appointment with her on the night of the fifteenth day of the waning moon because he felt sure that she would not have the courage to risk her life to keep the appointment. But there again, if you think that it was his fault, then the fault was caused by a man's ignorance of the true nature of woman!"

We kept silent for a long time after. I felt an indescribable tremor in my heart. Finally Harsa broke the silence. Her voice was strangely hoarse and tremulous:

"And the monk...er...that man, what happened to him?"

The old man struck a match and slowly lit his cigar wrapped in banana leaves. He took some time to exhale the smoke, all the while he remained gazing, but finally he replied:

"He tried to hang himself the next day. I am not quite sure whether it was his good fortune or misfortune that someone saw him and saved him in time. Since then he had disappeared from Pak Aow Monastery."

An instinct gave me a sudden thought. I looked hard at the old man and said quietly:

"You seem to know all the details of the story very well, Nai Chune."

The pilot looked at me straight in the eye; politely and guilelessly and with a sad smile, he said:

"I ought to know better than anyone in the neighbourhood, at least, as much as the preacher monk himself."

"Then you are..." Harsa broke in.

But the old man seemed to anticipate what she was thinking and hastily said:

"No, I am not that preacher monk. I was the Abbot of the monastery. It was I who advised him to tell her to come on the fifteenth day of the waning moon..."

The Me Ping River keeps on flowing. Many millions of lives depend upon it as a channel for existence, but the life of a poor and innocent girl has once turned it into a channel of love — and death!

A Place I Knew Once

John Hetherington

THE MAN in the raincoat came into the Cafe Phaleron and stood inside the plate-glass swing doors, blinking his eyes against the light. He was fairly tall, and the length of his raincoat, which reached well below his knees, made him seem taller. The coat was dry because it was a fine night, and cold, with a white winter moon.

"Can I get a feed?" he asked the fat man sitting on a high stool at the cash register behind the counter.

"Whatever you want," said the fat man, whose name was Melikos and who owned the Cafe Phaleron. He did not glance up from the newspaper he was reading. Melikos had massive shoulders and a heavy paunch and a mat of coarse curly hair grew strongly all over his head. He must have been handsome once, but now the flesh on his face had gone slack, his cheeks flabby. He jerked his head at the rows of empty tables and chairs. "She's all yours."

He went on with his newspaper, and the customer found his way to a table against the wall at one side. He hung his hat on a wall-peg and took off his raincoat and hung it beside the hat. He wore a dark suit with an old-fashioned double-breasted jacket; the suit had a flat creased look, as if he had resurrected it from a trunk in which he had stored it years before and forgotten about it.

He sat down and picked up the handwritten menu-card, and was still studying it when a waitress came to him from the back of the cafe. She was a blonde, and pretty enough, but her mouth had a discontented pout, and while she waited for him to decide what to order she tapped one high-heeled foot and her eyes roved resentfully over the empty tables and chairs.

"Rump steak," the man said. "Rump steak, with fried eggs and chips."

"Tea or coffee?"

"Coffee."

He waited, his hands lying clasped on the marble-topped table. He was about fifty, with a prominent nose, a tight mouth, and pale blue eyes sunk far back in his skull, and his thinning hair was grey. He had the look of a man who could wait forever. He stared at the wall, but

197

unseeing, as if shutters had dropped between his eyes and his mind. After a while the girl brought the food on a tray. She laid cutlery and the plate of meat, egg and potatoes in front of him, then a plate of sliced bread, a small plate holding two balls of butter, a cup and saucer and an imitation silver pot of coffee. She scribbled out a ticket and slid it, folded, under the edge of the breadplate and was moving away when the man spoke.

"Miss?" he said.

She turned back.

"You lived in this town long?" he asked.

"All my life," she said. She added then, with a crude attempt at hauteur, "If it's any business of yours."

The man cut through the egg and into the steak, and carried a forkful of food to his mouth. He chewed, the muscles at the angles of his jaws working. Then he said: "I thought you might be able to tell me about a place I once knew here."

"What place?" His words promised some small variation in the monotony of the girl's existence, and her interest was roused.

"The Keppler farm," he said. "It was a long time ago." She wrinkled her nose, concentrating, and he could see the name meant nothing to her. "About a mile out of town," he prompted, "back from the highway. An old limestone place, with a slate roof, and a windbread of pepper trees at one side."

"Yes, I know it," the girl said. "It's called Merrylands Farm now." She looked at the man. "Wasn't there something funny about it?"

"Funny?" he said. "I don't know ... Anyway, it's still there, is it?" He chewed steadily for a few seconds in silence. "Yes, I suppose you could say there was somethin' funny about it. Harry Keppler and his wife there. That was near twenty years ago" — he glanced at the girl — "before you was born, I reckon."

"I remember now," she said. "I've heard Dad say."

The man said, "What's your name? Perhaps I knew your old man."

"Benson," she told him.

"Charlie Benson's girl, is that right?" She nodded. "Yes, I knew Charlie a long time back, but he couldn't remember me." He poured coffee into the thick cup, added two spoonfuls of sugar, and stirred slowly. He started to say something, but the words died on his lips because Melikos, sitting behind the cash register, spoke.

"Shirley," Melikos said. "You got work out back. You go an' get on with it, see!"

"All right, Mr. Melikos." She glanced down at the customer, giving a half-shrug. "Sorry," she said, but nobody could have told whether she meant it for the customer or for Melikos.

She walked toward the back of the cafe, hips swinging, high heels tapping on the brown linoleum, and went through the bead curtain which masked the kitchen doorway. When she was out of sight Melikos slid from his stool, and, laying his newspaper on the counter, walked back down the cafe to the table where the customer sat; it was a fat man's waddle more than a walk, and he moved clumsily on his feet, shod in thick-soled carpet slippers, which were misshapen with bunions.

He stopped by the table and looked down at the customer for perhaps five seconds. Then he said, "I got you now! You're Harry Keppler."

"I'm ahead of you," Keppler said. "I knew you soon as I came in. You've changed a lot, but somehow you haven't changed."

"Why didn't y' say?"

"I don't know." Keppler's tight mouth gave a half-smile. "We never was close mates, and I couldn't tell if you'd want to know me."

"Ah, why not?" Melikos said. "She's all ancient history now."

He lowered his massive body into a chair on the other side of the table and face Keppler.

"Where y' come from?" he asked. Melikos had left Greece when he was eighteen and never been back in forty years, but his English was still imperfect.

"You could work that out pretty easy," Keppler said, but with no trace of bitterness. "I finished my time yesterday and stayed in the city last night, then hitched a lift here today."

"Why back here?" Melikos asked bluntly. "There ain't nothing for y' back here."

Keppler pushed his plate away and smeared the last of his butter on a piece of bread, which he ate. He watched the swift expert movements of his long hard-skinned fingers as they folded the paper round the tobacco and rolled a cigarette.

"I don't know, Con," he said at last, answering the Greek's question. "I didn't come to stay." He ran the tip of his tongue along the gummed edge of the paper, sealed it with a flick of his thumbs, lit the cigarette, and drew smoke into his lungs. "What became of Jarvis?" he asked then.

"You mean Tom Jarvis?"

"What other Jarvis would I mean? Of course I mean Tom Jarvis."

"He died," Melikos said. "Didn't nobody ever tell y'? He went away right after .." He nearly said "right after the trial," but stopped himself. "He went away right afterwards and nobody never heard of him for goin' on five, six years. Then news got back he'd been livin' near Wodonga an' had died there."

Keppler watched the smoke from his cigarette climbing toward the ceiling.

"No one ever told me," he said. "I s'pose no one thought it mattered by then."

"He had a bad death, the way I heard it," Con Melikos said. "It was cancer, an' he took a long time dyin'."

"I'm glad of that," Keppler said, with deliberation. "The bastard deserved a bad death."

"You shou'n't say that," Melikos said. "Like I said he's all ancient history now. You oughta try to forget."

"Don't you believe it, Con." Keppler's tight mouth half-smiled again, but the smile did not touch his eyes or any other part of his face. "I've had a lot of time for rememberin'."

He drank the last of his coffee and stubbed out his cigarette in the saucer, then pushed back his chair and stood up.

"I'll be gettin' along," he said, and picked his long raincoat from the peg and put it on, buttoning it down the front. " I got nothin' to say for now."

"Where y' goin' to tonight?" Melikos asked. "She's nearly nine o'clock. Y' won't get nowhere tonight."

"I'll hitch a ride north," Keppler said. "I'll find a job somewhere between here and Albury. I might as well get started. You said yourself there's nothin' for me back here."

"You got money?"

"Enough."

He reached down the old dark-grey felt hat and walked toward the front of the cafe. Melikos followed him and went behind the counter, and Keppler glanced at the ticket the waitress had given him and dropped it on the counter together with a ten-shilling note. The Greek pushed the note back, shaking his head.

"She's on the house," he said.

"I didn't come in for a buckshee feed, mate," Keppler said, his voice taking a slight edge. He flipped the ten-shilling note with his fingernail "Take the money."

Melikos hesitated a moment, then shrugged. He rang up the amount on the cash register, slipped the ten-shilling note into the drawer, and slid change across the counter. Keppler picked up the coins and put them in his pocket without counting them.

"Well, Con," he said, "I'm off."

"All right," Melikos said. He added, "Hope I see y' again some time," but the words were a mere formality and both men knew it.

Keppler went out through the plate-glass swing doors and stood on the pavement, looking left, then right along the broad main street. The street was deserted, in the clean bright moonlight and the hard radiance of the high sodium street lamps. A loaded semi-trailer stood beside the kerb in front of the hotel sixty or seventy yards further on, and Keppler started toward it, hoping for a lift.

It was twenty minutes before the driver of the semi-trailer came out of the hotel. He was a young man, hatless and wearing a leather wind-cheater. He badly needed a shave, and he smelt of beer but seemed sober enough. He glanced at Keppler standing, hands in the pockets of his raincoat and collar turned up, in the shadow of the semi-trailer.

"Any chance of a lift?" Keppler asked.

The driver looked hard at him, with sharp, wordly eyes, sizing him up, and decided in his favor.

"Sure thing, mate," he said. "All the way to Sydney if you like."

They climbed up the driving cabin, and Keppler lowered himself in to the spare seat. Humming a tune from My Fair Lady, the driver started up the engine and steered the semi-trailer out from the kerb. The semi-trailer rode smoothly with its heavy load, and presently the highway left the township behind and travelled between open paddocks.

"You live in these parts?" the driver asked.

"I did once," Keppler said, "but not for a long time."

"She's good country," the driver told him. "I'd like a bit of land here. It'd be a good life for kids here."

"You got kids?"

"Three," said the driver. "Boys. The city's no place for kids these days."

A mile or so from the township they passed a farmhouse. It stood back from the highway, square and solid in the moonlight, with a wind-break of pepper trees at one side and light showing from its windows. Keppler watched it from the time it came in sight round a bend and went on watching it right out of sight, twisting his head to look back from the cabin window until the house sank behind a low ridge and was hidden.

"See somethin' out there?" the driver asked.

"Just a place I knew once," Keppler said, settling back into his seat and huddling deeper inside his raincoat. "It looks about the same as I remember it."

The driver was not interested. He started humming again, the same tune from My Fair Lady, and the semi-trailer lumbered on into the night.

201

A Sawbwa Dies

Daw Mi Mi Khaing

THE SAWBWA lay on the high hospital bed under the very thick red Chinese blanket. The screen which shut him off from immediate view told us that the news of his critical condition, bringing us rushing here, was indeed correct. Ranged around the large emergency ward, silent, seated on chairs, were close relatives.

The uniting shadow of death was already over us. Sao Tun Aye and his wife we saw often; yet only now, seeing them already in attendance, I realized our kinship through that figure on the bed. Shan families are so interwoven by marriages and polygamy, we forget ramifications without surnames to remind us; we treat people as friends, to remember suddenly they are close relatives after all.

But one's thoughts should not wander irreverently. The Sawbwa is in dire straits. His habitual grunting snores beat the silence; beside him three nurses wipe away the injections from that burst vessel in his brain; his tongue is clipped with a clothes-peg to keep it free of his teeth; he has not been conscious since he reached the foot of this high hill on the road from his capital town, Lawksawk, whence they brought him yesterday. His squat figure, his completely vulnerable and helpless position, is visible from the side of the room where I have found a chair at an angle to the screen. Horror strikes. . . .

My averted eyes rest then on Sao Tun Aye's wife, Sao Kin Lay. A Shan beauty. Lily skin, soft eyes, plump cheeks, with a slender body, sweet expression, fresh from a bath, powdered, perfumed. As so often before, this man now dying, who enjoyed no physical beauty in his own person, has loveliness hovering in his vicinity, gently brushing by. His growth was stunted, according to popular belief, by a fall from an elephant at the age of ten. That was a bitter blow to the towering old Chief, his father. Regardless, the old man's will arranged for him a marriage with the best any Shan prince could hope for: a Kengtung daughter, Sao Van Kyiao, "Gem-Mirror," beautiful as well as highest born. From that shrinking bride of fifteen had come the love of a mature woman, and from his thwarted growth six whole handsome children.

But fourteen years ago he had lost this Gem-Mirror Mahadevi who had truly been the light of his life. Eleven of the years he had spent in uncomplaining grief and loneliness; and then he had remarried, for companionship he thought, for he was 64; but such is the wonder of Nature, such the potency of seed and germ, that a second florescence had brought him twin boys.

But I was forgetting Sao Leng, also called Jean, our niece, and the only one among the Sawbwa's four daughters to be present, quietly sobbing. While I comfort her with embraces, Sao Sai comes, with the confidence of her husband's authority: "Get up and go away, quickly."

I don't want to be flattered with ministrations, but this tone is never to be denied and I notice also a starting of other relatives from chairs. Sai hustles me toward the stairs.

"The doctors give him only a few more minutes. If he wants to die at home he must be carried there straight away. That won't be a pleasant sight, so hurry. Come, there is no use in looking at such things."

The heir, younger than the Sawbwa's four daughters, follows and asks urgently: "Could not my father last the journey to Lawksawk so that he may die among his own people?"

"No, no, the ambulance is waiting, and he will go to the Haw."

This is the modest house he has built in Taunggyi, in place of the old cavernous mansion. His son looks unconvinced. Though the Shan Sawbwas relinquished powers and revenues two years ago, by the desire of a Socialist-inspired government, they remain the Sawbwas to their people and their families.

We pause to head off cars which bring more inquiring relations, and then follow the half-mile to the Haw.

The ambulance is drawn up at the door, and immediately inside it is confusion. A staircase abuts right on the porch, and up and down it rush people who fetch things, throw things, catch things urgently demanded from within the closed ambulance. Jean has been living here in modern young-family style. Her husband an engineer, her son a toddler, her twin girls arriving so soon and her job as a school librarian given up.

Now, with a dying Sawbwa on the doorstep, there is this continuous flurry up and down the stairs to find the right kind of things. Cotton ... wool ... rags ... yes, surely. Sheets ... yes, plenty. But they need a silk carpet first ... it must be a silk carpet ... And blankets ... no, not a woolen one ... a velvet blanket. ... And, Jean, they want a gold chain! No, not like this, Sao, not with a locket, long plain ones.

Men pull furniture out of the sitting-room into the narrow hallway and put a bed in. More shouts and remonstrations: "Not a mug like this, I'm telling you! We need a silver bowl! A large one!"

"Surely not, he is there in the ambulance still. No one has said a thing."

But the taps are running full in the downstairs bathroom. It is a corpse that we bathe, not a dying man, and Jean sobs out suddenly with realization, making obeisances vainly into the air, "My father has gone without my last respects!"

There is a rush of feet from the back rooms of the house. Lawksawk has long been a sad and dying court, first losing prosperity from the internecine wars of the pre-British period; then suffering an eclipse of splendor with the death of the old Chieftain during Japanese occupation, and the fires which burnt his palace; and finally losing all heart with the loss of the beautiful Mahadevi. So, it is mostly old women who rush out now. This is their saddest hour. They could see through shabbiness, beyond poverty, across empty walls, to the innate kingliness that resided in that squat body. But now their lord, their rice-giver has gone, and they sob in greatest distress.

"Have you gone, Your Worship? Have you left us? Where are we now? Whom do we turn to?"

The shaky old women follow each other through the door wrinkles, tears, dismay on their faces; but in the arms of two of them are the twin boys, one apiece astraddle on ancient hips, but lovely, lovable, clear-skinned, succulent, plump, wide-eyed and unperturbed. Again, live beauty blooms in the shadows of this man's dark wooden pillars....

We went home for a bath and quick supper. When we returned, the Sawbwa lay, not yet in state, but still on silken rugs and under velvet covers; his two thumbs bound together with a gold chain, his two big toes likewise; a gold coin on his mouth; his drinking water by his head, pictures to the wall, and the floor carpeted end to end for watchers to sit by. The doctors had come and injected him to keep him preserved while relatives gathered.

There was quiet and calm in the Haw now. The two sets of twins, plump uncles and winsome nieces, were sound asleep; the sobs of the old women were stilled, and in their place could be heard the kitchen choppers preparing next dawn's meals for the helpers who were already collecting.

And so Agnes, the eldest daughter and herself a Mahadevi of another state, arriving after seven hours hard driving from Mandalay, did not break the quiet with sobs but carried her mother's beauty silently in her weary, utterly resigned face, beauty enhanced as never before by her grief.

With her here, the family could begin to discuss whether to cable the children overseas, how long to wait, when and how to transport the corpse to Lawksawk. Agnes, who gives to each of her eight daughters an English name, like Fern, Ellaline, Charlotte, and Gladys, alongside their Shan names, lived for these other matters in the climate of the past. Communities object to an alien corpse crossing their areas and trailing ominous shadows. To her, communities were still only Shans with state fealties, and she worried intensely that her father, having died out of his state, would have to cross Yaunghwe State's villages to get home.

But next day the Lawksawk elders arrived and decided all. The Buddhist New Year was due, it was not good to keep a corpse over it; so interment should be on the Tuesday, a suitable day by all calculations.

"Only one week's mourning? And for a Sawbwa!" This was unheard of.

"But why such a rush? Our father lay for twenty months, and he saw more than one year out."

"But there was a reason."

"Yes, by Kengtung tradition the old Sawbwa is not buried till his successor is proclaimed. The British were in full control then, and for their own reasons withheld recognition from my brother, for two years, they said. So father lay on."

"If I may respectfully submit an opinion, sir, this brought no good to Kengtung State."

"Yes, it is true. My brother was assassinated before recognition came, and both had to be buried together."

So it was decided.

"And then, please, sir, the Haw in Lawksawk is too small to receive the funeral crowds."

That was sad indeed. He died without ever rebuilding his power home. Poor modest man, so slow to act, so lost without his Mahadevi; modest till death, never assuming, never uttering an unkind or tactless word. He would be taken to his state only on the funeral day. Pavilions would be built beside the tomb for the last offices, and he would be buried without re-entering his home.

But the shortness of the wake was made up for by its intensiveness. This thriving and congested cosmopolitan town, owing no allegiance to him, spilled out its citizens to visit the Sawbwa, after office, after school, in the lunch-hour, after dinner, and before breakfast.

But none of its shops could supply the traditional grandeur. A short while, the Sawbwa's Kengtung mother-in-law had died. Her coffin had been encased in white velvet, on which delicately cut metal flowers covered with gold leaf were set in by skilled craftsmen of Kengtung taking twenty-one days to make, so how could our dead brother have anything fitting in seven days?

But grand or not, none of the symbols or steps must be omitted. Faithful old courtiers took over Jean's menage. One side of the driveway was cleared for parking cars; the other built over with a long bamboo pavilion. Here all the town could come for tea, cheroots, pickles, or sweets. Here also, an orchestra played. As we stopped our car the strains of the royal *sidaw* greeted us, sad in the peculiar Burmese way; for to us pomp and ceremonial are sad, perhaps in the dormant memories they stir of those deprived of pomp by a swordsman's stroke in the days of kings long ago; perhaps by the realization of their transitoriness, which sense is the real spring of poignancy.

But suddenly this music changed. A full jubilance of all the instruments tinkled, clapped, shouted, sang, and resounded as we went in.

In the chamber an ornate bed had been put. A canopy of white nylon in frills and flounces covered it, hung all around with gold and silver banyan leaves, not real gold nor real silver, but tinsel, light; yet effectively pretty, sufficiently evocative of pagoda bells and splendor associated with divine sanction. Umbrellas, white, gold and red—how surprising that mixtures of more frothy nylon, lacquer, and old oiled silk went so pleasingly—these festive umbrellas flanked the bed head and foot. The silk covers were bright red and green, not chaste white. A big red lacquered rod rammed the bed through from end to end, and under this the coffin rested, enormous, gilt, giving to the Sawbwa in his last sleep the full height he must have desired all his life, for he stretched out now as long, even, as his renowned father who had been a fierce enough warrior to stick the heads of rebellious tribesmen on the pediments of his palace walls as warning to all.

Every day, especially at evening time, the house overflowed; all rooms, passages and staircases too, filled with people sitting or standing. The Sawbwa's brothers-in-law, easy with their aristocratic origins, rarely came in to take seats of honors, stoop, laughing, joking, sometimes with antics, drinking whisky and comparing the merits of their parked cars.

We invariably sat in the carpeted room, a great contrast. On the first day silent or whispering. A day later mild jokes to lighten the wait, but still a painful effort holding jaws back from laughing widely in appreciation. Then the gambling at night started, to make it possible for some to stay awake all night. A day later talk and laughter came naturally.

It continued as the servant brought in a tray with the Sawbwa's meal and set it beside his dead master. He uncovered the dishes, poured drinking water, and as new plaintive music started from outside he fanned gently with a fan of peacock's feathers. After fifteen minutes of this, he backed out with the tray, returned with tea which he poured out, and cheroots and matches.

The tray was enameled tin, the china, plain utility. Yet symbols suffice for our people. No one in that crowd questioned that this man was as much a Sawbwa as my father-in-law who, lying under several tiers of magnificent canopies, during each day for twenty long months, had his meals served by his fair daughters in turn—no servant being good enough—on a table of carved silver, set with cups and dishes of solid gold, and lit by a giant taper before which the sad princess bent as she waved the fan gently to and fro.

But this short wake was soon over. The seventh day was fine and clear. We decided to drive ahead of the cortege. It would be a pleasant trip for us, for the forty-six miles to Lawksawk was now good road, tarred by the Army who had set up a military town beside it; and we invited Pete, our American friend, to join us.

"Will I not be intruding?"

"Heavens no! There is no such idea with us. The more people go, the better the bereaved ones like it."

Foolish Westerner's sensitivities persisted. . . . "It seems not decent to go out of curiosity or just for a trip."

"Will you believe us, Pete. No one expects you to feel sad, so for what other reasons could you be going, except to please Jean by your attendance?"

The drive took us across a flat stretch of plain, its extensiveness rare in these Shan hill regions. I could understand why the young heir had sometimes shown what appeared to us undue confidence about his future. Had it not been for a Union government which put an end to feudal rule, he would now have become lord of all these acres.

Lawksawk was an old and powerful principality in Burmese history, and approaching it from this end, one could understand that also. After forty odd miles of straight road, we swooped around a bend and faced abruptly a miniature canyon, not grim enough to dispel the smiling nature of this drive, but with its humped farther bank good enough for defense. The bends continued rapidly four or five times, and then we entered straight into the beautiful Lawksawk valley, suddenly open right before our eyes. Across the wide plain the eye leapt to blue hills whose peaks were topped, exactly as one expects peaks to be crowned, with great white massed spires with very thick, clumped foliage. The rest was lost in mystery and in distant loveliness.

Everything necessary to a capital was there as we crossed the valley. Fertile rice fields, a great banyan tree, sentinel to the town; further guard was provided by the Zawgyi river, a narrow stream that coiled around and again in a curve which enclosed the series of mounds forming Lawksawk town, like a heaven-filled moat. All this spelled a kingdom in the past, but today Lawksawk town consisted of one main street a couple of hundred yards long and a few lanes of villagers' houses.

We turned into the old royal town, and that did not disappoint us. No buildings except for a few small ones for school, for state officials, and for Sawbwa's relatives. But the remains of the old brick walls, the red roads ploughing deep through the dust, the old pagodas dating back eight or nine centuries, the vast enclosure in which had stood the old Chief's palace and where jungle was fast growing now, these were enough for us.

Standing on one of the prominences and looking back towards the entrance into the valley, we were silenced by the beauty that we saw, and the consciousness of its history too. With our ravaging weather, our destructive exploits of the past, our building for permanence, only those buildings seemed to continue the torch of Buddhism long after each poor mortal has left his pitiful accumulations of wealth. We can rarely become conscious of our past by man-made structures standing to remind us. It is Nature, only, which must remind us; the geographical formation of this or that place which made its history and which remains after all is destroyed; the face of which, being now bared, makes its events plain to read. Again and again has this consciousness come to me. It came when I stood at Mandalay and saw its site as the crossroads of all the land and water routes to the four corners of Burma, and understood, without the fabled palaces, why it had been the "Center of the Universe." In Lawksawk now it visited me again.

The cortege still not being in sight, we went to look at the military town. What a contrast to Lawksawk's softened decay. A mile away from the red village, the metal roads cut clear and uncompromising, signs posted everywhere, new bungalows, barracks; trim, orderly; green lawns, water towers, and motorized units. The Army with its corps of educated, hard-working and patriotic officers, would be the vanguard of our entry into the modern world.

The cortege was due. We returned and changed into all-white clothes. The men told us to wait at the monastery while they escorted the coffin on foot.

The monastery was a massive wooden pile, still holding together its beautiful old components, though for how much longer one could not say, before it tottered into decayed timber. Its grounds were full of milling people, from every Lawksawk house, from the Army lines, from all the villages in the 2,196 square miles of Lawksawk territory. They were eating the free food served without stop under the big banyans which shaded the cleared circumference of the monastery grounds.

We went to the bamboo dining hall nearby. Here everyone who was of any consequence or affluence from Taunggyi and the neighboring big towns had driven and were seated at tables and chairs. An impressive Chinese meal was being served from the steaming iron pans under the trees; little boys in Boy Scout uniforms ran in and out between waiters and put down opened bottles of fizzy drinks, a bevy of girls threaded *their* way through the little boys with trays of green Shan tea, and some youths in Shan homespun carried drinking water in enamel urns topped by a communal lacquer cup from table to table.

The meal turned out to be delicious. I wished I had sat at the next table where some relatives were eating heartily. Now with admirably controlled ladies from Taunggyi I had to hold appetite back like a decorous funeral guest.

After this we were shown into the monastery. I was struck by the attitude of the Lawksawk elders who arranged all this. They seemed anxious to spare Agnes and all of us modern creatures the physical discomforts of the ceremonies. Kengtung, which was a generation behind in relaxing its customs, would have assumed that it was our privilege to undergo every part of the ritual, rigors and all. After a long wake, we would by now have been walking from the entrance of the valley with the coffin, all holding on to a long white cotton cloth which would keep us in line and set the same tortuous pace for all. We still expected to do part of this, but here we were in the cool dimness of the monastery, eating pickles, drinking Shan tea, and chatting. When they called us at one o'clock, we found to our surprise that we were being hustled to the very last rites.

Even then an elder ran and implored us to go by car, the sun being hot, but this time we held firm. From all sides now the crowds were converging on the bamboo structure at the top of the mound. Though most of them were in working clothes, their number and combined pedestrian movements seen from the treeless slop still suggested a great occasion.

Is it because we are under-populated, is it because we lack material wealth, that in the context of our country-side traditions it is the human crowd which makes the festival, more so than lights, colors, structures or what have you, which may or may not be there? The grandeur of a man is measured by the size of a crowd he assembles; judged like this, the Lawksawk Sawbwa was having a truly grand end. Seven days' spread of news had been enough to gather a mighty crowd pushing towards the top of the mound. People in ordinary Shan and Burmese clothes like ours, hill tribes in various outfits of black and bright splashes, soldiers in uniform, Indian cattle-communities, and little buffalo-urchins in semi-nakedness, all toiled up the hill.

Now we entered the most beautiful part of the funeral. It had been baking hot on the slope, and then this structure greeted us, cool, bamboo poles and thatch, not cheap matting. On the earthen floor thick piles of clean straw; over that thick mats, fine at the front and coarsening away backwards. The thatch roof was low, but the tent was enormously spacious and airy. In front of us, raised on a bamboo dais six inches higher, sat a hundred or more monks in saffron robes. Behind them was the only closed end of the structure, a screen made all of thatch, with light entering between the tufts. Everything smelled of this thatch, of fresh-cut bamboo, and of clean earth. Before the monks, the offerings were piled, not arranged artistically as one could expect in a more organized function than this one; but piled in profusion they looked all the more: towels, umbrellas, slippers, spittoons, for each of sixty-seven monks. The completeness of this type of expenditure—to give to as many monks as one has lived years, all their needs, which are basic and regulated—makes further grandeur pointless.

The place filled rapidly. The surging hordes took seats behind us with no doubt as to who sat where. Late-comers among the mobs jostled in and laughed at their stumbling, sure that none of the family, though feeling grief imminent again, expected from them a solemnity they did not feel. There was noise all over; little cow-herds outside the thatch lifted tufts to see the better and were roared at by the Sawbwa's cousin, an ex-Army officer: "Get away, you young rascals! This is not your show!" Jean smiled quietly and said, "We need someone like him to handle naughty people."

The noise increased and so did the surging, pushing us till we were tightly packed. The drums could now be heard, louder and louder, the thumping deepened and resounded, the tempo increased, the low roof bore down on our ears, urgent shouts came closer, calling, "This way! Heave! More, more! Hey!" Panic, expectancy, death, finally, doomed in the air, all came nearer for those who listened, amidst the jostling which still went on; and then with a great clash of cymbals he was carried in, lancers, umbrella-bearers, pennant carriers, all furling their standards and coming in, directed this way and that by the ex-major, without detracting one whit from the solemnity for those who felt solemn, and adding to the curiosity of those who gaped at the show.

Flowers had been handed to us to hold during the prayers; also yellow and saffron rice to hold, but nobody knew for how long or why; we looked at each other and giggled a little at our ignorance.

The prayers were the shortest on record. As soon as they were over, the heir, guided by an elderly hand, knelt and presented each different offering to the senior monk in the regular way. He proffered it respectfully and got it acknowledged by a touch of the monk's hand, an act which can be performed only by males even when the real donor is a woman. But before he had quite finished, well-meaning people were already directing the carrying out of the huge coffin, umbrella-bearers, lancers, pennants also, directed again by the ex-major. My brothers-in-law rushed to be among the pall-bearers, my husband clicked his cameras. And by the time the son and heir had finished the ritual, the coffin was already at the grave twenty yards away. Those who ran in its wake must have got there with it. We were shut off by crowds pressing forward, Sai saying, "It's no use, some of the people are very dirty. Don't try to go, wait patiently here."

The heir wandered out looking lost, no one paying heed to him. He pressed slowly but determinedly through, without asking for a special way. With a sister-in-law I did the same.

Old voices behind us said, "Please, those who have stood long enough, give other eyes a chance also."

But there was nothing to see.

An open trench, in it the masons bricking up the coffin, across the trench perched precariously on the pile of loose dug earth Agnes, with her eight daughters and sister and brother. Soldiers, cowherds, and cultivators pressed round them. Little whispers from my sister-in-law came to me: "How odd...they should have marked out an area round the grave."

I called across then to the son, "Sao Sai Long, won't you ask some one to clear the crowd to make the last paying of respects easier?"

He woke; for an instant the mantle of all the Lawksawk Sawbwas descended on the playboy that he was, and squaring his shoulders he called with authority, without shouting: "Stand back there, we want a clear space." At once people took up his words, so eager in their obedience, and in a second the space was clear; the front people teetered on the invisible line with pressure from behind.

We kneet to pay respects; the last brick was in; with no guns, no more ceremony, the Sawbwa was laid to rest; and the crowd dispersed quickly down the hill.

The chauffeurs of all the cars had driven up to the mound to save their employer's legs. We waved ours away and walked. The air was cool, the people disappearing; the winding of the River Zawgyi across the plain made blue-green clumps on the pale ground again and again between us and the far hills.

"Isn't it beautiful, Sai?"

The little wild flowers and sprouting buds had not been crushed by those thousands of feet, and I could still gather a fresh and delicate bunch.

We had our Kengtung brother with us and found a side track which brought us back to the dining shed. The tables were already packed away, the cooks had washed up, the crates of pop bottles were being

211

loaded onto a lorry, the bamboo posts being dismantled. I could not help saying, "People have remarked about how this whole funeral has been rushed through. The procession was scheduled to start at two but he is buried now and it is just two."

The Kengtung brother had been closest to the Mahadevi and Sawbwa, and I felt at once I should not have spoken; he might be hurt; why must I always speak, why not be completely silent like others? But there was the purest laughter in our brother's voice and his smile was sincere as he replied, "Yes, he who was always so slow and so different we have made him brisk today. Let us hope we have given him confidence and that he will be quicker in his next existence."

Daughter-in-Law

Martin Wickramasinghe

FIRST THING in the morning Kathonis took his way to the beach.
The touch of the breeze brushing through branches still damp from the night showers was colder than usual. Kathonis unwound the towel from his head and pulled it around his shoulders so that it covered his chest and part of his back. A crow screeched as it swept past his head. To Kathonis, this walk to the beach and the dawn-song of the birds perched on the roadside fences had become a daily ritual.

A bull bellowed. He did not even turn to look. He knew that it could only be the bull that Aleis used in his buggy. Every morning Aleis took one or two people to the railway station; and then if any passengers got off the train from Colombo, he brought them back with him. In fact, whether there were any fares to the station 'or not, Aleis was always up with the first morning light and on his way to the station. Every morning Kathonis met the buggy about half-way between his own house and the big trunk road that ran parallel to the beach. For although neither's home boasted a clock both men regularly rose at the same time.

At the beach Kathonis would stand looking out across the water for a while. Then he would wash his hands and feet in the surf rippling up the beach. On some days he would clean his teeth with soft sea-sand, rubbing it around with his fingers. He would wash his mouth out with sea-water. Then he'd always take with him two lumps of lime stone, the size of coconuts, one in each hand.

Today, too, Kathonis went down to the water, washed his hands and feet, and took his way home again, carrying his two lumps.

"Kathonis, every time I meet you here in the morning, you have these stones," said Thepanis.

"I like to have my hands occupied," Kathonis replied. "I have never been used to going empty-handed."

"You must have got into the habit of going rope-collecting."

"Ah! That's right!...I must go earlier than usual today."

Kathonis threw the stones on to a pile under the breadfruit tree in his garden as he went up the steps to his verandah. His daughter, who

213

had been sweeping the little compound when he came in, soon put up a cup of coffee and a bit of jaggery* in his hands. He nibbled at the jaggcry as he drank his coffee; then he took a pair of scales and his purse and went out. He would return only about one o'clock in the afternoon, carrying a huge ball of rope on his head.

Kathonis is now an old man of fifty. When he left home in the mornings, he would go about the villages and across the countryside collecting thin rope that is made everywhere from coconut fibre. On Sundays, he would make all this rope up into a big roll or two, and cart it across to sell to Diness-hami Mudalali who had a contract to supply rope to a big firm in Galle. In the early days Kathonis had carried the rope to Diness-hami's on his head.

Fifteen years passed before Kathonis was able to change this manner of life. After fifteen years, he had amassed a hoard of four or five thousand rupees. But it was not only because he was better off that spinners had begun to bring their rope to him. Now he found himself getting seven or eight times the quantity he used to collect with so much of labour, and all without stirring beyond his own verandah. Before long he was buying a ton a week, and then he began taking the rope to Hayley's himself. From that time on he began to make profits undreamt of earlier.

II

All these years Kathonis had lived in a house of clay and wattles, daubed over with white-wash; now he built himself a house of fine stone, with plastered walls eighteen cubits in length. He did not have to spend a great deal on the building. The lumps of stone that he'd collected two by two for fifteen years supplied the stone for half the house. In a chest standing in a corner of the kitchen he had collected nails enough for the raftering of the house; and bits of brass for a blacksmith to turn into hinges and locks.

He had collected these in much the same way as he had got together his hoard of stones. He'd picked up old nails and fragments of brass by the roadside and in the compounds and verandahs of houses he'd gone to for rope.

The old man's first thought after moving into the new house was that now he must marry off his son. Diness-hami, the contractor, who had once been enormously wealthy, had now fallen on lean days. Kathonis thought that the Mudalali's daughter would make a good match for his son. And, before six months had passed Kathonis was celebrating the marriage.

---

* Brown, sweet 'rock' made out of coconut sugar.

Kathonis' daughter was already married, and he had asked her and her husband to come home two weeks before the festivities. But they appeared only the night before the wedding. This daughter had been given in marriage in the days when Kathonis had carried his rolls of rope on his own head. He had not been able to afford much of a dowry then — only seven hundred and fifty rupees, some simple clothes, pearl jewellery, and a chest of drawers of jak-wood. Because of this she was displeased with her father and brother. Besides, at that time, Kathonis owned only a bit of garden and eight acres of undeveloped coconut land. Later this last had become a fine high-yielding estate. When his daughter saw this, she had strained to get this estate written in her name but in vain. Then she asked for half of it. "Time enough," was all the reply she got. It was after this that they had harsh words over the division of the estate. The first time she merely shrieked at her father; the second time she left home calling down curses on her father and brother. Small wonder she did not go to the wedding till the last possible moment.

And she did not waste any time getting away either. The very evening of the wedding day she returned home with her husband and her two children.

Kathonis did not spend much on his son's wedding. He bought his son the black coat, the new shirt, the length of tweed made into a sarong, that every bridegroom must have. But he only borrowed a pair of shoes — this was not miserliness, it was more like thrifty good sense, for a young man of his son's social standing never wore shoes except for his own wedding.

And though Kathonis didn't spend much on dress and ornament, he was very generous when it came to feasting the guests. A table, twenty-four feet long, was laid out for the relations who brought the bride from her father's house. It bore four huge dishes of rice, and was covered from one end to the other with row upon row of plates; there were gravies and dry dishes, viands cooked and fried, preserves fiery and piquant. The sight of this magnificent wedding meal, on which a whole army of women had laboured, made Kathonis beam all over.

The guests talked loudly, not of the new couple, but of Kathonis Mudalali, of his wealth, of his eight acres of coconut. But the tears that filled Kathonis' eyes were not tears of mere self-satisfied joy, but of regret that his wife had not lived to see this day.

Diness-hami Mudalali gave his daughter only a set of pearl jewellery as dowry. The women who had gone to Diness-hami's to fetch the bride had many hurtful things to say about it. But Kathonis did not say a word against Diness-hami; here was no lessening of his happiness. "I didn't think of worldly goods when I arranged his marriage," he said over and over again.

215

III

"Miss Somi, you will have to see to the housekeeping now. Jinapala is a foolish boy. He does not know anything about managing a house," Kathonis said one day to his daughter-in-law. It was about a week after the wedding. "As for me, I am a weak old man now. I can't do as much as I used to do."

"Yes, father," replied Somi, a smile lighting up her face.

Now even Jinapala had to go to Somi if he needed a rupee or two. For his father gave the housekeeping money to the daughter-in-law and not to him. And the daughter-in-law handled the money with marvelous thrift.

The daughter-in-law lavished on the old man such solicitude, such food, such endearments, as he had never known from his daughter or even his dead wife. Kathonis seldom had to take his rice now without a dish of curry, beautifully cooked with not a condiment missing. Somi would also have prepared a dish or two of vegetable, and a *mel lum* of chopped herb and shredded coconut. When the old man had finished, the son and the daughter-in-law would sit down to eat together. But they'd have only the sambol. For unless the meat had been cooked in gravy, and had to be finished, the daughter-in-law always puts it away for the old man's next meal. Jinapala thought that his wife had to do this because the money his father gave her was not enough.

Once or twice a week Somi would go with her husband to visit her father and mother. She would go only after she had made her father-in-law comfortable and given him his midday meal. The couple usually returned quite late from Diness-hami's. Somi always took with her on these visits a cane basket full of vegetables and curry-stuffs, perhaps even a pound or two of sugar.

On these occasions Jinapala found that not only his father-in-law but even his mother-in-law were unstinting in their hospitality. Even Somi's young sister treated him with greatest thoughfulness and fondness.

"Our brother-in-law is getting thinner," she would say sometimes, looking at him.

"Oh yes, Jinapala is a little thinner," his mother-in-law would agree.

Some days Jinapala would stretch himself out on a lounger in the verandah. Somi's sister never forgot to run in then and fetch him a pillow with a fresh white cover.

Once Jinapala had made himself comfortable Somi and her mother would disappear into a room and they'd be talking for hours. Somi would emerge only after Jinapala had called out that it was time to go home.

On almost every visit, she'd put two rupees, or perhaps five, into her mother's hands, when they were alone. Although Somi saw her mother at least once, sometimes twice a week, Jinapala never dreamt of questioning her as to what there was to talk about so much.

Some eight months after their marriage, Jinapala and Somi, returning one evening from visiting the old couple, found Jinapala's sister at home. She was railing at old Kathonis, and she turned on them without a pause.

"All you've come here for is to carry away everything we have to your mother's! Did you think I hadn't heard?" and she snatched away the cane basket from the servant girl who was carrying it for Somi. She tore it open.

"Ha! It's full enough when she carries it away; now there's only the empty box!"

"It's none of your business!" shouted Jinapala.

"Then whose business is it? None of my business, indeed! I have a right to know what's going on here, all right! You aren't the one who got all this together, father and mother sweated for it. You and your wife can't fritter it all away just as you like!" She flung down the basket and smashed it to bits. "None of my business! So only you and that woman have any business here, huh?"

"Leave this house at once! You are a nuisance to all of us." Jinapala was furious now.

"Leave the house? Who are you to order me out?" Shaking with rage Gunawathie plumped down on a chair and fiercely crossed her legs. "And you! You are the schemer; you are trying to destroy our family." Gunawathie glowered at Somi as if she'd like to scorch her up with a look.

"Get out!" Jinapala shouted. He lost control of himself and shook his clenched fist at her.

Kathonis, who had taken the first chance to retreat into the house, now bestirred himself on his daughter-in-law's behalf.

"There is no need whatsoever for you to question our dear Somi Nona. What I had to give you, I have given. What is left does not concern you. I will do what I like with it."

"Somi Nona!" Gunawathie screamed. "Your dear Somi Nona! So you are for this fine new lady, too! When you used to come home sweating under loads of rope it wasn't this fine lady of yours who attended to you, it was I! Now you have forgotten all those things. After mother died didn't I suffer and slave for you for years? But you have a fine new lady now and you have forgotten everything. A curse on you, all of you! The gods at least are just!" Gunawathie burst into a violent fit of tears.

At this Somi ran out and hung on her father-in-law's arm. "Don't get angry, father. Everybody will hear us fighting. I don't want anything. You can give sister everything she wants, even if we are left paupers!"

"A nice piece of work you are! You have been ruining the family ever since you stepped into his house." Gunawathie flung out of her chair and into the compound. "You will be struck by lightning for this crime. You have completely fooled this idiot here and her old father, but don't think you will escape. You will never prosper!" So saying Gunawathie bent down, scooped up a handful of sand and flung it into the air. Then she stormed out.

It was late, and the village road was already bathed in moonlight. Gunawathie turned her steps homewards, still quivering with rage. A dog that had been lying in a verandah jumped up to bark as she passed by. Another somewhere joined in. The scent of Hendirikka flowers wafted across to Gunawathie from somebody's garden. It was a scent she knew well. Her mother had grown a few bushes of it in their own compound when she was alive, so that she could be sure of having flowers to lay before the Buddha Image every evening. Remembering her mother, Gunawathie remembered also that if she had ever known tenderness and attention it was in those days when her mother was still alive. Her father had never been demonstrative towards her, or even towards Jinapala; he devoted himself entirely to slaving at his business from morning till night. "Even when the children were little babies, Jinapala's father was never one for carrying them and fondling them," Gunawathie remembered hearing her mother say in those days.

Coconut and breadfruit trees grew in dense masses on either side of the road, so that it ran through thick shadow and lit only here and there by moonbeams breaking through the foliage. As she walked down the stretches of dark road fitfully brightened by that light, Gunawathie's rage melted away, and a dim fear took its place. The drumming, the strong smell of burning incense from a devil-exercising ceremony going on somewhere in the darkness a little way from the road, added to her uneasiness. She turned back to the village and got Aleis to take her home in his bugg.

IV

After the day on which Gunawathie turned on all three of them, Somi took to attending on the old man with ever more sweetness and consideration than before. Old age and Gunawathie's troubles were slowly losing his strength. Yet it was not a sudden decrease of strength, it was his daughter-in-law's untiring solicitude that made Kathonis give up the rope business. Even his wife had not lavished so much devotion on him. She'd insist on rubbing the medicinal oil on his hair, take a little of it in her soft, tender palm and gradually pour it into the 'Oil Spot' where the hair whirls round. Then she'd gently rub it while Kathonis was lulled into drowsiness, like a child that is being kissed and rocked to sleep. Often she'd read to him by night from the Buddhist Scriptures till he fell asleep.

Jinapala railed at his wife more than once, seemingly out of sheer jealousy. But Somi would never reply in anger. After their father had gone to sleep she would go after Jinapala and scold him playfully. It never failed, Jinapala's tempers always subsided.

"Miss Somi hasn't married Jinapala. She's married his father! What a crafty woman!" Jinapala had heard a woman who lived down the road say.

When he told Somi about it she said: "Your sister has put the idea into the woman's head. She tried her best to stir up trouble between father and me, now she's trying to make us quarrel."

Kathonis was filled with loving sympathy for his daughter-in-law, when he heard that Gunawathie was making her accusations publicly.

"Somi Nona, people tell me that Gunawathie has been talking in the village about us and saying that you are taking away everything we have to give to your mother. What I say is, you give her whatever you like," he told his daughter-in-law.

Before he got himself a daughter-in-law, Kathonis had been quite indifferent to the comforts of life; all his desires and pleasures were connected to the pursuits by which he added to his store of rupees. In the days when he used to go rope-collecting far and wide, his one day of rejoicing was the day on which his weekly trip to sell the rope that he had collected so laboriously. He would be jubilant if he had ten rupees, or perhaps a little more left, after settling all the expenses by the way. His joy knew no bounds if he succeeded in locating a new rope-spinner. Bringing back two lumps of stone with him from the beach every morning wasn't merely a means of getting some exercise; doing it was a real joy. Almost as great a joy as watching the pile of stones growing round the breadfruit tree in the garden.

At the time, Kathonis had never been troubled by even the mildest of illnesses, never had to spend even a day or two in bed. Thus during the time his wife and then his daughter managed the house, and until the coming of the daughter-in-law, he had never needed to take full draught out of the bowl of kindness and devotedness.

The pleasure he had got from collecting the stones, two by two, ended only with the building of his new eighteen-cubit house. And he put aside the joy of going about the familiar occupation of collecting rope only after he had a daughter-in-law, for seven or eight months. A man who had never before known the loving kindness of a woman, Kathonis now began to change his way of life gradually, after his daughter-in-law came to minister to him so fondly. His happiness depended on her kindness, her love, her wondrously gentle speech. Nothing pleased him more than having his daughter-in-law near, attending to him. If one day she had happened to delay in rubbing the oil on his head, he would soon be calling out, "Somi Nona, my head aches a little, let's try some of that medicinal oil." And when she had fetched the oil and was rubbing it into his scalp he would purr with pleasure like a fondled cat.

The man who once had seemed to have wrung out and cast away all tenderness from his soul now seemed to possess tenderness and responsive feeling. To Jinapala, separation from Somi for two or three weeks would have been no hardship. But Kathonis could not do without Somi's gentle care for even two or three days.

One day Jinapala pleaded with his father: "Please, father, it is now time you transferred to us whatever you are going to give us."

"No, there is yet time!" the old man said.

Several weeks passed. One morning Somi was rubbing oil on her father-in-law's head, and after a while she spoke to him thus: "Father, if you are going to give us anything, wouldn't it be good to settle things now? Our sister Gunawathie is even angrier than she used to be. She has begun to say worse things than before even about you. If you were to decide one way or the other, her ravings might come to an end."

"I have also been thinking about it for many days. I thought of writing the coconut estate in your name. Jinapala is rather a foolish boy..."

"Do whatever you think is right, father ... And this house we need, most of all a place to live in that is entirely ours..."

"For whom is the house, if it is not for you and Jinapala? I am putting it down in his name. Isn't that the right thing to do?"

"Why, father, do just what pleases you. If you give it to us, it does not matter in whose name it is." Somi stroked the oil into his scalp even more gently than before.

And she exerted herself more than on other days over the preparation of his midday rice. She rummaged in the kitchen shelf for a wood-apple, with which she made a cream to regale him with.

But although Somi went about her work that day with the air of one who was enjoying unaccustomed happiness, there was no happiness

220

deep down in her mind. Somi discovered within herself subtle feelings of guilt, like a thief's and she could not understand it. On her husband's face too, she saw not joy, but such a look as you might perhaps see on the face of a man who had committed a secret crime. The cat came rubbing itself against her feet, and it seemed to her that even its 'gnaw' was a cry of woe and foreboding.

After finishing the house-work Somi went out into the compound. She realised that she had forgotten to sweep it when she saw in a corner of the garden, standing up like lumps of rice cake, the earth thrown up by a dung beetle during the night. A crow flew down and perched on the topmost ridge of the roof. It cawed. The strange fancy came into Somi's mind that the crow was trying to say; "That's the one, that's the rogue!"

One evening about three weeks later, Gunawathie burst into the house looking like one possessed by a devil. "You, you, you're not fit to live! You thieving..." The words shot out like the flames of an explosion.

"You fooled that old man into giving you everything, didn't you? I came today to put an end to your meddling, no matter what happens to me afterwards. Yes; I'll set fire to this and..."

"I have nothing to say to you. Father had given away his properties just as he liked; why do you blame me?" Somi said angrily.

"But I have much to say to you. And to that buffalo there..." She glared at her brother so fiercely that he quaked. "Yes, you have found a buffalo to lead by the nose, too, you... You have danced such a dance before that old fool, he doesn't know what he's doing."

"Apoi! People who say such things never prosper. The gods should strike you with seven lightnings for saying such things."

"Shut up," Gunawathie screamed. She jumped at Somi and tore at the neck of her blouse. Somi tried to wriggle out of her grasp. Gunawathie clawed at her face. Jinapala came running out and dragged Gunawathie aside. Kathonis, too, ran out and raised his arm to strike her. She was beside herself with rage; she pushed him away, and he fell heavily to the ground. Seeing him lie there, stunned, she fled out of the house. She ran down the road screaming, "That woman has murdered our father!"

V

Kathonis was in the hands of the native physician for six months. One of the bones of his right arm had been broken, and it took six months of splints and poultices to set it right. For the first month the physician himself came twice a day to massage oil into the arm, put on a poultice, and fix the splints. After that it was the daughter-in-law who saw to everything.

Although Kathonis was able to leave his bed after six months, he remained a very sick man. The physician said that the fall must have injured some of his internal organs, already weakened by age.

Kathonis was very weak now, the barking of a dog was enough to enrage him, and he frequently railed at his son. Only Somi was spared his scoldings. And even Somi sometimes had to endure a hard word when she tried to give him medicine. After two months of constant, sleepless nursing, Somi was so tired that she got her younger sister to help her.

Those six months weakened Somi a great deal. Her days held no happiness now. She became irritable. She often snapped at her husband and sometimes even at her father-in-law.

After he left his sick bed the old man took to wandering about the village. And he started telling people that his son and his daughter-in-law no longer cared for him. He was lame in one foot now and walked with difficulty. Though Jinapala and Somi tried hard to make him put on a clean sarong and vest, he insisted on going out in filthy rags. The villagers, hearing his stories, were full of pity for him; they agreed among each other in praising his goodness openly. They had nothing good to say of his son and daughter-in-law. And Kathonis was greatly pleased. He went more and more often into the village for the pleasure of hearing such talk.

It was not only Kathonis whose clothes were disreputable now. Jinapala too was often dirtily clad. And if the daughter-in-law's clothes were not dirty, her withered face was a pitiful thing to see. The beds in the house were now covered with filthy old mats, the pillows were all stained. It had been Somi's habit to sweep the compound every day. But now it was swept only once every week or two. Cattle wandered in every night through a gap in the fence, and the dung they left remained just as it fell until the beetles got at it. If it weren't for the beetles the compound would have been a mass of dung in a few days.

"I have been through eight months of suffering. I cannot nurse father any longer. I am going home and taking the children with me," Somi told her husband one night. "Inspite of all the care I take of him, he is always in a bad temper now; he is no longer fond of us. And he is still as sickly as ever. And he goes about the village telling people that we don't look after him any longer."

After a pause Jinapala said, "Father is needlessly ... trouble... Perhaps Gunawathie has had him put under a spell, to make him hate us so much."

222

"What spell? He will never improve. I am going home with the two children."

"What will happen to us if you go? Won't people say bad things about us?"

"The people in the village have all had their say now. Father has gone about telling every body that we don't care for him, that we would be glad to see the end of him . . ."

"Let him say what he likes, let us endure it and go on as before."

Somi took herself and her children off to her parents' house. Jinapala too went to his mother-in-law's every day and returned late in the evenings, sometimes only after he had had his evening meal. Only a woman of forty-five was left to look after the house and attend to the old man.

Somi returned to her father-in-law's house only when Jinapala told her that the old man's illness was taking a turn for the worse. They got two native physicians to treat him. When their treatment did not seem to work, they decided to try western medicine, and they fetched a doctor.

On the fifth day after the doctor had started treating the old man Somi rose early as usual to give Kathonis his medicine. She poured it out and said; "Father, here's your medicine." Then she saw his face. Her eyes filled with tears. She bent down to make sure, then she went to her husband who was still asleep in the next room.

"Father is dead! . . ."

"Apoi . . . !"

Somi quickly put a hand over his mouth.

"They went into the room and changed the dirty old mat with a new one. Jinapala took the tattered sarong and vest off the corpse and put a fresh white cloth and a shirt on it. Somi put two clean pillows under its head and then drew a fresh sheet scented with 'Savanna' roots over his feet.

Then the daughter-in-law began wailing. Jinapala joined her. Hearing the sound of mourning the villagers began to run towards the house. They said; "In a previous birth Kathonis Mudalali must have died without acknowledging the kindness and devotion that Somi had shown him. It's only today that he has settled his debt."

Translated from Sinhalese by A. Halpe

Molten Iron

Tsu Hsi-Nin

THE BRIGHTNESS of the snow was reflected in the passengers' faces. This rare snow storm had lasted for two whole nights and a day, and it was because of the heavy snow drifts that the 3:20 passenger train had not come through.

Even when the snow stopped, the sky did not clear up and the streets of the little town were all closed. When the stores opened, the snow bank at the doorways was piled up as high as a man. At least, the people were not smothered inside; they could still see the cold, white sky. When they greeted the neighbors, they could hear their voices but could not see each other. However, they were all happy; they felt that Lao Tien Yeh* had played a joke on them; a gentle joke that was immensely novel and amusing.

Thus, the death of Meng Hsien-kwei, the opium smoker, at the East Mountain Temple was not known until late in the afternoon. Nobody knew when he had died.

The news spread quickly. A narrow strip was dug out in the deep snow and it was as if the people were walking in a tunnel. It was so many years since they had had such a heavy snow fall that they all seemed to feel they should salute each other. The news of Meng Hsien-kwei's death was passed on through the snow tunnel. When they spat on the snow bank the hot phlegm made a tiny green hole. They felt they had to express some regret for the deceased but in their hearts they really felt that this was just as rare as the heavy snow storm.

The train stopped and the town lay undisturbed by the smoke and rumble of the iron wheels. It was as quiet and peaceful as it was twenty years ago.

Several dogs were sitting around the dead body. When the people came running to it, the dogs sneaked a little farther off unwilling to leave. The corpse was coiled under a disorderly heap of wheat stalks as if even in death it was a little shy. But it was not hidden well, for one bare leg was sticking out. When the wheat stalks had been brushed

---

*Lao Tien Yeh literally means Old Man in the sky, meaning the Ruler of the heavens.

away, the railway workmen, who very seldom came to the East Mountain Temple, had all come by then to help in settling the affairs of the dead man.

The stiff body could not be straightened; it remained curled up; pretending sleep, or making fun of someone, as it lazily allowed the people to turn it, push it around, and lift it up. People would look just like that during sound sleep: mouth half open and eyes half shut.

The Meng line of descendants had already been interrupted so that there were no relatives to come and claim the body. The towns' people got together and produced a flimsy coffin, but it could not be brought to the East Mountain Temple because the snow trench was too narrow. The corpse could neither be left at the temple as they were afraid the dogs would gnaw at it and thus cause criticism from the neighboring towns. They ought to shroud and bury the body before dark.

To carry the body through the narrow trench so the only thing they could do was to take the worm out of the dog skin left behind by the dead man, tie two ropes to it and put the corpse on top, dragging it all the way to the northern section of the town, passing the railroad beside the pond at the south side of Deaf Hwa, the carpenter's shop. That was near the station and, not far over the tracks were the burial hills.

The corpse, still curled up, was dragged heavily over the snow-covered ground. A stiff arm was stretched out of the dog skin, trailing over the hardened uneven snow, moving up and down, and falling back again to its position. The movement was as regular as if the stiff arm was working at some simple handicraft; although it never used to do any kind of work at all. When people thought of the dead man it was always as a figure reclining under the caves of the temple corridors, urning his opium, his head pillowed on a piece of black brick, oblivious to discomfort.

The town's night watchman followed behind with a small cloth bundle with the end of an opium pipe sticking out. This was the only thing left by Meng Hsien-kwei. The watchman scattered round pieces of yellow paper that floated in the snow.

The flimsy coffin was not even painted. Most probably, the cost of painting it would be enough to buy another one just like it. The natural white color of the willow wood looked somewhat like the color of dead flesh.

The signal post was half buried under a circle of snow and there were several workers clearing the tracks at the rail switch. The coffin was in the clearing by the side of the pond. It was difficult to place the rigid curled-up body into the narrow wooden box. It seemed the dead man was not too willing to be put away in such a careless fashion and he was mulishly making a last demand. Some suggested to burn more paper money for him, then perhaps they would be able to manage to put in the arm that was causing so much trouble.

"You had better put in that opium pipe of his first. If you don't, he won't give up!" Someone reminded the watchman. A few of the old women began to get angry and threw a whole stack of paper money on the dead man's face, exclaiming:

"We have done our best for you, Opium Devil! Why should you seek retribution in death!"

Finally, they had to bend the stiffed arm — maybe breaking it — before they could place the cover on the coffin. Deaf Hwa, the carpenter, who had waited impatiently hurried forward to nail it down. The nails were six inches long and he hammered them down in a few strokes. However, he did not do well enough to show off his capability as a carpenter for he was too nervous lest the dead man would struggle up again.

They decided to leave the coffin there and bury it after the snow had melted. If Meng Hsien-kwei had offended the Dog Star after he died, the dogs would come and batter him with their heads and the thin boards of the coffin would not be able to bear up. So they decided to have the watchman mix up a can of lime with water and pour it over the coffin.

Dusk was falling and the people began to go home. Some people lived on the other side of the tracks; twenty years ago, there was no such thing as the other side of the tracks. The lone coffin was left encircled by a muddle of trammeled footprints. The ashes of the burnt-out paper money lightly twirled in the melted snow-pit, blown and scattered by the cold wind, chasing each other over the ice-covered pond. A black dog sat on the pile of snow by the road-side, constantly pointing his nose up in the air. Children threw snow balls at him but could not drive him away.

People began to talk of the number of years it took the dead man to go through his family's fortune and end up the way he did. It wasn't too long an age. Even those who were in their thirties could remember the time when there was the struggle over the contracting of the government-owned salt. That year, the railway had just been laid through and there were not as many businesses and trades in the little town. But the salt industry, which the Official Administration wanted to put out for contract, brought many outsiders into the village — country yokels from far off Shansi, and Moslems from over the border.

During the years when the railroad was being built, the people of the town were disturbed. They were hopelessly resigned to receiving an unimaginable catastrophe. In the simple minds of the half-farmers, and half-merchants, life was quiet and peaceful except for the primitive fears of drought, tidal waves, locusts and plagues.

According to hearsay, a huge monster would soon be barging in: No Cha's Wind-Fire Wheel* known to them through the songs and stories of the tale-tellers. Nobody had ever seen it.

The machine monster was an enormous black dragon, so tall, so big, so long; it belched out smoke and fire as it roared and rolled on. Houses would quake and fall when it would pass. Their ancestors would turn over in their graves and the spirits of their children would be plucked away. It was also rumored that the Royal Court had been defeated by the Foreigners, and this caused the black monster free entrance into the town.

Several lives had been lost during the survey of the prospective railway. The District Magistrate, went to the country, but nothing could be done to settle matters. Would the Imperial Court allow the people's ancestors to be dug out? They would die protecting their graves! Even if Master Chan, the Honorable Taotai** came with his soldiers bearing green flags and the Imperial orders; the Imperial Court should also understand that the machine meant no harm. They said that when the railway was finished it would only take a day to reach the city of Peking. That was Devil's talk! The people said. On a fast horse, it would take five days, by foot or sedan chair it would take over half a month to reach Peking. And what would anyone want to go to Peking City for? Even though for thousands of generations no one had been to Peking City, the crops in the fields were still producing seeds, the trades were still making profit. Who would want to rush to Peking in a day? It took three hundred and sixty suns to make a year and it was even bothersome to remember all the months. Birthdays were remembered according to the time of the harvesting of wheat or the flowering of the soya bean. The ancients had divided night and day into twelve hours;* that was already complicated enough without dividing it again into eighty-six thousand and four hundred seconds. That would be even more meaningless! And now they speak of a short day to travel so many hundreds of miles!

Two years after they had finished surveying, there was still no train. The people thought it had blown over, or the Imperial Court had driven away the Foreigners. But gradually, despite the suspicions and fears of the people, the railroad stretched day by day, towards the town: extending from south to north, from north to south. The peo-

---

* No Cha is a supernatural being in Chinese legend.

** Taotai — the former intendant of a circuit, the political division of a province.

* The original Chinese hour is equal to 2 English hours.

ple reported on the progress as if it were some impending disaster. They felt exactly the same way they had felt the year of the flood. The only ones who remained calm were the old women who went their way to the temples to lay their petitions in the laps of the gods. The buddhas, encircled by the fragrance of the incense sticks, only smiled passively, but they gave the old women more hope.

When Master Chan, the Honorable Taotai, came once again, everyone in the town came to the railroad tracks and knelt there. The Honorable Taotai smiled at them as hard as did the buddhas at the temple. He did not wear his court dress, [his face was burned dark by the sun]. He stayed overnight in the town, but not at the town elder's home and, under the circumstances, the District Magistrate had to submit to the inconvenience. The next day, both Honorables got up at an unaccustomed early hour to follow the rails down south on an inspection tour. Aside from the innkeeper who went around showing off the scroll that the Honorable Taotai had personally written for him, all the town people continued to curse, having lost all hope. They all waited for the foreign witch of a train to come with all its impending disaster.

"A fatal calamity!" They swore with resignation.

During this railroad business, another important affair disturbed the town: the time had arrived for the rebidding of the salt contract. There were only a little over six hundred families in the town and including the families from the nearby villages and farms, there were some thirty bidders. On the day of the bidding, Meng Hsien-kwei's old man, Meng Tsao-yu, took the bid at eleven thousand one hundred and eighty-nine ounces of silver. But he was not the only one; Shen Chang-fa had put in exactly the same amount. That amount was the nearest to the official estimates, so to decide between the two, the government sent down an official to personally supervise the lot drawing.

The Meng and Shen families had been enemies during the previous years fighting for this salt contract. By an unfortunate coincidence, these enemies had to clash again. The District Officer, Master Hung, came down twice to try and settle the dispute but achieved no results as both families refused to draw lots and were determined to stand firm and fight it out to the finish.

For the past two generations, the Meng family had been important people. It was due to having lost the contract that Meng Tsao-yu had looked down on his father due to their family properties. He was, however, even more of a rascal than his father. He possessed a scrupulous determination to stick to his word. He had always been used to winning in any argument that when he became involved with this dispute he was eager to win it so as to wash away the shame of the last generation, and earn, five years of prosperity for his family. Nothing anybody could say or do would force him to give way.

"I, Meng Tsao-yu, have waited and endured for two generations and now after thirty years, my time has finally arrived! Don't even dream that I will be as useless as my father was!"

Master Hung, the District Officer, was sent down and Meng Tsao-yu drew out from his leggings a small dagger with a sharkskin scabbard from which dangled a bright red tassle.

"You that are named Shen, if you have the guts let's try it the hard way."

Shen Chang-fa was the kind of man who could become anything you said. This time it was different. The prospect of having five years of great wealth could change anyone.

"Whoever gives way is a bastard descendant of mine!" Shen Chang-fa rolled up the sleeve of his fur-lined gown, showing the large red birth mark on his arm.

Master Hung drew on his water pipe, thinking of the quail fights. He reached behind him to loosen the tip of his pigtail that he had sat upon.

Shen Chang-fa was already mentally clicking at the abacus; the railroad had taken away five point six mous* of his farm land and he was planning on getting the salt contract to make up for it. He was willing to sacrifice the stab pains of a knife rather than lose five point six mous of land.

He yelled at his third son standing beside him: "Go home and get your grand-father's knife — the Shens have never given in to anybody yet. Thirty years ago, Grandfather Shen conquered the world with this sword, now wealth is about to fall on the Shen's tiled roof we shall not give way!"

This speech needled Meng Tsao-yu until he hurt all over. There was a tearing sound as he slashed off half of his trousers leg and planted his foot on a long wooden bench.

"Master Hung, your intelligence is as clear as a mirror, you and the other brothers gathered here, shall be my witnesses!"

Meng Tsao-yu held up the dagger in his folded hands and saluted everyone; then he quickly stabbed himself three times in his lower leg. The small dagger went right through the flesh before being pulled out again it was done with such flourish and neatness that it was as if were not his flesh at all. He lifted his leg on to the back of an arm chair and showed everyone his wounds: three cuts with six wounds, and the blood flowing down in rivulets on the floor.

---

* Mou — A measure of area; 6.6 mou equal one acre.
** denoted jealousy — vinegar is very sour so when you say eating vinegar it means you are sour with jealousy.

"Just a small gesture!"

Meng Tsao-yu stood erect on one leg, quietly letting the sticky, purple drip onto the brick-patterned floor. His ruddy face and neck had not changed color. The watchers could hear the drip of the blood as uniform as the sound of the iron hammers as they drove in the nails on the railroad ties in a distance.

The air began to fill with the sound of the clashing of metal on stone. The railroad had already come to the little town!

Meng Tsao-yu's woman brought him some hair ash to stop the blood but he threw it away.

The Shen's third son had come with the knife used for killing sheep. After Shen Chang-fa's ancestor had used it to get the salt contract from the Meng family, they had mounted it with a black wood handle and scabbard inlaid with silver. When the knife was drawn out the rough and the delicate handwork did not balance with the brightly polished blade.

Shen Chang-fa's eyes caught the blood on the floor, and although he did not show it outwardly, his courage cooled off a little. The sword in his hand carried the weight of his family's fortune. He grit his teeth and with a little too much strength, thrust the knife halfway through his leg. It took some time before the blood started to flow. The knife was stuck and it took two people to pull it out.

Pools of blood dripped on the floor of the hall, ending the fight. Master Hung went back to his office, leaving the matter to be settled by the town magistrate, since nothing was definite about who won and who lost.

Meditation in any kind of a dispute would have been easy, but this kind with two parties using their own flesh and blood to match against each other, it was rather difficult to decide.

Two days afterwards, a tray was presented to the town magistrate. The tray was covered with a square of bright red cloth on which lay three neatly cut off fingers. The family and neighbors Meng Tsao-yu pleaded but he would not listen. Three of his fingers for a family fortune was not asking too much, he would say.

"What, can I with the surname of Meng lose to that bastard Shen? That old man of mine has already burdened me for thirty years. The salt contract will be mine this time."

The tray went back to Meng Tsao-yu. On it were added three more bloody fingers which could be immediately recognized as Shen Chang-fa's. He did not think that Shen Chang-fa would also go to such lengths and in his anger, he kicked over the glass-covered screen.

"Who will stop me now? Whoever tries to stop me is a bastard son!" Meng Tsao-yu roared.

230

He had one son. The twenty-year-old Meng Hsien-kwei who was about to be married and was therefore, considered a mature man. Meng Hsien-kwei was pale, thin and tall. He always looked as if there were some bones missing in his body for wherever he stood, he always had to find something to lean on. When he walked, he twisted and undulated like a girl singer crossing the stage in a Chinese opera. He was not built for keeping up a family fortune. And seeing his father become such a bloody mess in this dispute, scared him into running away to hide himself at his grandmother's place, several miles away, where the railroad had already been laid up to that place.

Meng Hsien-kwei followed the workers around all day long, never getting tired of watching them. The cold weather, nor the bitter wind, did not stop him.

On the day when the railroad was finally finished, the first train came through, decorated with the dragon banner and red flags, section after section of cars. The people had never before seen such beautiful little houses made out of iron and steel; one after the other, flying by, back and forth. It was snowing and the train came and went in the midst of the snow, leaving behind a low trail of smoke, creating a sense of mystery and power. The people's fear and hate seemed to have been chased away. Meng Hsien-kwei, however, was left with a feeling of depression. He wondered if he could, in his lifetime, be able to ride on the train.

A messenger arrived from his home, having come through the wind and the snow to bring the news that his father had ended the dispute with his life.

Hurrying home for the funeral, Meng Hsien-kwei rocked back and forth in the mule cart, crying and thinking. After the New Year, the salt contract would be his and his wish to ride in a train would actually be realized. But, on seeing how terribly his father had died, he was scared to do anything.

In spite of the heavy snowfall, a group of people gathered in front of the town elder's home.

The town elder was of a family that had achieved recognition for meritorious service, so that in front of his door was a tall flag pole, on top of which, the square-shaped box was slanted over. It had not been painted for years, and it was covered with sparrow's droppings trimming the edges white.

Nobody had ever died like Meng Tsao-yu's.

There was an ironmaster who traveled around the villages who had come to this town to set up his furnace and show off his handiwork. No other handicraft was as welcome as this one, for this was a most popular pastime; and it has been a long time since monkey stage shows had been presented in town.

The people brought food, broken pots and pans, and broken ploughshares to exchange for new tools and utensils. Around the furnace was an array of sand molds, ploughshares, gun barrels and iron hoes. The furnace belched out blue and red flames while two stalwart fellows stood on the bellows, pumping it continuously, sending the quivering red and blue flames spurting upwards into the air. The mouth of the furnace yawned toward the sky and it swallowed bushels of coal and raw iron. The people kept calling out; one wanted a pot of so many inches, another wanted a ploughshare of a certain size. Everyone was fighting to get something from the first pot of iron ore. The bottom of the furnace was opened and the bright red molten iron flowed into the fire-proof mortar standing below.

The ironmaster used a long iron stick to scrape off the floating refuse and then stepped back with a wave of his hand. The two burly men who had been pumping the bellows came clumsily over, their legs wrapped up with water buffalo skins, lifted the heavy mortar and following the directions of the ironmaster, poured the thick red iron liquid into the various sand molds.

This was the first put and after they had finished pouring it all out, their faces were dripping with huge beads of sweat. The molten iron had heated up the surrounding area for a distance of over five feet around.

"Water melon juice! It's just like water melon juice!"

The people who had crowded around to watch forgot the cold. Their faces baked a bright red by the scalding iron as they watched the sweet red liquid squeezed from the ripe water melon.

"Water melon juice is good for your health!" some said.

"Not always good for the health! Who will drink it?" another said. It was all a great big joke, and the people were having a bit of fun.

It was at the ironmaster's shop that Meng Hsein-kwei's father met his enemy after losing each three fingers.

"You by the name of Shen, do you hear that? The health restoring water melon juice!"

The two, who suffered bitterly because of their dispute, stood on either side of the furnace, glaring at each other.

"Do you have the guts, you by the name of Meng? If you do, I, Shen Chang-fa will surely keep you company."

At that moment, someone came running up with the news that the train was really coming. The rumor that the train was coming had been told innumerable times but this man came running up, out of breath, and insisted that this time the train was really coming; it had already reached Cat's Valley.

The people had been cheated many times and yet they could not resist it. They hurried toward the north of the town, in groups.

Not many people were left by the door of the town elder, while the snowflakes kept on falling and stopping, stopping and falling.

"Master, your honor must be our witness!"

Meng Tsao-yu twisted his long pig-tail around his neck. "My good-for-nothing old man has cursed me with a life time of endurance, should I just wait to become like a cad for my son to chew on?"

The town elder was talking to the ironmaster, asking him how much he could make at this kind of work, how much coal he had to use to heat up one pot of ore, how much he paid the two workmen, how much his expenses were for a day.

"I, with the name of Meng, cannot endure to be under other people's feet for a lifetime!"

"I think you two should settle this matter peacefully!" The town elder sincerely advised them. He had not actually understood all that Meng Tsao-yu was shouting at him. "Tsao-yu, listen to me. The two of you divide up the cost of the bid and the profit. If you fight this out with your life, you can't take one single grain of salt with you into your coffin! Think more of what my third son has said to you about a new way of thinking."

The two elder's third son was studying at the university in Peking and the town people called him the foreign scholar. He had told Meng Tsao-yu:

"If you're just doing this in a show of temper, there's nothing more to say. If you're crazy for the five year's great wealth, I'm afraid it will be very difficult." Foreign Scholar, aside from having cut off his pigtail and talking with a Peking accent, was not at all foreign. "You won't believe me when I tell you that once the train goes through, I don't think you can go through with the salt contract; there will be the day when you will lose everything. This could be difficult to believe."

This was not only disagreeable to Meng Tsao-yu's ears, everyone else who heard did not believe it. Anyone who got the salt contract and did not become wealthy must have gone against the natural laws of heaven. There never had been such an example in all the thousands of years that had passed.

From a distance came a queer roaring and rumbling. The people had never heard such a sound before.

The furnace was heated intensively, the blue, red and yellow flames quivered and exuded a nose-stinging sulphur smell. The ironmaster used his stick to stir the pot and the fire sparks and the snowflakes intermingled.

The bottom of the furnace was opened and the second pot of molten iron flowed out slowly into the mortar filling it up with the bright red heavy liquid.

It has been snowing, but Meng Tsao-yu took off his upper jacket. Although he had already lost three fingers and the bloodstains on the bandages appeared to be still fresh, he was very nimble with his hands. He took off his gown and threw it on the ground. Mistress Meng who had been busy at home preparing for the New Year, came rushing out with her hands still covered with flour. Unfortunately, it was too late; the people standing around were also unprepared for this.

"Everyone listen! I, Meng Tsao-yu, have the contract; it will be my son's!"

The man was bare-chested, his pigtail wound around his neck in a knot, as he jumped forward and lifted up the half-filled mortar.

"I have it! It is mine!"

He gave a last shout at his enemy, Shen Chang-fa, and lifted up the mortar full of molten iron, higher and higher. Nobody dared to try and stop him. No one would dare to defy death by touching that scorching liquid. Even the ironmaster stood there, shocked and immobile.

Everybody watched him pour the bright red liquid iron into his wide open mouth.

It took only a short while, only a flash of an eye; and it was not really poured into his mouth. The molten iron was poured over his head, over his face and a sudden spurt of yellow smoke mixed with milk-white steam rose up into the sky as the air exploded. Immediately, the air was filled with the horrible smell of burning flesh. It seemed as if the people were also covered with the hot liquid and they shouted out their fear and pain. It seemed as if they heard a last shrill cry from Meng Tsao-yu; a cry that stuck to their ear drums and would not go away for a long, long time.

Then it was the train whistle blowing, a long long whistle; sharp and clear.

Meng Tsao-yu fell down in that spurt of smoke and lay with his face toward the sky.

The molten iron quickly became several vein-like lines of black solid, covering his bare chest. The raw iron looked like a huge black claw, tightly gripping the mass of rotten flesh.

One curled-up leg was still quivering weakly, lifeless.

The entire head was burned a crisp black, there was no way to tell where the nose was, where the mouth was that had just shouted: "I have it, it is mine!"

The black ashes from his hair floated around in a puff of wind, whirling in a circle, then disappearing. Smoke curled up from the dead body, the cotton-quilted trousers were still smoldering, although flames no longer danced.

A heart-shuddering rumble of iron wheels came from the north of the town, like the hurried striking of ironware or the running of countless horses over the frozen ground. Pitch black smoke covered half the sky and the day immediately seemed to darken.

The few faces of the people that were left standing there had all lost their human color, gazing apprehensively at each other, they did not know whether it was because of the pitiful death of Meng Tsao-yu or if it was because of the arrival of the devil-like train with its portent of seeming disaster, that they were reduced to such abject fear and terror.

The wind rose and the snow began to fall more heavily. As the day darkened the ground became even more pale. The snow wanted to bury the little town, perhaps bury it in silence.

Only the woman's pitiful grieving, broke the quiet.

From then on, the misunderstood and unwelcomed train began to disturb the town. It came and went as it willed, roaring, thundering, forcing the people to become used to it.

The train brought with it many new things that were not really needed by the people, nor considered important. The post office started a new building in the town, people from the other provinces came to sell: oil, newspapers and foreign soap. The train forced people to know how many hours there were in a day, how many minutes in an hour.

Six months after the train had gone through, only two people in the whole town had had the courage to walk into the stomach of this long black dragon; the foreign scholar and the young master Meng Hsien-kwei.

The salt contract was held by the Meng family and in six months they had made three thousand ounces of silver. This was really carrying out the contract in as honest a way as there ever was. At the end of the first year, when they added their accounts, they had made a solid seven thousand six hundred ounces. Meng Hsien-kwei bought land, built a house, took a wife and then a concubine. After that, he started to smoke opium.

The train did not bring any disaster to the little town, except for the terrible death of Meng Tsao-yu. Everybody said that it was the will of the gods and the devil, and that Meng Tsao-yu should break the evil spell. However, the foreign scholar's prophesy was not an empty one. Three years later, the merchants packed their salt into the train and it did not even stop at the little town. That year, they lost a hundred mous of land. They all began using gas lamps and foreign soap. The people came to have a fixed hour and minute for taking the train and, if the people still had any complaints, it was only that they had to wait for the train to come.

Five years passed, ten years, twenty years before a white coffin covered with lime was set in the deep snow by the railroad tracks.

That night, the moon came out from behind the clouds and mirrored itself on the snow covered tracks, and also on the lonely coffin where dogs waited in a circle. A white one padded restlessly back and forth, his shadow moving over the snow.

A wind-blown cloud just missed the moon. The white dog looked up and scratched at the snow with his forelegs, until he had made a deep hole and laid down in it.

Another cloud hit the moon. The people were all sleeping deeply.

Translated by Nancy Chang Ing

In Answer to Cimabue

Valdemar Olaguer

Beneath the oils, formality
Freezes like the Gorgons' stare;
And we who stare precisely, see
The stern bucolic style and air.

Vitality the sheep repeat,
As if by echoing a life
They can revivify their meat
Asleep beneath the butcher's knife.

And talks were of death. A painting stands
Without a theory or speech,
Though in the atmosphere pale hands
Ceaselessly flutter out of reach.

Byzantium, the great, was once
A vital wisely ruling power;
Byzantium and its hundred suns
Retired dejected, to a tower

To weep for so much excellence
Brought to an early pall and shroud
To ask resounding questions, whence
Her lamentation issues loud.

What are those saints from Goitte's hands? –
(Vitality of depthless fruit;)
As apple's rind and core can stand
Upon the nourishment of root.

Laugh with the Middle Ages, Florentine —
Your wise restraint can always pin
The distances in measured flight;
The pigeon's wing dissolved in light.

Dusk

Carlos A. Angeles

A battery of silence halts the day
And stirs a fabric air out of the loom
Of stillness, something to be tucked away
Before the night descends upon a room.

Low on the hand-scrawled wall, low on the floor,
Descending low, as story-books are shut
Against the heart's assignment and the hour,
Night pauses for a while and then slips out

Into the city's tired and peopled street,
A blind pedestrian lording traffic still
That rides along the shuffling rush of feet,
While day dies dully from a distant hill.

Lost in the dragnet of the sky, the sun
Relic of unskilled fish, swims out of reach,
Far from the swathe of green, the sea-laved one,
Beyond the stained and fabled, pebbled beach;

Beyond the logic of the bled horizon
Where tilts the tip of mourning and despair,
Beyond the hour that blotches all description
Vivid against the corner-grief of air;

Into the caverns of the sea to sleep
Beneath some monument of sand and shark,
Of seawood, down the sunk and submerged deep,
Inviolate, unfathomed as the dark.

Shoreward the softly wading feet of night
Tangle with salt and surf to subtly spin
A sudden pattern, intricate and bright,
Against the void that it must wander in:

Far from the precint of some fatuous fire
Streaking across the avenues like faith
Which reaffirms man's genius or desire —
And calmly smiles, and moves. The hour is late.

The Anchored Angel

Jose Garcia Villa

And,lay,he,down,the,golden,father,
(Genesis',fist,all,gentle,now)
Between,the,Wall,of,China,and,
The,tiger,tree(his,centuries,his,
Aerials,of,light) . . .
Anchored,entire,angel!
He,in,his,estate,miracle,and,living,dew,
His fues,gold,his,cobalts,love,
And,in,his,eyepits,
O,under,the,liontelling,sun-
The,zeta,truth—the,swift,red,Christ.

The,red-thighed,distancer,swift,saint,
Who,made,the,flower,principle,
The,sun,the,hermit's,seizures,
And,all,the,saults,zizags,and,
Sanskrit,of,love.
Verb-verb,noun-noun:
Light's,latticer,the,angel,in,the,spiderweb:
By,whose,espials,from,the,silk,sky,
From,his,spiritual,ropes,
With,fatherest,fingers,lets,down,
Manfathers,the,gold,declension,of,the,soul.

Crown,Christ's,kindle,Christ! or,any,he,
Who,builds,his,staircase,fire-
And,lays,his,bones,in,ascending,
Fever. Verb-verb,king's-spike - who,propels,
In,riddles! Six-turbined,
Deadlock,prince. And,noun,
Of,all,nouns: inventor,of,great,eyes:seesawing,
Genesis',unfissured,spy: His,own,Arabian,
His,loveflecked,eye!
The,ball,of,birth,the,selfwit,bud,
So,birthright,lanced,I,hurl,my,bloodbeat,Light.

And,watch,again,Genesis',phosphor,as,
Blood,admires,a,man. Lightstruck,
Lightstruck,into,the,mastertask,
No,hideout,fox,he,wheels,his,grave,of,
Burning and,thread,his,
Triggers,into,flower:laired,
In,the,light's,black,branches: the,food,of,
Light,and,light's,own,rocking,milk.
But,so,soon,a,prince,
So,soon,a,homecoming,love,
Nativity,climbs,him,by,the,Word's,three,kings.

Or,there,ahead,of,love,vault,back,
And,sew,the,sky,where,it,cracked!
And,rared,in,the,Christ,for,night,
Lie,down,sweet,by,the,betrayer,tree.
To-fro,angel! Hiving,verb!
First-lover-and-last-lover,grammatiq:
Where,rise,the,equitable,stars,the,roses,of,the,
zodiac,
And,rear,the,eucalypt,towns,of,love:
—Anchored,Entire,Angel:
Through,whose,huge,discalced,arable,love,
Bloodblazes,oh,Christ's,gentle,egg: His,terrific,
sperm.

Dusk in a Little Harbor

Chairil Anwar

At this hour there is no one seeking love
Among the gowdowns or in the old houses, nor yet
      among the stores
Of ropes and masts. Grounded ships and boats
Lie there abandoned hoping to be moored.

Rain precipitates the night and faintly comes the rustle
Of kites' wings: the soft sounds of day
Are hushed swimming to meet the end of sight.
      Nothing moves.
Land and sea lie sleeping and the waves dissolve.

Nothing moves. Nothing except I, strolling
Along the headland, my vanquished hopes within me.
The last sob smothered upon the beach.

Philosophy

Nissim Ezekiel

There is a place to which I often go,
Not by planning to, but by a flow
Away from all existence, to a cold
Lucidity, whose will is uncontrolled.
Here, the mills of God are hardly slow.

The landscape in its geologic prime
Dissolves to show its quintessential slime.
A million stars are blotted out. I think
Of each historic passion as a blink
That happened to the sad eye of Time.

But residues of meaning still remain,
As darkest myths meander through the pain
Towards a final formula of light.
I, too, reject that clarity of sight;
What cannot be explained, do not explain.

The mundane language of the senses sings
Its own interpretations. Common things
Become, by virtue of their commonness,,
An argument against the nakedness
That dies of cold to find what truth it brings.

Swan

Rodney Hall

In a public park
beside a lake
separate they sit
prim, discreet,
linked by a path —
she with her mother,
carefully aloof,
he with his wife.

They stare at lilies
turn from mallards
to a swan of black
of scarlet beak
of lonely heat
and yielding down,
no stranger to rain.

The unruffled world
must keep concealed
its hungry gaze
of secrecies.

Four Impromptus

Gwen Harwood

I

Changed by the fugitive light of dusk
the landscape melts and flows to peace,
but the heart fretting in its husk
of flesh is restless, seeks release.

As a young child I could not bear
to see the sun go down, and I
would pray for endless light; no prayer
could keep the sun firm in the sky,

and shadows one by one would claim
my world. At nightfall still, some fear,
some anguish that I cannot name
grips me, and evening finds me here

obscurely troubled, a plain fool
mourning for daylight's transience,
who cannot make of light a tool
to shape joy from the flux of sense.

Wholeness is elsewhere. At this hour
I sense and fear the involving shape
of absence, and a night whose power
the gifts of grace alone escape.

II

Early for my first lesson, afraid to knock,
I waited, an awkward child, outside a room
where scales, while a metronome pulsed like a feverish clock,
unwound their procession of notes; and in the gloom

of that empty hall the sounds turned in my head
to syllables of a language I must make
my own: clear-speaking, as airy and plain as bread
they summoned a hungering child to enter and take

nourishment in a world whose joy transcends
all temporal needs, where the heart understands
unquestionable shapes of truth, and mends
its mortal wounds.
                You enter, and warm your hands
by playing scales, and again as the notes unfold
heart stirs and wakens, waiting to enter in
its passion of sound. I listen, as of old:
this hour will change my life. All's to begin.

III

Those who are lucky find a few:
to the heart's innermost recesses
their words and looks and gestures fall
like light, and this is mutual.

Think of light entering a room:
nothing is asked, and nothing offered;
but mind and eye together wake
to see the commonest objects take

authentic clarity of form,
and fresh from rest the heart embraces
for a brief moment, unafraid,
the stuff of which the world is made.
This day will end. The world will end.
Light changes, and we change and suffer.
But for this hour I offer you,
whose warmth and words and skill renew

the heart, a poem, though words can never
contain as music does, the unsayable
grace that cannot be defined
yet leaps like light from mind to mind.

IV

Clear, simple as a windless day
calm in its paradise of blue,
when through the quiet of earth it seems
that earth itself will speak to you:

when eyes from every bush and flower
stare into being, and thoughts move
in visions, and love is answered in
the human faces that you love:

clear as a landscape filled with sun
issues this theme, a drift of air
brought into form by mind and hand.
Let heart put off its cloudy care,

rejoice to learn how in the plain
texture of truth its peace is found,
and rest in elemental joy
under this firmament of sound.

The Fever

Rosemary Dobson

Outside the children play like flames
Over the scorched verandah boards,
The sun burns through the shrinking vine
And Floury Baker calls; his bread
Will not be sold, although all day
He makes his one persistent cry.

My mind like a white butterfly
Moves from the curtain to the sheet,
From sheet to mirror which returns
All it receives of sky. I seek
The gravity of etchings, lines
As thin as veins, as light as cinders.

You take my temperature and hold
My wrist between your fingers, watch
The seconds pass, attentive, dark,
In city suit, late for your train.
The fitful fancies of my fever
Insist that you have called, a stranger:

Your brief-case is a doctor's bag
We have not met before, to you
I am a woman sick in bed
Whose children, unattended, play
Outside their shrill, staccato games:
Not yours and mine, of both our making.

If this were so would not my heart
Leap up to recognize with passion
The claim of love for love, to make
Insistent as the shrill cicada
The cry of need, the want of knowing,
One urgent phrase reiterated.

And would you from your unknown life
Of surgery and morning calls,
And home, and wife, and children doubtless,
Would you not meet with recognition
That doomed, entangled, piercing cry?
There is no need for you to answer.

The Kaleidoscopic Dark

Lola Jackson

Look down into the kaleidoscopic dark
Through childhood's bright and paper-sharpened mime
Where memory holds action or remark
In focus from the field of space and time.
A child in summer's copper-coloured glare
Graved deep on her unwitting memory
Her grandmother seeing in the vibrant air
That lent her years an ageless mystery.
Then as the needle wove across her span
Did she impart to cloth and child the fires
That under weary work day garments ran
With deep round dreams upon unfilled desires.
And did the child with wild and innocent eyes
Spy out herself in this most strange disguise.

Time Of No Return

Hsu Chung-pai

I

Uncle came back to live with us, bringing with him my new Step-aunt and Cousin Wei, a daughter by his first wife.

Uncle had been a government official most of his life. Because his asthma attacks were getting worse, he had come back to the country.

Before their arrival, a suite of rooms had been repainted and two huge parlors were converted into a study and a dining room. But Uncle and Step-aunt never went into the dining room to eat. It was always Cousin Wei sitting there by herself, reading a book while she ate. Cousin Wei was tall and slender, with very white skin and a straight nose. She had beautiful eyes, black as the black wei chi[2] pieces. Step-aunt may have thought of herself as the first beauty of the family, but Cousin Wei was much more beautiful.

The servants would tease Step-aunt Lee Feng Chieh[1] behind her back. She wore the latest fashions and she never left Uncle's side. If Uncle was smoking, she would be by his side ready with a light; if Uncle was playing mahjong, she would be looking over his shoulder; if Uncle was entertaining guests, she would sit nearby listening to their conversation; if Uncle was eating, she would be there picking out tasty bits of food for him; if Uncle was in the throes of an asthma attack, she would massage his back; if Uncle was writing, she would grind the ink for him.

Cousin Wei also wrote well. Once in a while she would do some painting and occasionally she would carve name seals. I often saw her in the study writing or painting. Her mother must have been more beautiful!

But she was always by herself and rarely saw her father. Uncle's bedroom was like a fortified castle. There was a big courtyard and a small courtyard behind the big one. Beyond the small courtyard was

---

[1] A character in a Chinese operatic play. The emperor Chien Lung (1736-95) was supposed to have taken a fancy to her after he had seen her serving wine at a country inn. He took her as a concubine.

[2] A Chinese chess game played with black and white button-like pieces.

250

a suite of rooms. There was a small parlor in the suite and behind that was his bedroom. It had a red silk curtain hiding his head. The servants began to call the room the Forbidden Royal Chamber.

Cousin Wei usually went only as far as the little parlor in the outer part of the suite. Standing outside the bedroom door, she would ask, "Are you well today, Father?" Uncle would call out, cough and say, "Better." And that was all. She would close the door softly and leave. When Uncle had guests, they would play mahjong in the small parlor. But Cousin Wei never went in to look.

II

Preparations for my brother's wedding took several days of hectic activity. By the time of the ceremony, Mother was already hoarse.

Among the many guests, Second Aunt's family drew most of my attention. She had married someone from the neighboring town and seldom came back for a visit. Her husband hadn't come to the wedding, so she brought along her son and her daughter. Cousin Chin, her daughter, had a very soft voice; she looked as if a wind could blow her easily. Her mother had a list of all the things Cousin Chin could and couldn't eat.

Her brother, Sung Kuo-ping, was exactly the opposite. He was tall, with a lock of hair falling over his forehead in the most careless manner. He was always laughing and joking.

At the wedding Step-aunt was greeting people right and left showing off her knowledge of etiquette. This was the first time she had left Uncle's side. She also kept busy changing her dress. It was as if she had decided to be the main actress of the show. Cousin Wei stood beside her, wearing a green *chipao,* green shoes, a pearly brooch and a ring.

I was scrutinizing my new sister-in-law and looking over all the dresses the guests were wearing. I was able to rest only the day after the wedding.

Mother kept the guests busy with various activities—some played mahjong, others played cards. The Forbidden Royal Chamber was opened, and two tables of mahjong were set up. Even the children had a part in the festivities. We played a dice game with a few cents at stake. I squeezed in at the table along with some cousins of the same age. Cousin Wei was there, too. My silver dollar rolled under the table while everyone was engrossed in the game and I didn't want to disturb them by asking them to move the table. I squeezed my way out of the crowd, got a flashlight and looked for my money under the table.

I also saw a pair of hands. A dark hand was holding a slim white one. On the white hand was a pearl ring.

I worked my way from under the table and looked up at Cousin Wei. She was blushing, her eyes shining brightly. The hand that was not being held under the table was toying with a pair of dice. At her left stood Cousin Kuo-ping.

Because of my suspicion I began noticing other things. A few days later, I discovered that Kuo-ping's eyes followed Cousin Wei. Once I walked up to him and said in sophisticated tones, "I think Cousin Wei was the most beautiful girl at the wedding." "Yes, she looked like. . . ." He said something in English. I didn't understand. Maybe he was saying she looked like some foreign beauty, or like some Western painting. I pretended I knew what he was talking about and nodded.

Cousin Wei was wearing a pale gray silk *chipao* with gray binding around the edges. "What do you think?" Kuo-ping asked me. "What does she look like to you?" I didn't know what to say and lamely answered, "She looks like a fairy."

Later, in the study, I saw Kuo-ping looking over Cousin Wei's paintings. Butting into their silent conversation I had to open a big mouth again, "Everybody says Cousin Wei has artistic talent."

"Cousin Wei herself is a work of art," Kuo-ping answered, keeping his eyes on Cousin Wei. Kuo-ping had thick eyebrows, and a square jaw revealed the determination of his personality. These last two days his eyes had been even more tender than my newly married brother.

Cousin Wei's face grew red. "It's just a pastime. How can you speak of artistic talent?"

"Why don't you leave home and study some more? The way you hide yourself at home is like burying talent."

"Father — I am his only child," Cousin Wei looked out of the window as she spoke. "And he's always sick or aching. Mother says I should stay here close to Father." She looked farther away from the window and smiled.

"This is a big place, how can you keep him happy if you can't even get close to him?" Kuo-ping laughed. "The only person who can keep Uncle happy is that mistress of the Forbidden Royal Chamber." He knew about the Forbidden Royal Chamber, too.

Mother came looking for me. I didn't hear the end of their conversation. But I couldn't forget Cousin Wei blush and Kuo-ping's soulful gaze.

Second Aunt was in a hurry to leave. But Step-aunt asked her to stay for a few more days. Kuo-ping persuaded her, too, until she decided to postpone her departure for ten days.

In these ten days, my poor mother was in and out of the kitchen, thinking up new dishes for the menu. Even Uncle left the Forbidden Royal Chamber and joined us at mealtimes talking to us about a long separated sister. Cousin Wei's hair was down and her face shone. Even Cousin Chin, who usually ate as if she were a trenchman shoveling the food in, or as if she were a nun who saw through such wordly matters as a lust, wasn't so choosy and enjoyed a bowl of rice.

When they finally had to leave, Mother took hold of Aunt's hands. Step-aunt was bustling all over the place, ready with her farewell speech. Only the couple that should have felt most sad at separation acted as if nothing was happening. Cousin Wei was sitting beside Cousin Chin, shaking hands in good-bye. Kuo-ping was talking with Brother. They had been schoolmates, but this was the first time I had seen them talking to each other.

The sedan chairs arrived and everybody was crowded beside Aunt's chair helping her in. Cousin Chin walked to the second chair. Everyone rushed to say a few words of good-bye. In the midst of all the activity and noise, I saw Kuo-ping walk over near Cousin Wei and say, "Don't forget what I said. The world outside your home is even bigger."

III

My brother, whose work was in a nearby town, had disappeared. Sister-in-law was crying, and Mother sighed, "Why is it that some people just don't like to stay at home, while others rush to get home despite the rain and snow?"

After Brother married, he and Sister-in-law got along well even though their marriage had been pre-arranged. Before he disappeared, he was often with Mother and his wife. He had even discussed taking Sister-in-law away with him. When he learned his wife was pregnant, he was happier. No one suspected that he would disappear as easily as a kite at the end of a broken string.

Just before the winter vacation, all letters written to his office were returned with the words, "This person has resigned," written on the envelopes. No one knew where he had gone after resigning. Mother and Sister-in-law were disturbed greatly when no letter came.

Mother asked some people to watch for him, but all the news we got caused her more anxiety. Some said they had seen him in a boat at the sea. Others said they had said hello to him at the Hsia Kuan railway station. Still others said something even more absurd, that they had seen him drinking wine by himself in a village not far away.

We still had no real word of his whereabouts. Why had he gone? Was it because he wanted to run away from his responsibilities? Or was it because he was exasperated with his past? He had never complained. I had been afraid at first that he and Sister-in-law wouldn't get along.

But the day after their wedding, he seemed to feel more at home with Sister-in-law than with me. He rarely went out of the house.

Sister-in-law had no complaint despite the fact that he liked to lie on the bed reading, so that the whole bed was piled high with books. She couldn't read too well, so she never knew what he was reading. Whenever he left home, and I went to their room, all the books would have been neatly kept in place.

Several times in the evenings, Mother would ask me to knock softly on their door and ask my brother to come into her room. There she would lecture him. Only then did I learn that after he had started working, Brother never brought any money home. Nor did he have any new clothes made. He always wore that long gown and seldom combed his hair. We wondered where his money would go.

Whenever Mother lectured, he would listen quietly. He never talked back and never argued. When Mother would cry, he would remain expressionless. The next day, he would appear perfectly normal, as if the lecture had never happened.

He never gave any hint that he would leave home. When he would come back from work, he seemed specially glad to be home. I remembered the last time he had left, just before his marriage, he did not also give a reason then. Because he had come back in time for the wedding, nobody asked any questions. When he had a wife, even less attention was paid to his comings and goings.

I don't know why Mother thought of asking Cousin Kuo-ping. Probably when I was at school, she had written to him asking whether he knew of Brother's whereabouts. Brother and Kuo-ping had been schoolmates for a short time.

During the Spring vacation, Kuo-ping arrived at our house — partly because he had received Mother's letter and partly because Uncle was ill. I was home then for a vacation.

Sister-in-law had given birth to a daughter, and she took the baby to her home town for the vacation period.

I accompanied Kuo-ping to the Forbidden Royal Chamber. Uncle was curled up in his bed like a bow, with a padded jacket thrown over his shoulders.

Standing beside Uncle's bed, I had a strange thought: If Brother should come back, he would jump over the wall just like he used to. So after I came out of Uncle's bedroom, I asked Mother if I could sleep in Sister-in-law's room that night.

"Your sister-in-law's not at home anyway," Mother said, "You can sleep wherever you like."

I went into the room early and blew out the light. Sister-in-law had pulled down the curtain of the north window before she left. I opened it and opened the east window, too. If he should come home, he wouldn't have to stand outside calling, he could jump right in from the little alley outside.

I kept my eyes on the east window, keeping my ears open for the slightest sound — listening ... listening ... and finally I did hear something! It was a low male voice, "You see I did come after all!"

The voice came from the north window. Probably Brother was hiding under the peach tree outside. I quietly got out of bed and went to the window. Why didn't he say something else?

Just as I was about to look out, I heard a woman's voice, "Why did you come here?"

Strange ... it was Cousin Wei's voice. I had thought all along that it was Brother. But the low-pitched, "I came after all" belonged to Kuo-ping.

"I came back to find someone."

"Who are you looking for? Brother?"

"I wouldn't look for him. I came to find myself."

"Didn't you tell Auntie that you would help find Brother?" Cousin Wei asked. "Brother shouldn't have gone off like this without telling anyone. He has a mother and a father as well as a daughter now. He has responsibilities."

"That's why I wanted you to go out and have a look at the world!" He added in a rush of words, "Responsibilities! Doesn't he have any responsibilities towards his own ideals and beliefs?" He suddenly changed his tone as if Brother wasn't even worth discussing. "You haven't asked me why I came back to look for myself.

"I think I must have told you in my letters," Kuo-ping said. "Ever since the wedding, I have left myself here. I don't have time to look for Brother. I have to find myself first."

"Now, go find him," Cousin Wei said with a laugh.

"But he won't be lost." He was holding her hand so tightly that Cousin Wei cried out sofly. I was afraid that the pearl on Cousin Wei's hand would be crushed. After a while he said, "But I'm afraid I'll never find myself again."

Kuo-ping had the strangest attitude toward my brother. Responsibilities? Didn't he have any responsibilities toward his own ideals and beliefs? Kuo-ping knew much more about Brother than I did. I never knew anything about Brother's ideals and beliefs. Could it be that Kuo-ping's ideals and beliefs were the same as Brother's? Did he know why Brother had gone away? Did he know where Brother was but wouldn't tell us? If they did share the same ideals and beliefs, why did Brother leave home so often and why did Kuo-ping stay here confessing love to Cousin Wei?

I couldn't find any answer.

255

My schoolmate, Hsu Wen-tien, asked his sister to look for me. He said he had something important to say and that he would be waiting in the hall.

He was standing at one end of the hall, one hand in his pocket, when I came.

"I've seen your brother," he said.

He had seen my brother? I felt as if a shaft of lightning had struck me.

"It was this way." He was very nervous and had taken a hand out of his pocket to gesticulate. "Yesterday I cut classes to go home and I came back this morning. I saw a man catch hold of a student from Tung Hua's School right in the middle of the street. You know that Tung Hua's school uniform is just about the same as ours. This man was trying to get the student to take a message to you and the boy kept on insisting he didn't know you. Because I heard your name mentioned, I turned around and asked him who he was. He said he was your brother."

"Why didn't he come here to find me himself?"

"I don't know if I should tell you." He rubbed his hands together. "He wasn't dressed very neatly. His face was all swollen and he was wearing straw sandals. His feet were bleeding. His hair and beard so long . . . maybe they wouldn't let him in the reception room."

He pointed with one hand. "Now he's at that bridge to the left of the school gate, waiting for you . . ."

I didn't even stop to thank him, but rushed to the gate. Passing the proctor's office, I suddenly remembered that I had to have a leave of absence slip before leaving school. I went into the office. Mr. Chu was the only one there.

I must have looked very nervous filling out the slip. Mr. Chu, an old friend of Brother's, asked, "Are you ill?"

I shook my head, not trusting myself to speak.

"Have you seen your brother? Where is he?"

How could he have guessed so accurately?

He poured a cup of tea for me. "Calm down and tell me about it." He continued, "I've been meaning to tell you that I had a letter from him." He took out a letter from a drawer. The letter was very thick and the writing was big and sprawling. I recognized it as Brother's. I only saw the first sentence, "The vagabond has come home!"

"Of course, he doesn't know that I'm here. He wrote this letter to the school where I used to teach so I only got it the day before yesterday. He said he wasn't going to come home for the time being and wanted me to look you up. I've been waiting for him ever since.

I wrote to the people at the other school to look out for him. I don't know if he went to the other school and couldn't find me and so decided to look for you here. Where is he now?"

I told him what Hsu Wen-tien had just told me. He said, "You go to class. Don't go out. I'll take care of everything. He wouldn't want you to see him in his present state."

He saw that I was about to protest. "Listen to me." He tore up my leave slip. "What are you going to do about him? You don't even have any clothes to lend him. Let me arrange everything."

I couldn't concentrate on my studies. At four o'clock, Mr. Chu came to look for me.

"He's sleeping on my bed now. Tonight we'll have dinner together. Before you see him, 1 have a few things to tell you."

It seemed as if he was going to give me a lecture.

"First, you must not ask too many questions. Just pretend that he's back from a casual trip.

"Second, don't force him to go home immediately. Let him stay with me for a while. My family is not here so it will be all right.

"Third, when we do persuade him to go home, he must be welcomed with warmth. Your mother mustn't scold him; your sister-in-law mustn't complain; no one must lecture him. He won't be able to stand these things. He left home looking for an ideal and he has been disappointed. He's suffered enough. There's no need for us to reprimand him. If we just give him a little understanding, we can keep him with us. Do you understand what I've been saying?"

"Not everything," I said, "But I'll follow your instructions. Can I ask just one question?"

"What?"

"Brother's leaving home — did it have anything to do with Sung Kuo-ping?"

"It was all Kuo-ping's fault," Mr. Chu scratched his head. He's been working on those who are dissatisfied with their situation, in financial difficulties or unlucky in love. Before your brother was married, Kuo-ping tried to recruit him. He urged him to leave everything behind and join their movement. He could give the excuse that he was dissatisfied with his prospective marriage. Kuo-ping promised he would go to your home and call off the wedding. That way, your brother could leave home without hurting your parents too much. But after he left, he found out that the invitations already had been sent. Your brother is very tender-hearted. So he came back hurriedly. Sung Kuo-ping had promised to go to your house and your brother expected to meet Kuo-ping at the gate. He didn't know that Sung Kuo-ping didn't go to your house at all."

I still had many doubts. But I had promised Mr. Chu that I would only ask one question.

That night I saw Brother for the first time in a year and a half. He had bathed and had a haircut, so I didn't get to see the long hair and beard. He wore Mr. Chu's clothes, so I didn't see his tattered ones. He was wearing proper shoes, so I didn't see his bleeding feet. I only saw his swollen face and the fact that his hair was turning gray.

He greeted me with a laugh and told me I had grown taller. I laughed, too, and used all my strength to keep my tears away. I nervously drank my tea. I had to pretend that all was well, and I mustn't cry.

During dinner I talked to him about his wife and his daughter. I told him Uncle had died, Step-aunt had gone away, Cousin Wei had gone back to school, and Sister had graduated and was working. Then I told him father and mother were both showing their age. Father has been sleeping in Uncle's room. I wanted to tell him that Father had been looking for him, but stopped before I got the words out and just said, "Father often thinks of you."

He listened quietly and sighed. Maybe he was sighing for his lost ideals. Maybe he was sighing because the old folks at home were too old, the young too young and the innocent too innocent.

Mr. Chu acted like a clown. Hearing the sigh, he turned toward me and said; "Tomorrow, when you write home, just say that I'm the one who's keeping your brother away. Your sister-in-law won't be jealous, will she?" He burst out laughing. Brother and I echoed his laughter.

Three of us were laughing — but it didn't sound natural.

After that dinner, I didn't get to see much of my brother. I couldn't leave school whenever I wanted to. Sundays when I went to see him, he and Mr. Chu had a lot of friends there and I couldn't get a word in edgewise. Because Mr. Chu was my teacher, I was a little afraid of him and couldn't talk and joke freely. Besides, Brother never considered me as mature. I was still that little sister with braids down her back, unable to understand anything.

I wrote to Cousin Wei thinking of Sung Kuo-ping. I had never gotten straight the relationship of Kuo-ping and Brother. Where had that troublemaker disappeared to? I put Cousin Wei's words together with what Mr. Chu had told me. My understanding was a little clearer. After Cousin Wei got my letter, she should understand Brother's departure and return better than I.

Two weeks after I had sent off my letters, I got a special delivery from Sister: "Please return with Brother at once. Father is ill." A sudden blackness spread before my eyes.

258

"Father is ill." Father had long been ill. If he was ill enough to call us all home, it must be that he was really ill. I wiped my tears away and discovered that Sister's letter had not been mailed from the town where she worked, but from Wuhsi. Sister must be on her way home already.

Nervous and tense, I walked to Mr. Chu's house, put down the letter and burst into tears. He arranged everything for me. He sent someone to look for Brother and wanted us to leave immediately.

"You've finished your final exams anyway. Don't bother to pack, and don't bother to take anything with you. I'll have your luggage sent after you. You two leave now."

Everything that Mr. Chu had cautioned me about seemed unnecessary now. The whole house was in an uproar. Nobody had any time to scold or reprimand Brother. Nobody asked him any questions, and they had even less time to lecture him.

V

In the great hall, tailors were sitting around two tables. At one table, father's clothes were being made; the other table was a sea of white where they were turning out mourning clothes.

Brother was walking behind me. I don't know what the people thought of Brother's return. I just said, "Brother and I have come back together" and walked in.

The Forbidden Royal Chamber was completely changed. The sofa in the little parlor was pulled to one side. In one corner a camp cot had been set up. Next to the cot sat two complete strangers. In the bedroom, the red curtain had been taken away. I immediately saw father lying straight out on the bed.

Father had closed his eyes as if he were napping. His thin face was yellowish, but not much different from the usual. I was ready to scold them all for making much ado about nothing. But when he opened his eyes a little, I saw the difference — he didn't recognize me at all.

I sat on the edge of the bed, calling his name. I wanted to see if I could recall his memory. It wasn't that I wanted him to see me — I wanted him to see Brother beside me. I stood up, letting my brother cry for a while. Brother also sat on the edge of the bed. He put his hands on Father's shoulders, calling him in a low voice. Standing there, I saw Brother's mouth trembling and his lids blinking back the tears. He stopped calling, fell forward against Father's chest and stayed there a long time.

Sister-in-law brought Niece in. My little niece had never seen her father. She just stood looking the stranger up and down. Brother looked at her, biting a corner of his lip. She let go of her mother's hand and walked to the bedside, calling out loudly, "Grandfather! Grandfather!" Her shout was louder than ours. Father opened his eyes, a slight smile on his lips. The smile revived our hopes. I started calling, too. But Father closed his eyes again and the smile left his lips.

Brother and I kept watch beside his bed. His eyes opened now and then to stare at the top of the mosquito net. Sometimes he said something unintelligible. Sometimes his hands would reach out in the air, as if trying to convey the pain he was suffering.

The doctor came, took Father's pulse, pressed his lips together, shook his head and left the room.

VI

At the time of the July seventh incident. I was at home on vacation. By then I had just completed my first year at college.

Our school had moved to Lushan and I had received the notice: Uncle and Father were both dead, Step-aunt had left home, Sister had married and Cousin Wei was working in another town. Brother had taken Niece and Sister-in-law to stay with her family. Only Mother and I were left at home.

Poor Mother was so agitated that she had left her hair in a tangled mess. With the school's notice in her hands, she didn't know what to do. Lushan was so far, and with times being what they were how could she let me go? On the other hand, she had always wanted her children to be well educated. How could she let me stop in the middle of my education and waste my whole life?

"I know what we'll do!" Mother said.

"I won't feel well if you go by yourself. But if you can find one of your schoolmates, you can leave together."

Brother returned while I was waiting for a reply. "How come you're still here? I thought your school had moved. I wish I could grow a pair of wings and fly away!"

So Brother was restless again. Ever since he had returned from his disappearance, he had seemed depressed. He was much older than I, and he was often away from home so that I rarely saw him. I had the idea that he was impatient with life. When he was away, he wanted to come home. When he returned, he wanted to leave again. His thoughts were always floating here and there, always restless.

When I was worriedly waiting for my schoolmate's letter, I discovered that Brother, too, was waiting for mail. He seemed unusually short tempered and, at the same time, unusually elated.

August 13 came and the Japanese army attacked our troops at Shanghai. The war was getting nearer and nearer.

After I got in touch with my schoolmate, Mother rushed around getting the beddings together, packing my suitcase, opening it, repacking it and then opening it again.

VII

The school had moved again, this time to Chungking.

On the journey there, I hadn't received any mail from the family. First I found out where Cousin Wei worked — it was at Koloshan near Chungking. I wrote her immediately and she wrote back telling me about Mother.

Cousin Wei's letter hadn't mentioned Brother at all. I wrote her again to ask where Brother had gone after the town fell to the Japanese.

She told me that soon after the town was occupied, he had left home by himself and had gone to Shanghai, intending to make the trip into the interior. She had no idea why none of us had heard anything from him since.

I thought of how Brother had been waiting so eagerly for a letter just before I left home. Whose letter had he been waiting for? And did it finally come? A lot of people who had started for the interior even later than Brother had arrived in Chungking. Why was there no news? If he had stayed on in Shanghai, he would have contacted Sister there. But Sister had written to Cousin Wei and hadn't mentioned Brother at all.

As far as I knew, Brother hadn't seen Kuo-ping since he came home. Kuo-ping had been there to visit, but Brother had never been at home.

I remembered the sudden appearance of Kuo-ping the second summer after Father had died. The whole family was startled to see him. I was glad that Brother wasn't home. Cousin Wei hadn't found a job that summer. Mother said that since she would be graduating the next year and that she would go away to work, there would be very few chances for a family reunion in the future. She particularly wanted Cousin Wei to spend the summer at home.

Mother remembered that Kuo-ping liked steamed pork chops wrapped in lotus leaves and wanted me to cut a few leaves.

"Where will I get the leaves from?" I said, pouting and rather unhappy at all the attention Kuo-ping was getting from Mother. "Why go to so much trouble?"

"This child is getting saucier," Mother scolded me. "Aren't there a few lotus plants in Uncle's little courtyard? Open the middle window in the little parlor and you can climb into the courtyard."

I didn't know why the lotus flowers were put in the little court-yard. They used to be in the large courtyard in front of the big parlor. When grandfather was alive, he often took a bottle and collected dew from the lotus leaves. He said the early-morning dewdrops on the lotus leaves could give long life.

I took the scissors and walked into the little parlor. No one used this suite now. Mother had given Sister's room to Cousin Wei and had changed Cousin Wei's old room into another parlor where Kuo-ping was sleeping.

Only the windows on one wall of the room were open, because not many people come in nowadays. I opened the window in the mid-dle and stepped out onto the stone steps. I saw the lotus flowers right away. They weren't in the middle of the courtyard, but against one corner of the wall. No wonder the flowers weren't visible from the room. Only one flower was blooming. It looked so lonesome, and all by itself.

As I was reflecting on this, a sudden gust of wind started banging the window to and fro. I hadn't caught the latch properly so I turned around and closed the window, shutting myself outside. Glancing up at the sky, I saw that it would rain soon. I hurriedly took the scis-sors and cut the lotus leaves.

Just as I had finished and was thinking of climbing back, I saw someone's shadow through the window. Backing into the room was Cousin Wei. Kuo-ping was facing her, pushing her into the room. Cousin Wei's back was toward me so she didn't know I was in the courtyard. Kuo-ping's eyes were fixed on Cousin Wei and he didn't notice me, either. I quickly pulled my head down.

"At last I have a chance to be alone with you!" Kuo-ping said.

Cousin Wei didn't say a thing.

"Don't look at the floor!" He must have raised her head. "Look at me! Don't look at anything else!" His tone was half pleading, half commanding — Kuo-ping had always liked to put a hint of violence in his voice. "I've always said your eyes could speak. And I also know you..." Suddenly he gave a laugh. Maybe Cousin Wei's expression pleaded him not to say any more. "All right, you don't want to hear any further so I won't say any more."

They were silent. I raised my head. Kuo-ping's lips were pressed on Cousin Wei's. He was holding her tightly. Cousin Wei's hands were at her side.

Lightning started to flash and big drops of rain fell, plopping on the lotus leaves. What was I to do now? I was afraid of thunder and lightning. And they were kissing as if they would never stop. What should they care about the wind and rain outside!

Luckily, Mother called to Cousin Wei, "It's raining! You'd better bring in those books you were returning."

Cousin Wei pushed Kuo-ping aside, hurriedly opened the door and left the room. Kuo-ping took out his handkerchief and wiped his lips. I pulled my head down again and heard his footsteps leaving the room. Just as he reached the door, he shouted, "Cousin Wei! Do you want me to come and help you?"

That was the last I saw of Kuo-ping.

VIII

Our school was in a southern suburb of Chungking. Cousin Wei worked at Koloshan in the north. So we didn't see each other very often. We made a date to meet for a weekend at the home of my old friend Yung-feng. My friend had a living room, dining room and two bedrooms, so both of us could stay at her place.

Cousin Wei was still the same; quiet and serene. Even the turbulent war didn't seem to have affected her at all. She still wore somber colors. Her hair had not been cut. It was parted on the side and fell straight to her shoulders, curling a bit at the ends. I hugged her and jumped up and down as if we had met again after a lifetime. We didn't know where to begin talking.

Finally the conversation got around to that missing brother of mine. Mother always used to say that Brother acted as though he had oil smeared on the soles of his shoes — he was always slithering off somewhere.

"Where has he gone this time?" Yung-feng spoke as if she were a member of our family. She was my classmate and came from the same town, so she knew about our family. She added, "He must have gone to the place he went before."

My heart skipped a beat and I said, "Impossible! He went through the experience before and had his lesson. The first time a person sins, it's excusable; he knows better than to repeat. The second time he commits the same sin, it must be stupidity."

"You may be right in principle," Yung-feng said. "But according to the facts, you have to give in to me. Your brother wouldn't feel that he's making the same mistake. Don't forget, the communists are fighting for the same cause. This time, he probably thinks his joining them is right. He doesn't know that they are wolves in sheep's clothing. If you go to the butcher's and find out that they're selling dog meat, you want to leave. But if the butcher is standing at the door with a big cleaver in his hands, how are you going to escape?"

"Don't worry," Cousin Wei uttered the first words she had spoken since we had started talking about Brother. "Brother wouldn't be a collaborator. No matter what part of the battlefield he's on — no matter whether he's north, south, east or west, — he's helping to fight for his country. After all, we all share a common enemy."

Cousin Wei said this without any display of emotion. It was as if she were patiently trying to explain something to the child.

"Even if he is fighting for the country," I asked, "Why is it he doesn't get in touch with us? Why should he be so secretive about it?"

"In many places, Mei-mei, the fighting is secretive," Cousin Wei continued. "For example, he may be fighting with the guerrillas. His movements may be uncertain and he has no way of getting in touch with us. Maybe he thought that if we knew of his movements, it would just cause us to worry all the more."

I didn't know whether Cousin Wei was guessing. She had always known more about Brother than I had. But no matter how much she argued and spoke up for him, I still couldn't forgive Brother for his silence.

We didn't see each other after that. When I went to Koloshan again, they said she had gone to the hospital and I inquired there. The nurse only laughed and said her ailment wasn't serious. But nobody knew where she had gone from there.

IX

After graduation, I started on the road to another world. The office where I went to work used foreign languages more than Chinese. At each desk there was a typewriter. With all the typewriters banging away, the place sounded like a factory and it was busy all the time. I noticed that the things the others typed were sometimes in English, a language I half understood. Others were in Russian, of which I knew nothing, or in Japanese.

Because I had to attend the press conference every week, I got to know some of the women reporters. At that time, the communist papers and the privately owned papers all had women reporters.

At one press conference, Chien Ming of the Central Daily News told that "someone has come from Yenan* recently to act as their liaison with the foreign reporters. "Have you met her yet?" I was asked.

I shook my head. I didn't go to the press club very often, so I never knew about the comings and goings of the people there. I asked, "What's her name?"

"She's called Fang Kang." So now there was a Fang Kang to add to their ranks and to their propaganda for the foreign reporters

---

* A town in Shensi which served as the Chinese Communists' wartime headquarters.

and correspondents. Fang Kang — sounded as if she would be rigid and steely; she was probably short and dark with a very cold manner. I knew that the foreign correspondents' club was a good place to send out feelers and the communists would never let this chance to propagandize slip away.

The press conference didn't break up until late that day. After the conference, office hours were nearly over. Chen Po quickly left with Lee Yun-hua, calling out for us to come over to her house early for her son's birthday party. Chen Po and Lee Yun-hua were with two other women reporters. Chien Ming said, "Seeing that office hours are almost over, I'll wait for you and we can buy a gift and go over together."

Chien Ming and I walked out of the office together. Just as we turned the corner past the press club, I suddenly stopped to pull off a piece of paper which had stuck to the sole of my shoe. I felt Chien Ming giving me a tug and heard her say, "Here comes Miss Fang Kang."

I don't know if Cousin Wei was as moved and startled as I was. Her expression betrayed nothing. She seemed thinner and older. But she was still the Cousin Wei of my memory — quiet and serene. She shook my hand and said to Chien Ming, "We've met before."

Her composure reassured me. I straightend up and said to my Cousin Wei, the new Fang Kang, "How long have you been in Chungking?" I tried as hard as I could to sound natural.

"Not so long," she said, still smiling faintly.

"Miss Fang, are you coming or just leaving?" Chien Ming asked. "If you're just leaving, we can walk together."

"I'm just coming." She was still smiling.

"Do you have many friends at the club?" I asked.

"Just a few newly made friends," she said.

"We've got to go now," Chien Ming said.

Fang Kang held her hand out in good-bye — that same slender white hand. I shook her hand and said without thinking, "How is Mr. Sung?"

She started, then recovered her composure, pulling a leaf from the shrub. "Mr. Sung?" She let the leaf fall to the ground, "Oh! Him? ... Very well." She turned and left.

So Cousin Wei was in Chungking. And she was working not far from my own office. It was she who was spreading all that propaganda in the press club. We had met again and we were so close to each other now — and yet so far apart.

Chien Ming broke into my thoughts and asked, "So you did know her after all."

"When I knew her, she wasn't called Fang Kang," I answered.

"That was why you hadn't heard of her," Chien Ming said. "You must have been surprised!"

"You don't know just how surprised I was," I answered truthfully.

"Do you know Mr. Sung?" Chien Ming asked again.

"Yes," I said, thinking that she hadn't changed her name. "Where is Sung?"

"He's not here," Chien Ming shook her head. "Fang Kang has just been transferred. Sung could be at Yenan. She's their reinforcement here. Both her Chinese and English are very good. They often criticize her for having a little of the capitalist in her. She likes to have flowers in her room and even though she doesn't use make-up and dress in the latest fashion, she always looks neat."

We bought the gift and went on to Chen Po's house. Lee Yunhua had arrived earlier. Chen Po said, "Now we just have to wait for Fang Kang."

She turned to me and asked, "Have you met Fang Kang?"

"I met her just now at the door of the press club."

Fang Kang came, bringing a toy for the boy's birthday. She kneeled down and handed her gift to the little boy, "Long life to you!"

"How old is your baby?" Chen Po asked her.

Fang remained kneeling and, without raising her head, answered in a whisper, "Younger than yours."

"I didn't know you were a mother," I interrupted. "Is it a girl or a boy?"

She still didn't raise her head. "A girl."

"How come you didn't bring her along today?"

She stood up this time and pushed her hair behind the ears — her hair that was still long and curled. She didn't look at me, but she said softly, "She's not here."

Fang Kang was always at the press club. The propaganda she brought was reflected in the slant of the newscasts that I read every day, and it was reflected in the speech of some reporters.

We didn't meet very often. When we did, we greeted each other casually. No one knew of our relation in the past. No one knew that we had grown up as two trunks from the same root. Our present seemed a complete negation of our former intimacy.

Among our circle of friends, no one knew of my relationship with Fang Kang. When she was in Chungking before, she had worked in the countryside and her former colleagues had no connection with the press world. None of them knew that Cousin Wei had a younger sister and now none would know because she had changed her name. Among my own colleagues, no one knew I had a sister working for those people.

The only one who knew was Yung-feng.

I told Yung-feng that Fang Kang had a daughter. We guessed that when she had left Chungking, she was already pregnant. She must have had an unusually bad case of morning sickness thinking she was ill. So she went to the hospital. I remember the nurse who had laughed when she told me, "There's nothing seriously wrong with her." Of course, she was merely pregnant. And I remembered Chien Ming saying, "Do you know her Mr. Sung?" Undoubtedly, Sung Kuo-ping was the father of her child.

X

The fever wouldn't go down and I found it was typhoid. I had to quit work and go to the hospital.

I was better now and could walk, supporting myself by holding on to the edge of the bed. I had gotten to know all the nurses very well and they often kept me company.

It was a Sunday. After my nap, I sat in a rattan chair and propped my feet up on a stool in front of me. A blanket was draped over my knees and I had a pillow behind my back. I faced the window with my back to the door. I heard the door opening but was too lazy to turn around, thinking it must be the nurse or the orderly.

How was I to know that walking in behind my back was that tall, slender — was it Cousin Wei or was it Fang Kang this time? She knelt down and caught my hands in hers, "Thank heavens, you're all right now." She kept her eyes on me and smoothed back my uncombed hair. Her expression was full of concern. It was Cousin Wei who had come, not Fang Kang.

"I just found out you were ill a few days ago," she said, standing up. "Otherwise, I would have come long ago." Absentmindedly I fixed my eyes on an old tree outside the window. The sun was setting. What should I say?

I pretended I wanted a drink of water and she looked around for the thermos. "It's on the little table beside the bed. Yung-feng gave it to me," I said.

"Does Yung-feng come every day?"

"When I was very ill, she came every day," I said. "These last few days she's been away and besides, I'm better now."

"Does the family know you're ill?" She took my glass away.

"No, they don't. I don't let Mother hear anything that might upset her." I lowered my head and looked at the fringe on the blanket. Suddenly, I felt that because of her question, the distance between us wasn't so great any more.

She stood behind me, silent for a long time. She started combing my hair.

"Some people say that after typhoid all the hairs fall out." She broke the silence, pretending at lightness. "But it's just as thick as ever."

She put the comb away and moved where I could see her.

I looked at her profile. Her face was getting paler. Her pointed chin made me think of Uncle when he was ill. The pale face contrasted sharply with her black, chess-piece eyes. I seemed to detect a new sorrow in those eyes. Kuo-ping was right, her eyes could talk.

I suddenly felt exhausted and asked her to help me to the bed. "Let me get in bed and lie back for a while."

She helped me get settled. "Watch out you don't catch a cold," she said as she pulled the flowered scarf from around her neck and put it around me. After she had taken off her scarf, I noticed that she was wearing a bright red *chipao*. Strange — Cousin Wei hardly ever wore red.

We talked about this and that, but her mind was on something else. Finally, she picked up the box she had brought with her.

"Guess what I brought you," she challenged.

I couldn't guess. She lifted the cover — inside was a round cake with a half circle of blue flowers around it. "Now you know!"

As soon as I saw it was a cake, I knew. This was my birthday. Time had passed without my reckoning during the illness, and I had completely forgotten. Yung-feng was not in Chungking and everybody else who would have remembered was far away. Cousin Wei was a thoughtful person; she had even worn her red *chipao* for me.

"I know you can't eat it, but I thought you might want to look at it." She stuck the candles in the cake one by one. "Oh, horrible! I forgot the matches!"

She rushed out again and came back with matches. She struck a match and the dim hospital room brightened. She lit the candles one by one until I could see her shadow dancing on the wall.

"My poor hoarse voice won't attempt to sing for you," she laughed. "So let's dispense with formalities."

I inhaled and just as I was about to blow out the candles, she stopped me. "Make a wish," she said in English.

I closed my eyes, praying that my wish would come true. I opened my eyes and said, "You help me blow them out."

"You don't have enough energy, is that it? All right," she said. We blew out all the candles together.

It was dark again in the room. She held the cake up, "You can't eat it, so just have a good smell!" She brought the cake up near my nose and then put it back on the table.

She said, "You'd better rest now. I have to be going."

I lay back and she pulled up the covers. "You have to be careful. Don't take your arms out." I watched her walk toward the door. She couldn't see the tears dropping from my eyes in the dark. I had tried to suppress them for so long. I had wanted to cry ever since she came.

She turned around at the door, "Take good care of yourself," and then she disappeared.

XI

We won the war!

It was August 15, 1945, more than eight years since the July 7 incident of 1937.

After the heady victory celebrations, everybody prepared to return to their homes.

Just at this time, I found out that Cousin Wei was ill — and seriously. It was Chen Po who told me.

Cousin Wei was at Kuanjen Hospital. I took a bunch of fresh flowers, for she had always liked fresh flowers, and went to see her.

It was so quiet in the hospital. I opened the door softly and tiptoed toward the bed. The patient opened her eyes — those black button-like eyes, so familiar to me.

"Cousin Wei," I called her name softly.

She patted the bed and indicated that I should sit down. She shook my hands so hard that several petals fell.

I stood up and put the flowers in a vase. Lowering my head, I asked, "Are you better?"

She shook her head.

"You'll be all right soon," I said. "When I was here, the doctors told me I had no chance. See how much alive I am now?"

She didn't say a word.

"I can come every day to keep you company," I said.

She was still silent and only clutched my hand tightly.

I guessed I was to perform a solo that day. "I saw Cousin Lei not long ago," I continued cheerily. "He thinks we should change our old house into a school dormitory. A new middle school has just been opened in our home town. Did you know that?" She nodded. "Do you approve?" She nodded again.

Why didn't she say anything? Her hair was spread out on the pillow. Her face was flushed and the hand that clutched mine was hot.

269

"Last night, I dreamed of home." She sighed softly. "I dreamed I was in our little parlor. You were there, too. And the two of us were arguing."

I didn't want to encourage her emotions. I laughed and said, "I'm really terrible! There's nothing I like better than a good argument. Mother keeps on scolding me, but I can never change."

"How is Mother?"

"Very well," I said.

"Does she ever mention me in her letters?" She turned so her back was toward me.

"She asks about you in almost every letter." I patted her shoulder. "You hurry up and get better."

"When are you leaving for home?"

"It's early yet," I said. "I'll wait until you're better. What's the rush anyway?"

She turned over, her mouth working a forced smile on her lips — a smile that hurt inside.

"When Mother sees you at home, I know how happy she'll be."

"You just hurry up and get well. She'll be even happier to see you. We can go back home together."

She gripped my hand tightly and called me, "Mei-mei!"

The "Mei-mei" brought my tears. I quickly turned my head and told myself I shouldn't cry in front of her.

It was silent again in the room. I pretended I was gathering the fallen petals and looked around for a wastepaper basket.

"This hospital seems to have some sort of destiny with our family. I've been here before and now you're staying here, too."

"In the hospital," she said, "It's like living on the brink of life and death. All values of life change."

The nurse came in, took her temperature and gave her medicine. After the nurse had gone, she took a photo from under her pillow and showed it to me. "This is my daughter."

It was a picture of Little An. Little An didn't look much like Cousin Wei. She had her father's hick eyebrows.

"The shape of her face is like yours." I looked at the photo and then looked at her. "Look at her nose. Don't you think it looks like Uncle's?"

She took the picture, and laughed, "It really does, doesn't it?"

"She also looks a bit like Little Lien." I thought of Brother's daughter. I peered closely at the photo — the more I looked the more I thought the two cousins looked alike.

"Really?" Cousin Wei said. "This child really looks like Little Lien?"

No one mentioned the eyebrows.

"What's she like now?" I asked.

"Oh, just another baby." She frowned.

I couldn't resist asking, "Her father?"

"He's away on business."

So Sung Kuo-ping wasn't in Yenan. But of course. He was one of their old stalwarts. If they were going around taking over as many towns as they could, he certainly wouldn't be in Yenan. Did he know that Cousin Wei was ill? Would he rush to see her? They had been separated for so long.

"You take good care of her," Cousin Wei pointed to the child in the photograph.

How could I take care of her? I haven't even seen her. But I put a smile on my face and said, "When she's bigger she'll be just like her mother."

"No," she shook her head. "When she's older she'll be like her aunt." She stared at me. "You promise me now that you'll let her grow up to be just like you!"

She suddenly swallowed hard, put her hands to her face and burst out sobbing. I could feel her shoulders heaving under the covers.

I let her cry. Maybe she would feel better. I watched her tears — each tear stood for the suffering of a mother for her daughter.

"Everything I've done, I've done for her," she said through her tears. "But it turns out I still can't have her."

I didn't understand. Was it because she and Sung Kuo-ping had quarreled again? Was it because she was sick in bed and thought she wouldn't get well and would never see her again?

"After you get well, you can see her," I comforted her.

"They won't let me go back to see her." She started sobbing again. "They want to send me off somewhere else to work."

Now I understood. Little An had become a hostage. Cousin Wei had worked herself almost to death to be reunited with her daughter. But according to the rules of their game, working hard meant the extinguishing of all except party ties.

I could guess at how much criticism Cousin Wei's capitalistic emotions had aroused. All she could do was gaze silently at Little An's picture every night. She didn't dare speak her thoughts to anyone. She couldn't even buy a toy or some clothes for Little An. In their circle, maternal love was looked on as a sin. I wished I could climb walls and fetch Little An.

As we were holding each other's hands the door opened and Ma Lin came in. She was also from Yenan. Cousin Wei quickly let go my hand

and brushed the tears from her cheeks. I put Little An's photo under the pillow.

Ma Lin was laughing and greeted me cheerfully. "How are you today?" She turned toward Cousin Wei.

"You brought some flowers," Ma Lin said as she spied the flowers. "Fang Kang likes flowers so much."

I didn't know if she meant to be sarcastic. I didn't know her very well. Her world was very different from mine.

"I think you'll be all right in a few days," she said, sitting down in the chair beside the bed. "You have to build up your strength."

Cousin Wei nodded.

"You'll have to take good care of yourself," I said.

Cousin Wei glanced timidly at Ma Lin and then looked at me. It was a long look. Her eloquent eyes seemed to say something. But what? Then she said, "You go ahead. I'll be better."

I stood up, "I'll be coming to see you again."

Cousin Wei turned her head away and didn't say good-bye. Ma Lin laughed.

When I went back three days later, she was gone. They said she left with a short fat woman. It could have been Ma Lin.

My visit must have harmed her. Ma Lin apparently reported to the higher-ups on how we had been crying and holding hands. What else had she reported? They didn't want me to visit Fang Kang, yet they couldn't prevent it. So they had to move her.

Where should I look? She was ill and could only submit passively. She had no way of communicating with me. My whole life seemed to be a long series of hide-and-seek games. This time, those who were doing the hiding would throw up smoke screens in every direction so that I wouldn't know where to begin.

As it turned out, I didn't have to start looking. Chen Po told me they had taken Cousin Wei to Yenan for "psychological treatment."

All hopes of our meeting again were gone. I remembered that Cousin Wei had lit the candles on the birthday cake and had wanted me to make a wish. I had closed my eyes and prayed that some day Cousin Wei would come back to join the family with me. Just as my hopes might have come true, she had been taken away.

I walked aimlessly in the streets. I felt so empty inside, so lonely.

I made plans to leave Chungking. At home I had an elderly mother waiting for me — waiting for me to lighten the load of her last years. My heartbroken sister-in-law was waiting for the comfort I could bring her. My fatherless niece was waiting for me to help educate and bring her up. Our family resembled a play race. Sister had carried the burden long enough. Now we were in the home stretch and it was up to me to carry on.

XII

Mother's room hadn't changed at all. The big closet, the huge trunk — they were all in their old places. Even her red wedding scrolls were still hanging in the same spot on the wall.

Mother asked me softly when we were alone, "Do you have any news of Brother?"

I shook my head.

"Do your Cousin Wei and Kuo-ping have any news?"

1 shook my head again.

"Other people had faith in us and so they let their precious daughter marry into our family," Mother sighed. "What am I to say to them now?"

What could I say?

After Sister-in-law had gone back to her own home, Mother told me, "Brother is your responsibility now. You have to find him in some-way. Put an ad in the paper. By now, everybody knows that the war has been won. He should be able to come home now."

I promised.

"And then there's Cousin Wei." Mother could never forget her. "Her share of the money from the house is here. If she can, she should come back. She may not miss me, but I still miss her very much."

How could I explain things to her? It wasn't that they didn't want to come home. They wanted to come home so much but they couldn't.

Adapted and translated by Pan Shih

Nang Phanthurat's Gold Mine

"Riem-Eng"

$\Large S$EE THAT crazy guy?" Vicha put down his glass of beer and gestured with his mouth towards the table on our left.

I slowly turned halfway in that direction to take a quick look through the smoke rings overhead. For a second I was prevented from seeing clearly by the shadow of a red paper bag put under the lamp to catch fallen insects. When my eyes got more accustomed to the light, the picture cleared.

It was only nine o'clock, still too early for a commercial and communication centers like Jaknam-pho market to be rid of a crowd—especially in the rainy season. That evening, however, the roof-terrace of the yellow building was deserted but for Vicha and the young man with his girl looking very much like a couple running away from their parents to some secret rendezvous.

It did not seem right to me that "crazy guy" should be used for an old man of about 60 with snow-white hair simply because he was quiet, took nothing but orange-ade, and kept to himself. His eyes were half-focused beyond Yom Island where the Mae Pring and Mae Wang rivers end, and where the Chao Phraya river begins. He smiled enigmatically as if he alone owned and understood the whole world.

I stole another glance at the whitish eyebrows above that pair of still very bright eyes and noticed the fresh look on his face. I was careful enough not to stare and be impolite. Then I answered Vicha, a cigarette between my lips.

"Yes. But I don't think he's crazy."

Vicha pushed his glass nearer to the sixth bottle of beer that the waiter had just opened and brought. Propping his arms, he leaned towards me.

"That's him ... one of the 500 types of crazy men." He spoke through lips which were hardly opened.

"According to Luang Vichian's or Dr. Phon's theory[1], he might be an 'ex' type or an 'in' type. I don't know. But what else do you

---

[1] Luang Vichian, and Dr. Phon: Thailand's first two psychiatrists.

274

expect me to call a man who threw away a King Solomon's mine, the chance to be a rich man . . . a millionaire . . . just like that, if I can't call him crazy?"

Vicha loved to pose ruthless questions whenever his blood warmed up after guzzling down the product of a local distillery or one from a cutglass decanter. I even thought that if he wanted to, Vicha could have roused a dead man with one of those curious and strange questions fired every time he felt the warmth of alcohol.

"The man would come and rest here every year," Vicha continued, "for a few days, or as long as a week or two. Then he would disappear and nobody would know where he had gone. Some said he lived somewhere as far as Khan Kwang Thong, some said he lived in the old elephant stables of the Bombay Burma Company, and some said in the middle of the Khao Nor range off Ban Daen. At first they wanted to know his whereabouts with a motive that went further than mere curiosity, but after several years of trying nobody could make anything concrete out of the facts covering him. So they all gave up interest either in the man himself or in that gold mine of his."

"Oh . . . so there's a silver mine or a gold mine involved in all this?" I said continuing to blow smoke rings. "This must be the same type of legend as that one about Nang Phanthurat[2] at Khao Nor."

"You fool!" Vicha suddenly pulled himself together and sat up straight. He filled his glass and drank every drop as if to wash down his annoyance, "So you think this is a tale to be told only to children, eh? Anybody who has been in Paknam-pho for as long as I have, some ten years now, would know this much about Luang Thorani Vidhya—all of them from high-ranking government officials down to the kids who swarm in front of the theater — even the sampan boatmen know!"

I listened to him attentively at first with the expectation that the story might be more of the light kind that aids the digestion rather than the kind that might upset one if taken seriously. In general, people are too often interested in other people's business, to be of help. Since I belong to the profession that depends on pens and pencils, Luang Thorani's story was much too fascinating to be ignored even if I knew I could not in any way be of help to him. My silence served to let my old classmate know that I was beginning to get interested so he leaned forward with his arm on the table and continued to talk in a very low voice, so low sometimes that I had to strain my ears in order to hear him. There were times when he would burst out laughing as if forgetting himself. So loud this time that I was alarmed my friend was ill or

_____
[2] Nang Phanthurat: a female giant from a Thai legend, who possessed fabulous ponds of gold and silver. Here, the name is given to a site believed to hold hidden treasure.

275

drunk or something. Half an hour later, old Luang Thorani had gone back to his room and only the young couple were left whispering and giggling to their hearts' content in the darkness at the other end of the roof-terrace.

I could not help wondering if Luang Thorani actually did have quite a few of those "ex" or "in" qualities.

According to an old story told by Vicha (and the boy himself had been up here in the timber business for more than 15 years, so he ought to know it well enough!), Luang Thorani, who had just then resigned from government service, came up here with the intention of setting up a farm, a plantation, or to be in the timber trade or to hunt, nobody seemed to know for sure. He rented a house at the other end of the market, which served as his temporary refuge, and then went out to make a survey of the countryside around Khao Nor Ban Daen, continued to Thalok-bat, Bo Tham, Samnak Muang Raet, Lat Yao, Khao Kwang Thong, Thung Tabaek on Klong Mae-Wong up to Khao Mokochoo on the Thai-Burmese border. Nobody knew what he wanted exactly until a year later when his former guide who, unable to stand the illnesses and hardships any longer, refused to accompany him, and that Luang Thorani was in fact looking for gold.

Those who had been itching with curiosity began to laugh at the idea. Many government officials of long experience tried to convince Luang Thorani that his efforts would all be in vain. Quite a few hunters and wood traders who knew the country around confirmed that throughout their long experience of travelling they had never heard even so much as a rumor of the presence of gold! It is true that some iron pyrites were found on certain hills and along the edges of certain streams, but that was not gold! Even so, Luang Thorani fostered his conviction that there was gold in Nakhon Sawan region.

With the help of a roughly-made map and some evidence which was a little over one baht's weight of refined gold, he said that, towards the end of King Rama VI's reign, an old friend of his, an official in the Department of Forestry who went to serve at Amphur Lat Yao, met a Burmese with whom he became so well acquainted that they often went hunting together. When the Burmese was stricken with fever, Luang Thorani's friend took good care of him until he died. This man was entrusted by the Burmese with a bit of refined gold along with a statement that he had found a gold mine, which was of the purest quality, and in fabulous quantity that none would ever be able to estimate it. But where? Without a knowledge of geography or geology and depending solely on his experience with the country so far covered, the Burmese man could only give a description of the area, a description which proved to be of practically no value what-

276

soever, since every hill, meadow, stream and trail of land in this forest, one of the biggest in Thailand, had nothing distinctive about it.

Of course Luang Thorani's friend believed every word the Burmese said. Without a word to anybody, the rest of his life was spent quietly searching for this gold mine, this invaluable treasure. He spent all the time while he was Inspector for the Department of Forestry in that region in his quest for the gold. The expenses and hardships he encountered exhausted not only his possessions, but also robbed him of his health. Within a scant three years his efforts were defeated in that huge forest which for centuries had never been conquered by a human being. And in the same way like his Burmese friend he entrusted Luang Thorani with the secret and the map of the treasure.

"Isn't it wonderful to see how a man's conviction and faith can prove to be so great in the face of nature's approaching danger and despite the objection of the majority?" said Vicha, his eyes half-closed, still sitting there amidst rows of beer bottles.

"Luang Thorani was already over 40 when he came up here; he was no longer young. There was no record of his family. He befriended nobody save me, and yet, not to the point of trust. To all of us, he was a very mysterious man whom nobody could understand. Many accused him of being a little bit way off because a forest spirit had gotten into him as had happened to his other friend and the Burmese before. That's why even with the evidence, the sample of gold, the map and the fabulous story with it, everybody still regarded the whole business as a fairy tale or the dream of a demented man.

"Many years after, five or six I think, after he had gone off alone for more than eight months, so long that everybody took it for granted that he had fallen victim to jungle fever or wild beasts or that he had starved to death after having lost his way — he came back with big news. It was like a bomb in our midst. Can you guess what it was all about?"

"A white queen just like the one Aloysius Horn found in the middle of the Dark Continent, I suppose." I yawned. "Or a discovery of a Maeo[4] plantation in the jungle among one of those hills?"

Vicha knocked his head against his fist as he was wont to do when interrupted or annoyed.

"When will you ever grow up?" He quenched his annoyance with the beer that had been in the glass so long that its foam was gone. "Believe it or not, Luang Thorani came back that triumphant time, just like Caesar when he marched with his army into Rome across the Rubi-

---

[3] rai: a Thai land measure, equal to about 1600 square meters
[4] Maeo: a hill-tribe in Thailand.

con. He found the gold mine! Not only found the site, but he also brought back nearly two tamlungs of ore!"

I could not help opening my eyes wide with surprise although I was sleepy because of food and drink.

"Are you trying to tell me that Luang Thorani's fairy tale is now true?"

Vicha pinched his nose with his fingers as if stung by a bee. "Fairy tale? Hell no! The whole thing was true from the very start. All of us who had been laughing at him were nuts. Luang Thorani alone was in his right mind."

My face must have evoked an inimitable expression. "You must have had too much to drink ... Better wait until tomorrow. Haven't you had more than two dozens by now?"

"I'm not drunk!"

This was the first time Vicha had ever raised his voice at me. The couple in the corner stopped whispering to each other to look at us and then sneaked quietly downstairs.

"My goodness, those kids must have thought me crazy!"

"Perhaps," I said. "I even suspected it myself. A moment ago, you said Luang Thorani was crazy, and now you are insisting that he's not. Then ... somebody must be crazy..."

Vicha turned to me laughing, his white teeth gleaming. "No, I am not crazy and I still stand by my former statement." He said. "Listen to this.

"The day when the news about Luang Thorani spread to Paknampho market through Wat Sai, Na Pha down to Saphan Dam, and even across Khwae Yai and Wat Phao, I was already closing shop when Luang Thorani suddenly appeared. He looked so gloomy, so different from the Luang Thorani Vidhya we met earlier at the coffee shop that same day. He sat on the chair I pulled out for him and remained silent for quite a while as if mute. Finally, with a heavy sigh, he spoke as though to himself: 'What's the use?'

"There was much meaning in the expression on his face and in his manner that I did not quite understand. Instead of brimming with excitement, brightly and full of joy, realizing that he was practically standing on top of the world, Luang Thorani looked sad and downcast as if he were carrying a load the size of a mountain on his shoulders. Confronted with this perplexity which I could not make out, I had no choice but to keep quiet as well, because I did not know what else to do. To press a man when he is not in the mood to talk is tactless. To offer words of consolation or sympathy is likewise careless when one still doesn't know what the actual situation is. However, after another minute or so of silence, Luang Thorani continued.

" 'I meant my discovery of the gold mine ... the gold mine that you and the people around here thought I was so crazy about.' He pulled out a canvas purse from his pocket and poured valuable pieces of ore on the table, in just the way he had done all day before so many people at the various shops, clubs and at the hotel. 'Just think, Khun Vicha, what can I do with it next?'

" 'Ask for a concession to mine, of course.' I voiced out my opinion. 'If you haven't got enough money, then set up a company calling for investment shares. That shouldn't be any problem. Anybody would be willing to give you a hand. Everybody is ready to lend you support, individuals as well as government authorities. You're holding the whole world right in your hand. It's like having a wishing ring. You can wish for anything: comfort, pleasure, even love, any or all of these to make up for all the trouble, difficulties, suffering and bitterness you have had in the past.'

"Luang Thorani looked at me with compassion. Then he said, 'That was my idea before I discovered that gold mine, the gold mine that is richer in yield than the one at Bang Saphan, the gold mine which I roughly estimated to yield for at least 20 years, if modern machinery could be acquired to operate it. The area at the end of the stream at the foot of the hill alone would have a daily yield ten times that of Tomo.'

"His eyes shone as he spoke, but the glow faded...a moment later. Once more he looked the same old man with a sunburned face that reflected hardships.

" 'Yes, that was my original idea since the first day I came up here. Financially speaking, I have never been rich. In my whole life, I have never known a love that really lasted. A wife is nothing more than a vessel of desire, meant to fulfill the natural law of reproduction more than to be a friend of the heart. Children represent little more than disappointments. Forgive me for telling you my personal life, but there should be at least one person who understands this life which I shall continue to lead. Yes, personally I have no family ties. Do you know how everybody at home felt about this whole thing before I came up here? My wife was only interested to know if my pension would be sufficient to support her and a few young acquaintances of hers during my absence. And my son was only too glad to be rid of the one who controlled him and his unruly behaviour. My daughter sighed with relief to know there would be no more obstacles to her sneaking out to meet that delinquent boy friend of hers. As for friends, I have plenty as long as I can still be of any use to them.'

279

"Here Luang Thorani stopped short as if he were suddenly feeling very tired. He fixed his gaze on the light from the table lamp for a long time. I presumed he must be thinking of his past life. The expression on his face seemed to change with each thought. He finally resumed:

" 'Yes, I once thought like you. I wanted to be a millionaire, an owner of a gold mine. I wanted to rule the world! At a snap of my fingers, men, big and small, would crawl to me whether they were old enough for the grave or young with a face like a newly peeled hardboiled egg. But what's the use? My wife and my children may be pleased. I may get more love, more attention and care from them and from friends and even from the society to which Luang Thorani, that old pensioner... could never belong before! All charity organizations would sing me praises so that they might more easily dip into my pockets and divide what they got among themselves. Honor and Fame would follow. That's it — that's society for you. I know it well — the society that has nothing but its name. Everybody is trying to correct and improve everybody else except himself!' "

"Luang Thorani pushed back his hair with his hand and smiled faintly. 'I don't want that kind of life. I don't want false love, happiness and praise. Had I succumbed to these desires like any other man might have, and struggled to be a millionaire in Thailand, I would never be able to run away from them all. But nothing is more important than the lesson I've had during the time I was wandering up there in those parts searching for the hidden treasure, using the map that other people thought was silly. Just guess what I've found?'

"His eyes sparkled as he fixed them intently on my face. He went on to answer his own question without giving me the chance to say a word.

" 'I've discovered one thing I've never known before in all my life — peace! Peace, the thing that I have been looking for all these years. I had not known until then that this was the thing I wanted all along.'

" '... with that gold mine,' I interpolated.

" 'With the gold mine,' Luang Thorani repeated, 'My eyes were opened for the first time to the fact that the real object of my search was not it at all, but something else to which it led me.'

" 'I don't understand,' I felt my curiosity aroused.

" 'I mean that hill, the one with the gold mine of Nang Phanthurat. This is the name I gave to it,' he said with excitement.

" 'A peaceful hill covered with Pradu⁶ trees, with Uang Champa and Chang-nao⁷ blossoms clinging to the branches. On the edge was a platform, at the back of which were a cascade and thickets of bamboo. The hill itself was not high enough to be fogbound during the day, or low as to be oppressive with the heat. I built a small hut in the middle of the platform, my only tools being an axe and a knife ... these plus lots of effort and the hope that happiness awaited me. It took nearly a month to complete my not-so-neat hut, but it was good enough to ward off the wind and rain. There was no disease or sickness to fear, no wild beasts to bother about. For six full months I spent my life there. Each day was spent not in searching for gold in the stream, or exploring for gold deposits — these tasks would take only a few days — but in spending my life fully, the way I had always wanted to. The woods were full of fruits and edible roots during each season. I lived on that hill the way Crusoe and his Swiss family did on their lonely island. I might have been reverting to a Stone Age type of life but it meant no one any harm. There has never been any period in my entire life during which I was as happy as during those six months there. It was paradise on earth for me! I would not exchange it for the price of a gold mine, or the life of a millionaire or a king. My life there would never have been such a paradise had I yielded to the idea as I first meant to.'

" 'Just what do you mean, Khun Luang?⁸ I asked and could hardly recognise my own voice as I said it.

"Luang Thorani pulled out a roll of papers filled with signs in ink and pencil from his coat pocket, and spread them out before me. Then he struck a match. The expression on his face told of an excitement hard to describe.

" 'Nang Phanthurat's gold mine will continue to be 'her' mine. Nobody will ever find it, not even I myself. Let those six months be engraved in my memory. Let that hill remain the way it has always been for hundreds and thousands of years and continue to remain that way instead of being turned into a village or a district or a town, where men live to fight and destroy each other in such disgusting ways.' "

Vicha lifted the nearby empty beer bottles, poured the remaining drops into his mouth, then put it down looking sad and dejected.

"All gone," he murmured with disappointment, and said, "When I saw him put to flame one corner of the maps, I nearly jumped to grab

---

⁶ Pradu: big tree which blooms once a year yielding yellow flowers; known for its hard wood.

⁷ Uang Champa and Chang-nao: "uang" is a northern Thai word meaning "orchid." Uang Champa — a kind of orchid. Chang-nao — another kind of rare orchid.

⁸ Khun Luang: a polite form of address used with one who carries the title "laung."

281

the lighted match from his hands, but I must have been too surprised or too stunned beyond words so that all I could do was sit there and watch the flames consume those pieces of paper. When the flames nearly reached his hand, he dropped the burning maps in a spittoon where they extinguished themselves.

" 'There's the end of Nang Phanthurat's gold mine,' he murmured while rubbing his hands together. His face looked at that time as bright and enlightened as that of a man who has just found a new light in his life. There were no traces of regret or feelings of concern or worry in his face or in his eyes.

" 'It may be lost forever for everybody else in this world but not for me. It will live here,' he pointed to his head with his finger, '. . . until the last day of my life.'

"He left me that lump of ore and a feeling of wonder and amazement."

Vicha got up trying to support himself on a chair. He heaved a deep sigh.

"Did all that make any sense to you?" he asked while rubbing his eyes with his hand, then pushed back his hair, yawning.

"Do you mean to tell me that all you have been telling me is true?" I asked, raising my brows in query.

"That's right. You...," the fellow dropped rather heavily in a chair and rang for a beer to calm his anger. "After all we have been talking about, you still can't understand it? Let me tell you that my story is as true and as real as we are. The only thing I cannot tell you is what was in the mind of Luang Thorani at the time he made his decision. Since then, nobody knows for sure where he has gone. From time to time he would show up here 'just to see which way the earth was turning,' he would answer some of our doubts. But if Nang Phanthurat's gold was ever mentioned he would suddenly shut up. Some would quietly follow him as he leaves but they all failed. They saw him in the company of log-drivers, then with farmers or with people who went to the forests to look for herbs and roots. Sometimes he came down on log rafts with the people from the north and then disappeared, just disappeared like stones thrown into water. And just when we would all think him dead or gobbled up by a tiger, he would unceremoniously show up, looking contemptuously radiant and wearing his broadest smile. He bothered nobody, frequented nobody's home ... acted as if he were the richest man in the world, owner of King Solomon's mine. Now tell me, can a man be as happy when he's rich in beer or women as when he is rich in heart?"

"Perhaps...perhaps!" I half agreed with him, feeling a little uneasy about discussing so complicated a problem of the heart with a man whose stomach was full of a couple of dozen beers. Even though the fellow was my best friend.

But I think I can guess Luang Thorani's reasons for having destroyed the maps of the gold mine and crushed the least desire to become a millionaire in Thailand even if he had embraced the life of a wanderer, without family, without relatives and without friends!

The Donkey Cart

S. T. Hwang

A T TWENTY-FIVE I was a teacher in a small town in the Northwest of China. The town was sparsely populated and, being so remote, lacked modern means of communication. In the evenings the wolves howled in the nearby hills and occasionally entered the town in quest of prey.

I spent only one year there and, being unable to endure the isolation, packed my bags when the summer holidays arrived and prepared to return home.

A traveller had to take a donkey cart to the nearest railhead, some twenty-five miles away. On arriving at the departure point in the centre of the town, I found that all the carts, being mostly engaged in carrying local products, had left. I began to despair.

"Sir," a sibilant whisper came from a young foki whom I knew slightly (he was from the tiny Moslem restaurant) "all the carts have gone out into the country districts." I left his remark unnoticed. As time passed, I began to feel tired and hungry. The foki approached me again, "Sir, why not come inside for a rest? There may be a donkey cart somewhere else in the town. I'll try to find one for you."

"All right," I agreed, "take my baggage inside."

Having taken a table facing the street, I ordered a small pot of wine and a dish of mutton which were promptly served. A stout cheerful man, the owner of the restaurant must have learned of my problem and came up to me.

"Relax, my friend, and I'll see what can be done," he said, rubbing his hands together.

"It's already four o'clock," I complained, "and if I can't find transport before five my journey will have to be postponed."

"Don't worry," said the innkeeper, "dry weather like this is good for travelling at night."

I sat there quietly, looking at my watch occasionally, hoping to see a cart through the open door. The entrance was suddenly barred by the figure of the foki who came shouting that business was good at the market and that all the carts had gone and were not expected to return until the morrow. The foki moved away revealing an empty donkey cart. I leaped up, hurried to the door and was just about to hail the driver when I realised who he was. My hands dropped and I returned regretfully to my seat. The innkeeper gave a sympathetic smile. The driver was Lin Ng, an old man with a most unsavoury reputation. Among the drivers, he couldn't be trusted. Even the children called the villain in their games Lin Ng. I had used his cart once when I arrived in the town and I remember him vividly as a melancholic with thick eyebrows, wide cheekbones and a pinch of white moustache.

The story goes that when he was young he had been a member of a gang. They had all been wiped out by the law but he escaped and returned to the town. He had taken the job of being a transport driver. Soon afterwards there occurred an event which seemed to confirm his reputation. He was employed to drive a local merchant who carried a substantial sum of money. The day after the journey, the merchant was found clubbed to death in a ditch below a stretch of plateau some miles from the town. Everyone was aware that Lin Ng was the driver who had been employed to drive the leather dealer home and there seemed little doubt of his guilt. He emphatically denied this and asserted that the merchant had transferred to another cart, driven by Ngau Lo Tsun at the halfway stage.

The local Magistrate made a formal investigation of the case but could find no definite evidence except for some bruises on Lin Ng's arms. He was, of course, acquitted but the people of the town still considered him guilty. They avoided him and seldom made use of his services except for short journeys during the day and along well-frequented roads.

The clock struck five and I realised that there was little hope of catching my train now. Unless...?

"Ask old Lin Ng if it is still possible to catch the 9:45 train if we leave now." The innkeeper looked sadly at me but went outside, nevertheless, to inquire for me.

Old Lin Ng, his shabby hat in hand, said with some confidence, "I'll get you to the train in time, sir, but we must start at once." I looked at the innkeeper hesitant to leave but obstinacy urged me to put my faith in him. I had to make that trip.

"Is the weather suitable for a night journey?" I asked.

"It is perfect, sir," was the reply. When I paused again he seemed to sense the cause of my worry. "You could always take another cart in the morning," he went on.

"No," I had decided, "I have to catch the train tonight." I paid the bill and went outside with my baggage which Lin Ng lifted onto the cart. As I climbed in he said, "We are ready to go now, sir. You can take a nap if you want to."

285

Flatly I answered, "I don't want to." And with a crack of his whip we lurched forward.

Some three hours had passed and we were travelling across a barren plain under the darkening sky; the only signs of life were the occasional barkings of the dogs as we passed near some habitations. The countryside seemed to be asleep with the night wind singing a lullaby. The feeble shadow of the cart was cast by the single lamp at the front. The driver rocked and swayed rhythmically now and again giving a flick of the whip to the donkey. I leaned against the side of the cart grasping a large stone which I had picked up before climbing into the vehicle.

Lin Ng glanced at the sooty lamp and at the starry sky, then turned to me. My hand gripped the stone harder. "Are you dozing, sir?"

"No."

The cart began to slow down and the driver made the whip sound loudly in the night air. The poor beast stretched its neck but to little avail. We were having difficulties climbing the hill from the plain. "Get on, damn you!" yelled Lin Ng, jumping down from the seat and moving to the rear of the cart. I felt nervous now wondering if this was a calculated move to get behind me.

"I'll have to push from the back if you will shout at the donkey."

"Shall I get down to make the cart lighter?"

"No. Just sit there, please," he replied.

"I'd better get down for a while if only to stretch my legs."

I jumped down and walked behind the cart while the driver strained until we reached the crest of the hill.

"Thank you. You are very kind to help my donkey. He is almost as old as I am now and he has not been along this route for a very long time. He has been doing short journeys around the town and has forgotten this hill."

I resumed my seat and by then the night grew even darker, the way more rugged. The wheels creaked and groaned as though in protest at the rough terrain. Suddenly he put his whip down in the cart and fumbled at his waist.

"Would he attack me now?" I wondered. I put one foot on the seat and held the stone, ready to defend myself. There was a rustle and he half turned in his seat. He struck a match and the familiar smell of tobacco smoke drifted by me.

"You want to smoke, sir?"

"No, I don't."

"I have not been so far out of town a long time, it seems very strange to me now."

"It's certainly strange!" I replied.

"You are a Southerner, sir. I wonder if things are strange in the South?"

I replied that things were strange in any part of this world.

He laughed, "Things are all strange under the sun." The smoke drifted over his shoulder toward me. "Have you heard strange rumours about me in the town?" he continued, dispassionately.

"Probably." I tried to appear indifferent, slightly afraid even as I wondered all the more why he had asked that particular question.

"I have had no long journeys for years because the townsfolk are afraid of me. They say I was a robber once."

"Are there such rumours?" I pretended to be ignorant of the story.

"That's why I say this world is strange. Rumour is more vicious than an angry serpent. Once you are bitten by it you seldom recover. When I was a young man and trying to earn a living, I tried many jobs. I was a soldier for a while, worked in a vineyard later where I was so unhappy that I decided to return home. Just before I arrived a large gang of robbers was arrested near the town. People had suspected that I had been one of the gang and had escaped."

"But how could they suspect with no evidence?" I interrupted.

"Everyone has two lips," he went on, "we can't stop them from talking. Sir, you may have heard a much stronger rumour about me."

"Well ... vaguely," I answered.

"Let me tell you the truth. It was a night such as this and on this same road when I was taking a leather dealer to the station. He was as friendly as you, sir. He kept talking about the business situation while smoking one cigarette after another. Midway we met an empty cart going slowly in the same direction. I knew the driver, Ngau Lo Tsun, and asked him if he would like to take my passenger the rest of the way to the station as I was very tired and wanted to be home early. He explained that he had lost his whip and that his lamp had run out of oil. I loaned him my whip and filled his lamp. My passenger gave me the half fee and I took leave of them glad that I could go home.

"The next day it was reported that the merchant had been found dead in the ditch below the road and, several people knowing that he had been my passenger, I was arrested. But there was no proof, so I was eventually released. I went to see Lo Tsun who told me that his cart had been ambushed by three robbers who demanded money from the merchant. When he refused to pay they clubbed him to death and chased him away. Lo Tsun went on to say that as long as we remained poor, people would not suspect us of robbing the merchant but then, in spite of my poverty, sir, no one believes me."

I felt uneasy, while I contemplated his trouble. It seemed rather unfair. I loosened my grip on the stone and lit a cigarette.

"Look, sir," he pointed, "there is the very spot where I handed over my passenger. There by that date tree which has grown up so well."

I saw the shadow of a date tree. "I believe you."

"I can't really blame you for not doing so," he continued, "once a rumour has begun it is difficult to stop it."

We remained silent for a long time. The singular sound of the revolving wheels emphasized the loneliness of the autumn night. In Northern China, the evenings are usually quiet.

"Are you sleeping, sir? What time is it now?"

"I wasn't asleep." I replied, bending towards the lamp to look at my watch. "It's almost nine."

"If only my donkey were more energetic I would have been on my way back by now." I cautiously dropped the stone over the side and Lin Ng stopped the cart. "Did you drop something, sir?"

"No, perhaps it was a stone thrown up by the wheels."

He waved his whip and the cart advanced once again. We could see some lights in the distance. A locomotive whistle could be heard and I realised that my journey was almost over.

"Sir, write if you please to your friends back in the town so that I can have more long distance journeys."

"I would," I assured him.

We entered the city and I gave the old man a double fee. He made his farewell and left to get a drink at the inn. His shadow soon disappeared. I must write that letter. It may help the poor man.

The Two Pots of Orchids

Phan Du

EVEN now, every time I see flowers growing in those great earthen pots, or when the conversation turns to flowers and the art of enjoying them, I cannot help but think of an elderly gentleman, the scholar Nguyen. He was my father's dearest friend. But this fact has impressed itself upon me only later, when I had matured and accustomed myself to seeing what lies beneath the surface of things, that is to say, it is only now that I fully understand the depth of this friendship.

For, at that time, I never saw the old scholar among the very important people who attended those sumptuous feasts given at my father's house. And rarely would he come to pay us a visit in the palace.

But one thing struck me in the way my parents welcomed the old scholar. The reception was simple, without any ceremony, and very different from that reserved for high-ranking visitors. But in this simplicity there was a special care which revealed a particular esteem and a deep respect for the elderly.

Every time my father saw the old scholar coming he himself took the trouble to prepare the tea service, the incense burner, the chessboard, the brush, and the ink-stone. Besides, my father saved for the occasion the best tea, and the most perfumed. The two old men then played chess, sipped rice brandy, recited verses or discussed in the fragrant scent of santal. Some games lasted the whole morning, or at times all day, and yet victory was undecided between the two players.

My father only returned the visit of the old scholar once every two or three months. But, any time my father had good tea, or high grade cinnamon, he had my brother or myself take these gifts to the old scholar. Never did he order a servant to run the errand.

In that way, I had many opportunities to go to the old scholar's place. It was through those occasions that I began to understand the lofty poverty and the noble inner life of the old man.

His house was but a thatched cottage built in the middle of a garden that was not very large, located in a poor suburb. But it left in my soul, with the garden, many beautiful and poetic memories.

The old scholar's garden was a flower-garden. When entering the door, I felt as though I was wandering in a full-bloomed forest of trees.

289

All the garden was more dazzling with brightly colored petals than with sunlight. It was a peaceful world, very different from the noisy world outside.

I met the old scholar more often in the garden than in his house. And never shall I forget the image of this old man, white-haired and bearded, but majestic with his high forehead, his kind eyes behind the glass of his silver-rimmed spectacles, his tall slim body draped in the brown clothes he wore for every season, in the middle of the garden, standing near his granddaughter and smiling at the sight of me.

This image, even now, is for me the symbol of an always pure, noble, and introspective life. It comes to my mind in those moments when the uncontrolled waves of human desire are trying to destroy in me any faith in the noble significance of life.

The old scholar lived in this peace with his granddaughter and an old servant. Actually, he lived more with his flowers. For he loved to cultivate them, to tend them; to follow change in their lives were his most cherished pleasures, save that of declaiming verses and reading books.

At first, I looked upon this pleasure as a very common one. For to cultivate flowers in large earthenware pots was common to all men in this divine capital. A pleasure that at 16 I found very complicated and even boring. Furthermore, with his traditional scholar's way of behaving, the old gentleman had little in common with me. So that in the beginning, to go to his house was for me an obligation in which I found no pleasure. But, by dint of seeing him often, in the long run I found in this traditional scholar a very young soul, a simple and cheerful heart. The more I frequented his place, the more I respected and loved him, and my old fear faded. The old scholar looked upon me as a member of the household, like Boi-Lan, his granddaughter.

The flower garden attracted me more than anything else. I felt a true happiness gamboling behind the old scholar in the garden, helping him water his flowers, clearing plants of caterpillars, making props and performing a thousand other little tasks. In these walks, the old scholar would chat with Boi-Lan and me as with grown people. He talked of flowers, of characteristic traits of each specie, and made amusing remarks about them. It was through these talks made in the shadows of these flowers — talks I did not always fully understand, that I came to grasp that the old scholar's pleasure in cultivating flowers was something very lofty and very exceptional. It was not a selfish pleasure. And later, after an incident related to the fate of some pots of precious flowers in this garden, I realised that with the old scholar this pastime was raised to the level of a religion, the religion of flowers.

I remember one day, while changing some chrysanthemum plants to a basket, the old scholar told me:

"So, I must change, otherwise these plants will return to cavern life."

"Sir, what does it mean to return to cavern life?" This question, naive for those who are familiar with the art of tending flowers, made the charming Boi-Lan chuckle.

The old man answered:

"To return to cavern life for the plant means to lose all its leaves. Even though the plant is rich in flowers and buds, if it returns to cavern life, it has no value. In the cultivation of chrysanthemums, this is a great fault. But it does not suffice just to change the basket or to bring new soil. Much depends upon the nature of the soil, the fertilizer you add to it, and the way you bring it to the plant."

Boi-Lan, while bending to put soil in a basket, spoke softly to the old scholar:

"The main thing is that the flowers are numerous; even if the plant returns to cavern life, this does not matter very much. You are very particular, Grandfather, and it would be very hard to sell a pot of flowers to you."

The old scholar said, smiling to his granddaughter:

"Yes. Besides, that is why I never buy flowers just as I never can sell flowers. A pot of flowers you yourself cultivate, for pleasure, is above price. The rich who use their money to buy flowers do not always know how to enjoy them. For the pleasure is not in enjoying their color or their perfume, but in attending to their growth. A young bud that shoots up, a leaf that is going to unfold, these things are enough to satisfy the eyes and perhaps these joys are more rewarding than contemplating the flowers. For they are proud and delicate creatures! They do not ask any part of our wealth, but only our care. Only, those who devote themselves to them, who tend them with all their hearts, can fully enjoy their beauty, their apparent beauty that is hidden in their soul. For flowers have a soul; nobody can deny that. But people cannot see it as long as they spend their money to buy them."

As for the care given by the old scholar to his flowers, certainly few people could equal it. Among flowers, he preferred orchids, and among orchids, he liked most the "untainted heart" species. It was Boi-Lan who told me so. And she went into great detail on the precious orchids of the old scholar.

"Granddad is a little whimsical. He loves his orchids more than he loves me. He compels me to tend them with more care than little children. To water them, he demands the water which has served to wash my face. Every morning, I must wash them, leaf by leaf, and truly, to obtain a beautiful orchid requires much care."

I was astonished: "Why is it necessary to water them with the water which has served to wash your face?"

"Granddad says that orchids are like women and young girls. He says also that orchids are beautiful creatures, but silent, beautiful creatures. What does it mean — beautiful creatures?"

And I teased her: "A beautiful creature is a beautiful woman, a nice young girl like you, for example. And silent means the one who seldom chatters, I think that is what he intended to suggest..."

Boi-Lan burst out laughing.

I remember saying those words with the innocence of youth, without any afterthought.

At that time, I thought Boi-Lan to be as lovely as the beautiful flowers that were blooming in the garden. When I was with her, I felt the same joy I had with my dearest friends. That was something which I only understood later — when my mind was matured enough to grasp and analyse the imponderables hidden in happy or sad remembrances of days past. It was then I began to take an interest in the precious orchids, from the day I learned of their history, and when I knew that Boi-Lan herself took care of them. And especially when I learned that they were bathed with the water which had served to wash Boi-Lan's face. I found much poetry in the art of tending flowers and I valued the orchids much more when Boi-Lan reported to me what took place between the old scholar and the man who came to buy these flowers:

"He offered a bundle of piasters for two pots of 'untainted heart' orchids. But my grandfather did not agree to sell them. Furthermore, he found a good pretext to get rid of the buyer."

A bundle of piasters for two pots of orchids! I could hardly believe my ears. At that time, with one piaster, one might obtain a hundred measures of rice. Somebody was willing to exchange a bundle of piasters for two pots of orchids. Truly, this buyer must have been a passionate lover of flowers.

Seeing my astonishment, the old servant who tended the garden stopped hoeing and sighed:

"A bundle of piasters: oh, that is nothing. He would offer much more, provided that he gets the orchids. It is not that he likes those flowers, but he wants only to be known as the one who was able to buy the orchids of this garden, and chiefly to please his protector. His son, I think, is secretly in the Residence Superieure[1] or in the Res-

---

[1] Governor's cabinet.

292

idence.[2] But he was a fool to propose to the old master to buy his flowers. Had he asked for them, maybe he would have some hope that the old master would give them to him freely. What nonsense to rely upon money with the old master. That is the best way yet to meet his refusal. Happily, he chose a moment when the old scholar had not had anything to drink! Otherwise, he would have received a beating with a stick, which would have opened his eyes!"

My respect for the old scholar deepened upon hearing this story. I began to understand why my father respected the old scholar so much, and why, in his relationship with him, he brushed aside any ceremony usually observed in the mandarins' world. When he received the old scholar, or when he visited the latter's home, my father was another man. Nothing remained of the great mandarin that he was. And he was happy, at home, with the old scholar more than with any other person. This made the deepest impression on me.

With my increasing respect for the old scholar, my attention to the pots of orchids also increased. Boi-Lan and I gave the orchids our most attentive care, which brought us nearer to each other. Together we removed caterpillars, washed leaves, watered plants, and made supports that we put in the pot. I remembered having contemplated, through the orchid's leaves still wet and gleaming, an innocent, delicate face, framed by black hair which set off the brilliance of the complexion. And on this beautiful face, two dove-like eyes were dazzling in the light reflected through the drops of water hanging at the tips of leaves, shining in the morning sun. I almost see now as then two thin lips, often pressed together, as though they retained a smile. And those lips, one morning, told me through the orchid leaves:

"Granddad loves most these two 'untainted heart' orchids because they will bloom just in time for Tet.[3] Then he will have prepared the sprouting barley sugar, orchid-perfumed for a whole night, to be taken with rice brandy. And Granddad will give us some as a reward for our care. One more month, and it will be very beautiful, even more beautiful than the "white Jade" orchid."

And those dove-like eyes looked at the orchid leaves with that same tenderness I sometimes caught in the old scholar's eyes when he drank his cup of perfumed tea under the ly-arbor[4] in the backyard, and looked at the newly blooming flowers.

All the capitol was bustling because Tet was drawing near. Scarcely five days remained and the rain had not quite ceased to fall. But the dull melancholy of heaven and earth seemed already to be di-

---

[2] Mayor's cabinet.
[3] Vietnamese New Year celebration.
[4] ly: creeping plants of Vietnam which produce yellow green flowers.

luted in the tender and gleaming green of the leaves, as well as in the liveliness of the streets, full of spring colors.

I went to the old scholar's place late in the afternoon. I came to see the two pots of orchids whose growth Boi-Lan and I had been following every day. No changes, however small, escaped us. If I were away for a day, the following day, when I came, Boi-Lan, in her prattling voice would make me a detailed report of all the changes in these plants. And the old scholar listened in silence, smiling affectionately as an indulgent grandfather who enjoyed spoiling his granddaughter.

This time, after two days' absence, I was sure Boi-Lan would have many things to tell me — new buds just forming, a leaf which was sprouting or withering away, flights of variegated butterflies which were probing the flowers, and so many other things, so small, so original, so poetic. I entered the gate, my heart beating with joy because of the approaching Tet, and because of those many things Boi-Lan was to report to me.

But barely had I entered the courtyard when I stopped, stunned. On the threshold, leaning against a pillar, Boi-Lan looked out with a despondent face. I had never seen her face as pale as on that day. It reminded me of the hibiscus flower, beaten by the rays of the noonday sun.

I gasped:

"Boi-Lan: What is the matter? What has happened?" Boi-Lan went down the steps, and, leaning on an apple tree, sadly answered:

"Granddad sold..."

"Sold what?"

Her eyelids were fluttering rapidly. I saw that she was on the point of crying. I repeated:

"Granddad sold what?"

"Both pots of orchids."

Astonished, I asked: "This is not possible. You are losing your senses, or Granddad has been teasing you. Never would he sell these orchids. If he had wanted to sell them, he would have done so the other day. But why would he sell them?"

Boi-Lan shook her head.

"Yes. He sold them to the man who came the other day. If you do not believe me, go to the backyard and see for yourself."

I darted to the backyard. Though Boi-Lan had spoken very seriously, I could not believe in so absurd a thing for I understood the character of the old scholar and his love for flowers. A man like him, even when in dire need of money, could never sell those flowers. No matter how badly his need for cash may be, the pride of a man who valued the inner life so highly would transcend it. To sell flowers for the old scholar was shameful as it was for anyone for whom raising flowers was almost a religion. And these flowers were the most beautiful in his garden. He and his granddaughter put so much care in tending them for Tet. He confided part of his soul to them, and loved them as a mother would her children.

Moreover, though poor, thanks to the economy and the order the old scholar had established over all the household expenses, he did not lack the basic needs unless an emergency would arise. But for months, no misfortune had beset the family of the old scholar. I thought that Boi-Lan misunderstood, or that the old scholar had been teasing his granddaughter.

But arriving at the backyard, my perplexity increased when I overheard the conversation between the old scholar and a stranger. The latter must have been about fifty years old and, with his flat face, looked like a pig. He was wrapped in a satin gown too tight for him; its seams looked as though they might split at any time. He had a big paunch which went well with his thick face and grease-laden eyelids. He breathed heavily saying:

"Sir, if you had sold them to me the last time, everything would have been all right. You would have the money, and I ... my business would be done. But, now, sir, truly, I cannot, truly sir, I cannot repeat my offer of the other day."

The old scholar frowned:

"Then, what price are you willing to pay now?"

"Sir, yes, sir, I came, because you sent for me. But, truly, sir, I do not want these flowers any more ... Because ... last time, you refused, and I had to buy some elsewhere, yes sir ..."

He caught his heavy breath and went on:

"Sir, truly sir, to be frank, if you sell them very cheap, then ... I will force myself to buy them. If you maintain your old price, then, sir, I will have to leave them with you."

After saying this, the stranger laughed, showing two rows of irregular teeth overlaid with gold. His look, his way of speaking made me hate him. I knew that he said "yes, sir" often out of habit, for he was one of those men who had access to the houses of the great by the back door and that actually he had no respect for the old scholar. On his face, I then saw a satisfaction and, though young, I felt he was saying bitter-sweet things to the old scholar to make up for having been thrown out of the house the other day. I was afraid the old scholar might become angry. But he retained his composure. I saw him biting his lower lip and then he slowly answered:

"Make your proposition as you wish, if it is possible, I shall sell them to you."

The man lifted his face and opened his beady eyes and looked at the old scholar.

"Yes sir, yes sir ... It would be better for you to fix the price. It would be too delicate a matter for me."

The old scholar fondled his beard, looked at the two pots of orchids and said:

"I will lower the price by five piasters. That's a lot. But I have urgent business, and I must ... otherwise ..."

The buyer laughed again, showing all his teeth.

"Yes sir, that is it ... Men like you, indeed, who love flowers so much, never think of selling them. Yes sir, it is a good thing for me that you have urgent business. It is why, yes sir, why you did me the honour to send for me. Yes sir, but truly, this price is still too high, and if I haggle with you, it would not be decent. So, sir, allow me, yes sir, to withdraw."

The old scholar looked at the man, stunned. His face flushed slightly and he bit his lower lip harder, it seemed as though he no longer wanted to speak to the man. But when the latter bowed deeply before him to ask his leave, the old scholar coughed to clear his voice and said:

"Then I lower the price by ten piasters."

The man stopped, and answered: "Yes sir, yes sir, I will offer thirty piasters if you agree... sir."

The old scholar's face grew pale. In his eyes, lightly turned up behind his glasses, I saw that indignation, contempt, and sorrow were rending his old heart. The unmannered and overbearing attitude of this low-class fellow hurt his pride deeply. His hand was shaking when he stretched it to grasp a match-box near him. I heard him answer with a long sigh:

"All right, you may take the flowers." Near me, the old servant mumbled in a discontented voice:

"What a genuine thief he is! He still needs these flowers. The last time, he was insisting, got down on his knees in order to obtain them. Now that he has the opportunity, he becomes difficult. He knows very well the old scholar would have refused any further concession, otherwise he would try to lower the price even more."

After the buyer had carried away the two pots of orchids, the old scholar leaned on a cushion, motionless as a statue. He looked at the sheaf of bank-notes lying on a betel tray, then looked away, hands on his forehead. He heaved a long sigh. I thought his body would double up.

From outdoors, Boi-Lan hastened to the side of the old scholar. She looked at him, looked at the bank notes and lastly, at the place where the two pots of orchids had been.

"Tet will be spoiled. Granddad will not have orchids for Tet. But why did you sell them?" There was a flash in the old scholar's eyes: "All the hamlet suffered from the fire. One lost his father, another her husband. Houses were burned to ashes. How can anybody still enjoy flowers? With such great misfortunes amongst our neighbors, how can anybody still enjoy flowers?"

He stood up as he saw me:

"Yes, it is you, Mr. Ngoc. Very well, come with me. Boi-Lan, give me my umbrella and my stick. Do not weep any more."

The old scholar took a handkerchief, wrapped the bank-notes in it and leaning on his stick, made for the door.

I followed him. It was a winter afternoon. It was not raining but a cold wind was blowing ceaselessly. We took a foot path leading to the hamlet's end. Then I understood why he sold his flowers. Three days ago, a fire had destroyed part of the hamlet. Two persons were killed and four or five families lost all their houses and belongings.

On the way, the old scholar told me:

"Poor Boi-Lan! She is right to weep. But what else can I do? To enjoy flowers is a pleasure which relieves and uplifts the soul, and should not be a selfish one. The religion of flowers brings true believers to love their neighbors. Flowers are never selfish. Scent, colors, they give all to the world before dying. The creator put the deep significance of life as a hidden symbol in the flower's being. To love flowers without loving men is monstrous."

The old man bent to pick up a bough of thorns fallen in the path. He threw it into a hedge and went on:

"These days, because of the fire victims, I cannot sleep. Their misfortune makes me suffer. But as you know, money is rare in the first month. Where could I find, in time, the amount of money required, if I did not sell those two pots of flowers? To sell flowers is a shame. And to come upon people who take advantage of the opportunity to impose their demand on us is a greater shame. But we must swallow our pride and sell those flowers. It would be very easy to drive these people out, but the widow and the orphan, what shall they have to put into their mouths? To sell those two pots of flowers wrenches my heart, as though I have lost a loved one. Boi-Lan is right to cry. But how could we enjoy flowers when people around us are suffering?"

More than ten years quickly passed away. The old scholar Nguyen also passed into the other world. And Boi-Lan too. This celestial perfumed branch broke in the middle of her eighteenth spring. And the old servant, doubtlessly, followed his master to the hereafter.

After a long absence, on revisiting the old places, I did not find any more any trace of the people of the old days. They have disappeared, and seemed to have agreed to leave together.

The old thatched cottage no longer looks the same, the flower garden falling away in ruins is also difficult to recognize. But before these changes, before these things which have entered the past disappear forever, I feel in myself something that remains and will never perish.

And this imperishable something urges me to watch the whole night to write the story of those two pots of orchids, in a garden of the past.

Champoon

BEFORE we went up the special ward, the director of the hospital
warned me. "This patient comes from a good family and the story
which I have pieced together from his relatives and friends is connected
with people who are still living, wealthy and ... influential. And his
symptoms are such that, well, we in this hospital ... we cannot come
to any definite conclusion. You see, we hesitate to call him insane especially in the legal sense.

"Officially, I can only state that this patient received a violent
shock. It has been five months now, and yet, he cannot shake himself
free of it. The whole world is shut off from his consciousness. Only
what led up to that shocking event is remembered. His brain cannot
accept any other impressions. This is the whole trouble. We have tried
everything to bring him back to normal, to make him react in the normal
way. If we can do it, he will be cured, we think, but if we can't,
then ..."

The doctor shrugged, drew up his hands in a rather hopeless gesture.

The patient was about twenty-seven or twenty-eight. He was
well built, and his illness in no way affected his looks. He was not
pale or emaciated as one might suppose. In fact, he did not look sick
at all. He was good-looking and seemed intelligent: his clothes were
proper. He got up to greet us in the manner of a well-bred man. His
personality reflected that of a leader and not of a follower.

After the usual introductions by the doctor, he gazed vaguely at
me and maintained a disturbing silence. Nothing that I did or said
elicited a response. I remembered the doctor's warnings.

"You must have stayed for sometime in Bhuket?"

"No, not in Bhuket. It was at Taimuang, in Pangnga where I
stayed for many years."

"Taimuang is the center of many mining districts, isn't it? It
must have been great fun."

"It was hell."

I was alarmed. "What? Did it have anything that other places didn't have? Like Hadyai, for example?"

"Hadyai and other such places had women, drinking and gambling. But Taimuang had champoons, crocodiles and iron chains."

"I don't understand. What had champoons, crocodiles and iron chains to do with the three vices you mentioned?"

"I will tell you," he said.

FROM THEN ON, the current flowed. I had succeeded in breaking the dam that barred his voice. What follows is the story I got from him. I have, however, filled the gaps with information gathered elsewhere. The names of all the persons and places are, of course, fictitious.

"My father was governor of Pangnga. I was educated in a boarding school reputed to be one of the best institutions in Bangkok at the time. When I was sixteen, I became a little wild and my father ordered me to go back to Pangnga and I went to school there. I stayed there for five years until I finished my schooling. It was at about the same time that my father retired.

"My father was one of those rare people who had long realized that we Thais should do something about freeing ourselves from foreign economic domination. He had always tried to lead me towards going into business rather than work in the government, and he convinced me quite easily. I was cut for it. My father retired and went back to Bangkok. I became independent and took a clerical job in an Australian mining company in Pangnga. My rather irregular life and education equipped me for this job since I spoke Malay, Hokken and Hailam. The firm was ready to pay any price for someone who knew three languages in addition to English and Thai. I was paid two hundred bahts, a salary I couldn't dream of getting if I went to live with my father in Bangkok.

"However, I only worked for two years with the Australians. An American firm, the Yukon Gold Mining Company, opened a mine near Taimuang and wanted someone who could control all its Asiatic labourers and also act as liaison with the government officials. I applied at once and out of more than ten applicants, the company chose me, the youngest. I was paid about four hundred bahts. Aside from this, the manager allowed me to handle the building and other contracts, so that, in a very short time I was earning an average eight hundred bahts a month.

"For a young man of twenty-four who earned eight hundred bahts, though this was not unusual in Bhuket, it meant a significant and inevitable change in my life. When I was earning two hundred bahts, I

300

always had enough money left to save. I led a quiet life, I read, and listened to the radio after work.

"But when I began to earn eight hundred, my money rarely lasted through the month. It was not all anything to wonder at. Nai Amnuey had made a reputation for himself, a reputation for all the vices there were in the garden. Yes, I was always news where women, drinking and gambling were concerned.

"I was also ahead in other things. I never allowed anybody to act superior to me. I was always the leader, never a follower. And I played the role well too. I believe my social background came in handy. I felt at home in any company, whether of Thais or of foreigners. And what is more, my money made me a friend of everyone.

"The places where I loved to spend my time best were the various clubs in Taimuang. The town was the centre of travel in the region; from it roads led to all directions. From there one would go to many places, and my company's headquarters was only a short distance away. All the most interesting dens were there too.

"I would like you to pay close attention because what follows is important.

"There were two ways of travelling from Taimuang to the mouth of the river where the company headquarters was. From here, you could go upstream in a boat up to the Taquapa-Tungmaprao Road, on the other bank. You wait for a bus, then you go downstream to Taimuang, towards the mouth of the river. This took a lot of time. It meant sitting stiff in the boat for five or six hours. On top of this, you are never sure whether you can catch a bus.

"The other way was to get a boat that would take you across the river right to the area near the mouth. Then you trek on foot across the jungle to Taimuang. This would take only about three hours. But there are serious disadvantages travelling this way. You could easily lose your way in the jungle unless you know the paths very well. Besides, that part of the river swarmed with crocodiles, the fiercest that I have ever seen. When my father was governor of Nakorn Sritammaraj, I accompanied him during his crocodile hunting trips in the Pak Payur district which was believed to be ideal for crocodile hunting. But really that cannot compare with the river near our mines. Here the crocodiles would jump without warning at men in a boat. No wonder that part of the country was desolate with just a few families along the banks of the river. You can imagine why very few people would venture to cross this river, especially in a small boat. This district was widely notorious in the province of Bhuket. Taimuang people, who wanted to visit our mines, refused to cross that river unless their boat

301

was firm enough and equipped with high, protective walls on both sides.

"I, of course, used the company's boat which was big and safe. That way I was able to cross even the dangerous spots. From the bank I would cut across the jungle. I mastered the paths very well since I used them often. Still, I saw to it that I would be out of the jungle before dark. Tiger's footprints were not rare in the place.

"You see how attractive vice is. Even tigers and crocodiles would not keep one away.

"I don't want to boast, but I must say that I was very popular at Taimuang. And this led to a clash with one important person of Taimuang, in fact the whole of Bhuket. The man was Taokae Soon.

"Taokae Soon was also known as Big Brother Soon. Now if this man had prospered in Bangkok, his name would have been pronounced in a way that the Chinese meaning would be kept. But in Southern speech, it was pronounced either to sound Chinese like a foreigner's name as suited the occasion. Taokae Soon was friend and acquaintance to every man in the regions around Bhuket. But the areas in which his influence was most felt were Taimuang, Takuapa, Pangnga, Koakloy and Tungmaprao. As it were, every case — legal and illegal — was taken over by Big Brother before it reached the court or was settled outside of court. He entertained all high government officials. All of them travelled in Big Brother's car when they visited and he brought them to the best places.

"All the luxuries available in the region would then be put at their disposal. If an important official made a wish known, it was at once fulfilled. Big Brother had the reputation of being the most lavish entertainer. Young government officials easily succumbed to the comforts he offered and soon were made into useful instruments.

"Big Brother was strongly nationalistic; he worked for his country, of course. He was beyond reprimand as far as that goes. I, too, was violently nationalistic, but what enraged me was when he would for a moment forget himself and misbehave in any way. Taokae Soon, of course, never insulted anyone in public. He was always sarcastically subtle. I thought I would match his subtlety; I was therefore never openly hostile. He was a veteran gambler, while I was young and new in that sort of game. Although several times, I managed to weaken the 'tiger's stripes' with some of my private, original tactics. People began to talk about my strategies and secretly laughed at him. It was something Soon could not forgive.

"Though we never met in open battle, our conflict became known all over the area, and it was always incomprehensible to me how everyone, both Chinese and Thai, seemed to await our meeting and managed to confront us with opportunities by which we could clash. It seemed to be some kind of an exciting game for them to see me, a greenhorn, at war with an old tiger like Soon. I was anxious about the day when they would force us into open battle. Soon had been the king of the jungle for so long that it was impossible for him to tolerate the situation. How could a tiger, the king, allow a strange animal to invade his territory without doing anything about it? I told myself that this would eventually happen to me, if not in broad daylight, then in the dark of night. I passed the precarious grounds between us more and more carefully. Until . . .

"Do you know the champoon?"

I WAS STARTLED by his question and the new turn in his narration. The doctor left me alone with this patient. Am I safe? I quickly replied, "I have heard of it, but have never really seen one."

"It's a rare flower in Bangkok, but in the southern provinces it is quite common, especially in the areas around Taimuang. I will describe it.

"It's of the family of champak. It looks like a champee, but with a velvety calyx which first wraps up the petals inside while the flower is a bud. Then this velvety part opens and later the petals spread out. You can imagine the fragrance released. The petals are waxlike, thick and stiff. They don't fade like those of the champee. After it has bloomed the champoon lasts for several days. Its scent marks that of all other flowers around it. The scent is overpowering, compelling and unyielding.

"Isn't it strange that Soon with all his nationalism should name his only daughter after this flower? Champoon. Probably he knew how it suited her. At nineteen, Champoon was a bright, attractive girl. She did not attract at first sight just like the flower, her namesake. But once you take a second, earnest look, her beauty is revealed to you. Her emotions are exactly what you would expect from a girl with that name. They changed frequently and they have the same power as the scent of that flower. They made of Champoon an overpowering, compelling and unyielding person. When Champoon's mind was made up nothing in the world could change it. No one could stop her from carrying out what she was determined to do.

"Champoon went to school in Bhuket until she was twelve years old after which her father thought it was time she stayed home like a good Chinese girl. But Champoon was at that time in Matayom IV, and had tasted enough freedom to rebel at the idea of spending her life the way her father had mapped it out. Somehow, Soon appreciated the fact that Champoon inherited his willfulness. He compromised by allowing her to continue her education at a convent in Penang. This shows that it was not the education of girls in itself that he objected to, but he wanted to prevent Champoon from becoming absorbed into Thai life. It means, of course, that he did not wish his daughter to marry a Thai.

"Soon after Champoon's return from school her father's will clashed with hers. Taokae Soon continued to be strict with his daughter. And Champoon would not accept that treatment. A cold war ensued between father and daughter. Champoon would yield to a certain degree, such as refraining from going out all by herself and staying away from the front of the house which was un-Chinese. This would somewhat offend her father, but when Champoon decided to go to a place or if her presence was required somewhere, she would not let her father stand in her way. Her father would pretend he knew nothing about it, because his courage failed before her stubbornness, and he would not press obedience whenever it was more convenient to compromise.

"I must describe to you the way houses are built in the South, so that you would understand what I meant when I said Champoon agreed not to be seen in the front porch.

"Lodgings in the southern provinces are built so that they look more or less like lodging houses in Bangkok, one room after the other along the edge of the street. The houses appear to have the same length from the street as lodging houses in Bangkok, but they usually are much longer. Each house may be thirty or forty wah in length. A wah is nearly one metre. To obtain sufficient light, the roof is open in certain places. The openings are covered either with glass or tin according to what the owner can afford. The glass or tin covers are movable so that they could be slid over the openings when it rains. The wealthiest Chinese in the region lived in this kind of house. Chinese businessmen built beautiful mansions for show, but they preferred to live where they had prospered in.

"Taokae Soon's home was built in the way that I have just described. But the house was outside the town and did not face a busy street, while the back of the house touched the fringe of the jungle. In Chinese homes. girls were rarely seen in the front part, and though Champoon did not approve of the practice of keeping women in the house, she did not care to show herself there and be conspicuously different from her neighbours. She really enjoyed keeping herself busy with all kinds of housework and homecrafts. She read a great deal, had books sent to her from Penang and Bangkok, and she enjoyed excursions to the jungle.

"We met by accident, and fell in love as if it had long been planned by Brahma. Our love was sudden but strong and deep. The fact that we had to keep it secret and that it all seemed hopeless only intensified it. We knew very well that Taokae Soon would rather see Champoon dead than see her married to the man he hated and regarded as his worst enemy.

"I want you to take note of this. Champoon was a very determined girl. Yet, she refused to elope with me. Her education and upbringing held her back. As for me, I can swear to all the gods that I loved her truly and deeply. And I, too, was held back to take undue advantage of her. Although we could have eloped, we preferred to keep within the bounds of tradition and Champoon chose to suffer rather than take the easy way out.

"Taimuang was a small community, and nothing remained secret for long. Especially a love affair like ours. The talk spread in town and soon reached the ear of Champoon's father.

"I could not see her again. I knew that she was kept in the house and was not sent away because I had men posted around her house to tell me. Don't let me tell you of what I went through. I tried every means to communicate with her. I even offered a reward to anyone who should succeed in taking my letter to her and more reward to the one who could bring her letter to me. Several attempted but no one succeeded in transmitting our messages for each other. They only put their lives in danger.

"During the period of our earlier hostilities, Taokae Soon and I still observed certain rules of civility. We were outwardly polite to each other. But now it was an open war. We glared at each other when we happened to meet, though we tried to avoid each other. As for Champoon, I got some news about her from some of my agents. She had been lashed, tortured, and was like a prisoner in that long, dark house.

"I was exiled from Bhuket for a long time. This became a topic for discussion in several circles around the region. A group of friends hired a motor boat and threw a wild party in my place to console me.

"That party was memorable. It was in the style that Bhuket was famous for. Food, drink and women. I don't have to tell you about the quality of the food and wine. But there was something which no money could buy.

"There was a courtesan from Penang who was brought along specially for me. But on this occasion, she came on an invitation which she accepted.

"On a dark night a little light is enough for a darkened soul. So when one suffers because of the absence of one woman one finds consolation in another. My friends thought they were helping me. I accepted the gift of the devil.

"She was called Anita. She was a Filipina with a trace of Portuguese. She could pass for a Thai. She was beautiful beyond doubt and her personality was fascinating. A beauty that she was, it was difficult to believe that she was dirt.

"My friends and I spent three days and three nights on the boat. They wanted to take me to Ranong but I could not join them because of an important business which detained me. They left to go on while Anita stayed behind with me. In five or six days they would be back to pick her up and bring her back to Penang.

"I told Anita to go with my friends to Ranong. But surprisingly, she chose to remain in that wild, remote place. I asked her later why she preferred to stay. She liked my youth, my looks and my good manners, she said.

"How those attributes undid me! Yet, what could have laid in store for me? What could the beautiful Anita do to my life and my soul?

"As soon as my friends had left, Anita and I went to my residence. It rather excited us to really know each other.

"My residence was a roughly built wooden bungalow. Three rooms opened to the verandah from which steps led to the ground. The first room was my bedroom, I had my meals in the second. A passage from this room takes you to the kitchen and the bathroom. The last room was always locked since I kept my documents there. Even at night, however, I seldom locked my bedroom.

"My bungalow was a little away from the other houses of the company, just a short stretch from the river and the fringe of the jungle. It was usually quiet and often deserted. I had a servant and a cook in the daytime. In the evenings, all the workmen were mostly in their own lodgings, gambling or enjoying themselves.

"The evening before Anita was to be fetched by my friends, I accepted an invitation to a dinner at the house of the company's engineers by the sea. There was dancing after dinner and the two engineers had a very good time.

"I knew that they wanted to meet Anita; hence, the invitation. It had been quite a long time since the engineers were with women and the presence of beautiful women simply melted their reserve. Nevertheless, they were very proper and behaved like gentlemen. They danced and flirted with her. The party lasted till dawn.

"I am a light sleeper and it always takes some time to put me to sleep. But after the party that night, I was soon asleep. After a short while, I awoke. I heard the creaking of what seemed to be the front door whose hinges were never properly oiled. It was rather strange since I was sure I closed the door before I went to bed.

"I got up to find out when the morning sun glared right on my face through the open door, then I saw someone's silhouette at the doorway. I could not believe it and I rubbed my eyes.

"God! Was I dreaming? Have I gone crazy? With eyes closed, I still saw what seemed to be an apparition by the door. It was Champoon all nude, her long, black hair fell down her shoulders. An iron chain, around her ankles and her waist.

"We were speechless. I saw her eyes move away slowly from my face. I followed them as if they had been hypnotized.

"I held my breath as our eyes fell on Anita, her body pressed against mine on the bed under a gauzelike and nebulous mosquito net. She was sleeping, breathing softly.

"I don't know why I found no shame in the nudeness of Champoon but Anita's exposed flesh so shamed me that I quickly drew the coverlet over her.

"I could not look at Champoon. I waited for her to say something. My head reeled. Was I dreaming? Was this real? I pressed my eyes. When I looked up, Champoon was gone.

"CHAMPOON CONFESSED to her father that she was in love with Nai Amnuey and that they have had trysts. But she assured him that I had done nothing to her which would bring shame and dishonour to herself or her family. Soon would not believe her. He did not believe because he could not understand how a woman could still preserve herself after several secret meetings with a man. Soon himself had six concubines in his home. Besides being a normal young man, prone to the unusual temptations, Nai Amnuey had been his enemy, the only man who had dared to stand up against him in that part of the country over which he had ruled for decades, and therefore, was likely to put out his rage for the father on his daughter. In allowing herself to love the very man whom he hated, he thought Champoon had betrayed him. He refused to listen to her pleas and explanations.

"When both father and daughter had the same obstinacy and determination, and neither would give in, the result could be foreseen. They recoursed to violence. He aimed a big piece of firewood at Champoon. She dodged and he missed. However, Champoon was severely beaten. The noise attracted the attention of the neighbours. Champoon tried her best to utter only faint moans even when the pain was too great for her to bear. And when Taokee Soon was done with his brutality, she raised herself from the floor.

" 'I told you I am still untouched, and you don't believe me. You cursed and beat me. I will now go to Amnuey and give myself to him, heaven be my witness.'

"Everyone knew that Champoon would keep her word, for she had not said anything which she did not carry out. A week later, she left the house while her father was out.

"The word of a Chinese family head was law in his household. Soon had threatened to punish everyone — wives, sons, servants — if Champoon should ever get away. It was hard for Champoon to escape. The whole household literally grabbed her back, while some fetched the master of the house. Champoon was punished for her first attempt.

"She tried again several times but failed. To stop her, Taokee Soon finally ordered that she be chained to a post in her bedroom. At night, to permit her some freedom, he allowed the chain to be loosened from the post but still he kept it around her ankles. Finding that Champoon tried to escape in spite of the chain, he ordered one of her stepmothers to divest her of every piece of clothing she wore before she went to sleep every night. This last measure would be more effective than any other, he was sure. He had sworn that he would not relent even if the conflict between them would eventually destroy one of them.

"One morning Champoon's bedroom was empty. The roof was open and the glass cover was slid back. Champoon apparently used her bedsheet to hoist herself up.

"Champoon had fled to Nai Amnuey, her beloved. What pains and dangers she must have gone through to reach my dwelling!

"Champoon must have held up her chain from her ankle and tied the free end around her waist. She must have climbed on to her wardrobe and hauled herself up the roof. She probably used her foot to push open the roofcover and finally slipped away. She was strong and healthy and it shouldn't have been too difficult for her to escape that way.

"But it was a miracle how she found her way to my house. How did she cross the crocodile-infested river? No one could answer this. People concluded that the bedsheet which Champoon must have used to cloth herself with had probably been washed away in the river.

"So it was really Champoon that I saw at the doorway across my bedroom. I was certain that she had really been there. The opened door proved that it was no illusion. I rushed to the verandah but it was too late. There was no trace of her. I pursued her to the bank of the river. I searched for her wildly and desperately till morning. I then realized that she intentionally kept away from me. It was impossible for her to have gone far enough and missed my calls in the short time it took me to recover my senses.

"I ran to the workmen's quarters and ordered twenty men to spread out to the river for any sign of her. I made them search until dark. At sunset we returned home.

308

"I set out for Taimuang without going back to my bungalow. I told myself that I would kiss Taokae Soon's feet just to learn if Champoon was safe at home.

"When I reached Taimuang my secret agents confided that Champoon had not been home. Nevertheless, I wanted to be sure and went to Champoon's father. After all, Champoon was dear to both of us and should merit our concern no matter how we hated each other. But the wretched Chinaman was a perfect beast. He laughed at my face and said that if Champoon should be shameless enough to return he would beat her to death and send me her corpse in a coffin.

"I went home and gathered again about thirty men, dividing them into two groups. They marched on both banks of the river in search again of Champoon. She couldn't have passed anywhere except through the river. I thought she might have crossed the narrow part. I followed both groups in a boat which I rowed upstream.

"I had been walking and running for the last twenty-four hours. I did not remember having taken anything except four or five gulps of brandy. I must have dozed off; I woke up surprised because the bow of my boat was pushed hard against the bank of the river. What happened, I asked, and one of the boatmen pointed to something.

"Do you know how crocodiles make a meal of a human being?"

"No," I said.

"No matter how big a crocodile is, it cannot swallow whole a human body. Though its mouth is big, it cannot bite pieces off, and its legs are too short to help tear the prey's flesh. It must always take the body on land to make a meal of it. It would hold a part of the body with its mouth and beat the body against a tree. It would eat whatever part fell off the body. It would eat one of those parts each time and would go on beating and eating until the whole thing was in shreds."

The patient stopped talking at this point. He gazed into the distance. The silence made me nervous so I blurted out:

"Did the boatmen find Champoon?"

"No," the patient said. "What they found was a piece of chain tied around a human leg that was torn away at the knee. It was on a low branch of a tree . .

"Sir, can you tell me, did Champoon throw herself into the river to be purposely eaten by crocodile? or, did she try to swim back to go home to her father and confess that she had loved the wrong man?"

The Grandmother

K. Surangkhanang

WATCHED EVER carefully, with kindling sticks placed one by one from the woman's side, she sat there and put them on top of the old sticks which were almost burnt. The fire did not take long to burn, licking at the new tinder until its flames gradually came back to life in the half-light of dawn.

By the blaze, bright under the three-legged iron stove on which sat a big steaming-pan, under the flooring, a close cropped head of hair could be seen, the color of white weed-flowers, bobbing up and down five or six paces to the right of the stove. The head was bent down below the level of a flat, smooth, bamboo pole, polished to a shade of shining yellow at the middle. The two ends of the pole were small and slightly bent up. At the right places scoring marks had been made on both sides by four old rattan strings, plaited at the top and hanging down to form a kind of two old crumbling baskets, black with age, one at each end. The baskets themselves each held a flat plaited bamboo tray, on which were placed, one on top of another, a few white enameled bowls with cracks and black chipped spots on them. There were also an old cigarette tin containing bamboo pins and a small piece of rag serving as a cloth for wiping the hands.

These baskets represent a "mai-khan" and "sarak."[1] The "mai-khan" was carried on the shoulders. It shone in a beautiful color of gold.

The sound of water boiling came from under the two-tier steamer. Steam was pushing its way through the seam where the cone-shaped cover met the steamer. Sitting by the side of the stove was a middle-aged woman. She was wearing an old creased "pha-lai"[2] with several patches and a long-sleeved, grey-flannel blouse. When the woman stretched out her hand to pour some water into the pan, the boiling sound subsided while a heavy cloud of steam billowed out for the last

---

[1] mai-khan and saraek: In Thailand, peddlers, especially women, carry their load in two baskets which hang from the two twisted-up ends of a pole (mai-khan). The 'saraek' are the strings of rattan which form the slings for those baskets.

[2] pha-lai: a kind of printed cloth popularly used by Thai women as a version of the "sarong".

time before it gradually disappeared. The woman got up and took off the cover of the steamer, laid it on its back on the ground, lifted the steamer up and put it on a wooden stand where a girl was sitting adroitly, rolling dough into dumplings and putting them into another empty steamer. The soft and well-kneaded tiny tapioca grains were flattened in her palm by the tips of her fingers, then wrapped around a sticky filling, which had been well fried and seasoned with both salty and sweet tastes. The white dough was then rounded off and pinched tight over the dark brown pork-stuffing. When her hand got dry, the girl dipped it into a small bowl of water, then moulded more dumplings into round and smooth shapes before placing them in the steamer, ready-lined with banana leaves oiled with fat to prevent the tapioca paste from sticking to the iron of the steamer. The uncooked dumplings looked white and different from those already steamed. When she heard the noise made by the steamer being put there by her side, she took a quick look towards one of the thick posts forming the piles for the house above. There she saw the bending form of an old woman, huddled up against the cold. A pitiful sight indeed!

This was a daily scene, too familiar for any other feeling to be aroused in the girl except the usual sympathy. She lifted the steamer filled with dumplings arranged in neat rows with her own hands and passed it on to her mother to set on the pan, before calling out to the old woman: "Oh, Grandma. Bring your bowl over here. I'll count the dumplings for you."

Her whole body starting up from slumber, the old woman lifted up her wrinkled face to look at whoever had called. "Yes ... what did you say, my dear girl? My hearing isn't so good any more."

"I said ... bring your bowl over here, Grandma. I'll put the tapioca dumplings in it for you."

Once she had heard clearly, the old woman got up awkwardly, then clumsily poked about her for the bowl in her basket. With her back bent she walked over, bringing it to the young girl. Fixing her gaze on the cooked and shining dumplings, still steaming hot, she opened her mouth, with the chew of betel still in it, to say: "Only fifty today, my dear. I want to go home early so I can have time to look around for something to offer to the monks. Tomorrow is a holy day."

The daughter of the wholesale pudding dealer did not answer. She had her work to do, and apparently it called for quite a lot of attention and patience. She dipped her hand into a chipped bowl; the lard inside was hard because it was cold. She spread it on the dumplings to prevent the tapioca from sticking to her hand. Then separating the dumplings from each other, she arranged them neatly in the bowl. When the heat was too much for her hand, she would blow hard on it...so hard that sometimes a fine spray of spittle would land on it . . . But, why worry about a little thing like that? She was not going to eat those dumplings. The bowl was soon filled. She patted the dumplings with her hand to make them look smooth and even, topped them with some golden fried garlic, red and green hot peppers, then handed this to the old woman.

Watching her all the time, the old woman reached out for the bowl, taking care that her grasp was firm enough so that the bowl would not slip. But before walking back to her baskets, she could not help but look back to ask in a voice, tremulous because the teeth were not there any more to bar the way of the breath coming out: "Have you put in the three extra dumplings as usual, my child?"

"You needn't worry about being cheated, Grandma. If you don't trust me, you can count them yourself!" The young girl was sensitive and a bit snappy. The tone for her voice showed that she was not in a good mood.

"I didn't mean that; bless you, dear. I'm just afraid that you might forget," her voice dragged on, while betel-juice trickled out from the wrinkled corners of her sagging lips. "If you haven't forgotten, then it's all right, bless you. Then they're there all right."

She shuffled back to her baskets, put the bowl of tapioca dumplings on the bamboo tray, mumbling something to herself the way old folks do, touched this and that for a moment, then lifted the pole on to her shoulder where patches could be seen on the creased old flannel jacket, stained all over with spots from the betel juice. Tottering a little, she trudged from the house.

Gold and silver were on the horizon, but mist was still covering the whole area. The cold penetrated into her bones. Those bare feet, which had never worn shoes, stepped gingerly on the gravel road. Everything seemed to hurt because of the cold season; even this fine gravel cut into the soles. The old woman took a short-cut across a patch of grass growing under a row of trees by the road-side. A car's horn sounded just behind and she faltered. Only when she felt the sensation of a car speeding past her in a commotion of noise did she feel relieved. She stopped at another house to get some "miang-lao," put them in another basket, to balance the weight of the two baskets, so as to get to where she was going in time.

"Sakoo-sai-moo[3] . . . . miang-lao![4] Buy hot sakoo-sai-moo, my ladies!"

---

[3] sakoo-sai-moo: a kind of dumpling made of tapioca paste with stuffing made of pork and peanuts. They are eaten with parsley or lettuce.
[4] miang-lao: another kind of dumpling with nearly the same kind of stuffing wrapped in pickled cabbage-leaves, to be eaten with fried popped rice.

312

The people came early to market. They bought vegetables, fish and pork, until their baskets were full, but no one bent down to ask for hot tapioca dumplings or newly wrapped miang-lao.

Some passed close enough that their skirts even brushed against the rattan strings which supported the baskets. Instead of feeling sorry when they turned around and saw her, they would abruptly turn their faces away as if they had brushed against a log. The old woman could only follow them with her eyes. Her mouth, which was just opening to cry her wares, would slowly close. She remained sitting there until the sun was high and the market stalls had nearly all packed up. Still she could not sell anything. She had already chewed three or four mouthfuls of pounded betel. With no more patience left, she was preparing to leave when a woman's voice in front of her said:

"Grandma, give me three satangs' worth of sakoo."

The hands that were wrapping the dumplings in banana leaves trembled. She was fastening the package with a bamboo pin when the buyer stopped her:

"Where's the parsley, Grandma?"

She looked around, but could not find any. She searched everywhere, even at the bottom of the baskets, but in vain. She must have forgotten to bring it along. Her lips trembling, she pleaded, "I forgot to bring it along. Please wait a moment, my good lady, I'll buy some for you."

"I can't wait." The customer was a woman of a little over twenty. On her waist was a little skinny child. "Have you ever seen anything like it? Selling sakoo-sai-moo, and forgetting to bring any parsley along? If there's no parsley,—then I don't want any!" She croaked with displeasure.

"Well then, so you don't want any, my dear?" The old hawker looked up downheartedly at the buyer. She was blaming herself for being so forgetful. She could have earned three satangs!

The young mother could not get more than three steps away, when the child on her waist began to cry for the dumplings. The mother had to turn back.

"All right, Grandma, give 'em to me. Curse this greedy boy!" she said. "Don't bother to wrap them up. I'll give 'em to him right now." She threw a five-satang piece into the bamboo tray, took the dumplings, smelled them, bit and chewed half of the dumpling herself and stuffed the other half into the mouth of the child.

The old woman lifted the tray, put her hand into the basket and pulled out a piece of cloth which was once red, but which had now turned nearly black, untied the knot and counted the one-satang coins in it: one... two ... not this one, it's still new. Let me give her an old black one instead. Before giving the change, she looked at the coins well once more to make sure whether there were two or three. Once assured that there were only two, she handed them to the woman. Then she picked up the five-satang piece and dropped it on the cement floor. It sounded all right ... not counterfeit ... so she put it back into the old cloth, tied a new knot, and put it back into the bottom of the basket. As she was lifting the pole on to her shoulder, she stopped, remembering something, and set it down again. Once more she lifted the tray up, pulled out the cloth, untied the knot and took out a few copper coins[5]; they could be used to buy some parsley!

Leaving the market, she then edged along in front of the row-house shops, the dwelling-houses, stopping occasionally to hawk her wares. She had been walking since early morning, when the air was still chilly, until it was noon, and then through the afternoon in the hot sun, all the time painfully making her way on hot gravel and asphalt roads. She kept looking at the dumplings still left in her bowls while she walked on. Little by little she sold them. Every time she stopped to rest, and to grind herself a mouthful of betel, she would untie the knot to count and recount the money. In one knot was the money to be invested in sakoo-sai-moo, in the other that for miang-lao. Today's profit would be put together with those of the previous days in a separate knot.

Once she had regained her strength, she put the load back on to her shoulders, and continued hawking:

"Come, buy my sakoo-sai-moo and miang-lao!"

"Master, would you like some sakoo-sai-moo? Here's your hawker."

"Where? Oh, no ... better not. The hawker is an old woman. She's dirty!"

"Mommy, I want to eat chakoo-chai-moo!" pleaded a child.

"Wait till I give you a good slap! Asking for this, asking for that when the evening meal is so near. You didn't bring along any bags of gold or silver at your birth, you know! Old woman, go and hawk your goods somewhere else, or you'll be making me spend my money."

"Come, buy my sakoo-sai-moo and miang-lao," the hawking sounded more feeble now.

"Buy my sakoo-sai-moo! I've got miang-lao too!"

"Grandma, give me five satangs' worth of sakoo ... What? They're all gone? Then why were you still hawking it?"

"I did forget, master. Old folks are forgetful, you know."

Putting the load, which was by then much lighter, back on to her shoulder, she continued her painful steps. The sun had already gone

---

[5] copper coins: In Thailand the one-satang coins are copper, the five-satang nickel, the tens and the quarters silver. One baht has 100 satangs.

down behind a row of trees. Only ten or more miang-lao were left. It would not matter even if they were not all sold since they would not spoil. She could keep them until tomorrow. Passing through the market, she stopped to buy two salted eggs, a salted pla-too[6] and five well-ripened freckled bananas, put them all in the empty basket and headed home. Her legs felt so tired and she hardly had any strength left.

Those who were left at home would be waiting and expecting her return when the evening approached. Not to welcome home this poor old soul as would be expected of those whom she cared for. As soon as the mother saw old grandma, tottering along in the distance, she hurried to tell her daughter and her three sons:

"Look, children, your grandmother is back. Go and ask her for some sweets."

And the children would run out to surround their grandmother. The quick ones would snatch whatever was left in the baskets and put them into their mouths. Those who were slower would cry and fight for some. So, the minute the old woman reached home, with the load scarcely taken off her shoulder, the eldest boy, in one greedy jump, reached for the bowl of left-over miang-lao. He was a boy of eight, wearing a shred of shorts with no shirt on, dirty and grubby all over. His eyes were quick and cunning. When his sister and brothers protested, they fought noisily until the mother had to tell them sharply to share the food. Only that could quiet them.

The old woman could only look at the disappearing miang-lao, and would not dare interfere or stop the children from eating them. What a great pity! She had been hoping all the way home that she could keep them for tomorrow. She should not have forgotten that these grandchildren would come around and snatch whatever was left over from today's sale, just the way they had been doing every day. She could only look at them putting the miang-lao into their mouths, chewing and swallowing. Nothing was overlooked, not even the popped rice[7] in the tin-box.

She hurried to put the load away in its usual place because only then did she remember the salted eggs and the freckled bananas that she had put in the basket. If one of the children happened to find them, they would also be gone. She did not mean to keep these two things for herself to eat. They were meant as offerings to the monks. It would not matter much if she would have to eat only one meal out of two. With all her good deeds and the offerings she had made, she might be born again as a great king's daughter in her next life.

---

[6] pla-too: a fish of the same family as mackerel, one of the cheapest in Thailand.

[7] popped rice: usually eaten with miang-lao.

The mother looked as if she could hardly wait for the old grandmother to get home. She pretended to scold[8] the children: "What, children, snatching Grandma's things? Leave them alone so she can sell them tomorrow. Get away, get away from here, go and eat them somewhere else."

The old one could understand only too well that her daughter was only pretending to scold the children. She often pitied herself for all the troubles and all the hardships that she had to endure, for having a grown-up daughter who had married and had children on whom she could not depend for anything, not mentioning the fact that she had to strive and labor so hard to earn her own living, even at her old age.

The old woman did not utter a word, for she felt too hungry to bother about anything. Furtively she reached for the red rag holding the money and put it in the pocket of her one-sleeve tunic, tiptoed into the kitchen, opened the earthen rice pot with a broken edge, only to see some burnt left-over rice at the bottom. The few dishes of food scattered around the rice-bin bore the look of something waiting to be taken away and washed up more then something that could be eaten. Anyway, taking out a wide bowl, filling it with rice, she sat down and reached over for the dish with a few legs of salted crab left. In a tiny bowl was a ball of namphrik-som-makham[9] the size of a thumb. She mixed together whatever leftovers there were; it would be enough for a day's life.

As she was lifting the first mouthful of it to her mouth her daughter came into the kitchen.

"Mother, have you got some money? Lend me about thirty, will you? There's no more kerosene for the lamp."

The hand that was lifting the rice was weakly lowered. In order to avoid looking at her daughter's face, she looked down at the grains of rice in the bowl, and remained silent for a while. With whatever small profit she had made today she had bought food that was intended as an offering to the monks. What was left was only the money she would have to hand over to the dealer as the cost of the dumplings, so that she could get a new lot for tomorrow's sale. It was a long while before she was able to utter a halting answer: "No, I haven't got any. I only have enough for the cost of the dumplings."

"Why, didn't you make anything at all selling things today?" asked the daughter in a tone of displeasure.

---

[8] mouth-scolding, eye-winking fashion: in Thai "pak-wa, ta-khayip" meaning scolding with your mouth, while winking with your eyes — away of saying things which one does not really mean.

[9] namphrik-som-makham: "namphrik" is a kind of sauce made of shrimp paste. This particular kind is prepared by adding "som-makham" — tamarind paste.

"I did not sell them all. Didn't you see the ten leftover miang-lao that your kids have eaten up?" This was the only answer the old woman could make, feeling hurt and about to cry at her daughter's words.

Already in a bad mood by the thought of not being able to get any money out of her mother, the daughter was even more irritated by her mother's mentioning the miang-lao that her own children had eaten. Taking it as reproof for ingratitude directed at the children, she raised her voice and retorted:

"If I had known it, I would not have let them eat at all."

She abruptly left the kitchen, went straight to one of the girls who was enjoying a game, slapped her once on the cheek and spat out: "Here, you wicked brat. Why did you have to eat your grandmother's things? That's for being so greedy, not knowing what you should eat and what you shouldn't. Didn't you know that they were not for you, you little devil?"

The little girl howled because she was hurt and unprepared for the punishment. She was absorbed in her game and did not know what it was all about when her mother slapped her.

"I did not eat them. Phi Choi[10] did," she cried and struggled, "Please Mother, don't hurt me."

"You're all alike. Come here, Ai[11] Choi! Come here you villain, or I'll have your blood, I will!"

With her hands akimbo she yelled at the boy. A few bamboo sticks were stuck between the slats of the wall. The sight of Choi, trying to hide from fear behind the water jar, made her temper worse. She grabbed a stick and rained blows on him without mercy. She called him names while beating him: a child who was born to ruin his parents, born to waste all the money, born to make her bankrupt. But Choi, though the blows hurt, was not the only one to howl. His other two small sisters also joined in this unison caterwauling.

The grandmother saw everything and heard every sarcastic word directed at her by the daughter she had born and brought up with all due care until she could get married and raise a few children of her own, and even then, still had to depend on her old mother. Instead of being cared for by her children like other mothers, she had to go out to peddle in order to earn a bite here and there to support herself. She could not hold back her tears thinking of this. She bent down to dry her eyes on the lap of her skirt.

---

[10] phi: in Thai means "elder brother or elder sister". A Thai often uses this same word to address anybody who is older and who deserves his respect. In this case, the child means her brother named Choi.

[11] ai: contrarily to the word "phi", "ai" is used with a person one hates or disdains or for whom one holds contempt.

The rice she was trying to swallow seemed to get stuck in her throat. Every word that she heard hurt her. She would not blame her daughter, but thought instead that all this must be the result of bad deeds she had committed in a former life. Joining her hands and putting them above her head, she murmured: "I'm doing good deeds in this life. Do not let me come across such a heartless child in my next life . . . . please!"

What was left over was all eaten up, but the poor woman still had not eaten enough. Only a lump of rice remained at the bottom of the pot . . . yellow because it was burnt. She poured some fish sauce on it, them mixed it up and ate it. She could not help thinking of the time when she was still raising her own children . . . . never would she let any of her little ones eat plain rice with fish sauce. There had to be at least rice mashed with bananas or with bai-tamlung[12] soup. In better days they would have rice with meat-curry, sweet-and-salted pork stew. But now that the time had come for her to ask the children to take care of her, all she got in return for the kindness she had bestowed upon them was some rice left at the bottom of a pot mixed with fish sauce, which tasted more like salt water than something that was supposed to be made of small shrimps and fishes.

Well . . . . at least with this daughter she could still find a roof to sleep under and something to eat. From the other four daughters and sons she had received nothing except signs of disdain. Her eldest son was now an abbot of a monastry in the country. Since he was a monk and not an ordinary person, the temple boys would insinuate that old Grandma went there to be fed with whatever food was left over in the begging bowl, which by right should belong to the serving boys. So now she had to force herself to feel that her eldest boy had no more place in her life.

Her second daughter was married to an orchard owner with two big wooden houses. The old mother once dragged herself over to stay with them, but found it impossible to remain after a few days, because that daughter, Piam, would keep nagging her: "Do help Phi Boon to cut down those weeds in the ditches of the orchards, Mother, or he will say that I brought you into this house only to treat you like a princess. Near the bamboo clump over there . . . . the hired men have done it so many times already, but they just don't seem to get rid of them fast enough."

So, not long afterwards, she had to bring her old frail self back across the orchards in Klong Mon, to come and stay with her third child. She could not get any sleep: this son would come home nearly every evening drunk and start beating his wife and children. If she intervened, he would push her so hard that she would be sent reeling.

---

[12] bai-tamlung: a kind of vine, the young leaves of which make delicious soup.

The fourth child was the most wretched of them all. When the mother asked to stay with her for a certain length of time, she burst out crying and complained: "How can you stay with me, Mother, when I myself can't stand the harsh treatment of my mother-in-law yet? They are all people of blue blood. I'm so afraid that you'll come here and do something awkward and funny, then I'll have to be ashamed of you. Please don't stay here with me, go and stay with Nang Phew!"[13]

Phew was her fifth child and the youngest ... the one she was now staying with. She was poorer than the others, because she was married to a man who did not like to work. He could never stay long at one job, giving as reasons that the work was too hard, or that he was not strong enough for the work. Things being like this, the old woman could not help but get herself a pole and a pair of baskets, and go out peddling whatever she could.

When the son-in-law and her own daughter were able to make some money, they would quietly spend it themselves without letting her have a share of it. But if she ever earned any the daughter would be there pressing her for some money. She did not mind this so much; she realized that she was living with them, so it was only natural for her to help out. But, showing displeasure toward her by beating their own children! This made her cry often, pitying her poor own self and wishing for death to come as a means of escape from all this misery.

Phew kept it up for a long time, scolding her children with the intention of directing her spite at her mother, until she was tired that she had to stop. Dusk came, but she pretended not to notice. Since there was no light, her small children stumbled over uneven planks in the floor and cried.

The old grandmother could stand it no longer. In the dark she had to look for the bottle and then went down the steps to go out and buy some kerosene for the lamp.

Around half past seven her son-in-law came home with a few packages of sweets for his family. They got around together to enjoy the sweets ... but who would expect them to hand some over to the poor old grandma? The good smell of the food came wafting past her nose and she could only swallow betel-juice and choke over her hurt feelings.

That night .... before the tired grandmother could fall asleep, she had to get up several times to get a drink of water to calm the pangs of hunger and to quench the thirst caused by eating salted food that evening. She thought of the freckled bananas which she had hidden in

---

[13] Nang Phew: literally means "Mrs. Phew" but also used with a younger person one is close to or a person one is familiar with. Sometimes this same word is used with a woman to show disdain.

the basket .... but they were intended as offerings to the monks. It would not matter if she had to starve herself, but let the holy ones have them, so she would have merit in the next life. She did not realize that the monk who came around to receive the offerings, would say to himself words that would have shocked her: "Here comes this old wretched woman again! Hasn't she got anything else except salted eggs and freckled bananas? I'm sick of the stuff!"

What would she get in return .... this poor creature who so deprived herself in order to give to another? Would she get a heaven?

It is nature's law that ripe fruits will finally fall off the branch, and this old creature was thus like a ripe fruit: old and ripe. How many more days could she last? Every night before going to sleep she would repeat in her prayers her wish for the god of death to come soon to take her, and she prayed she would go in such a way that it would cause neither grief nor trouble to any one. Little did she know that these wishes were soon to come true—on a day she would have least prayed for or expected.

That morning, she woke up earlier than her daughter. She cooked rice and then went to make merit with her offerings of a salted egg and a package of cake wrapped in dried banana leaves. After breakfast, she went as usual to get the dumplings for her daily round of peddling. She still felt strong, both in body and mind. Then came midday when she began feeling faint; she had been walking in the heat of the sun, without any rest. But she forced herself to keep on hawking along the street. She took a different route today. On the left side of the street there was a small canal with water about one meter deep. She intended to turn and cross over to the left bank of the canal by a little bridge made of a single plank with a rail of bamboo to hold on to. A small lane led from this bridge to the house of a man who was a good customer.

The minute she stepped on the bridge, her sense of balance faltered and thousands of little lights danced before her eyes. Her heart felt funny, but she thought it was nothing serious, for she could still see her way. She grasped tightly the bamboo rail and supported herself, until the middle of the bridge. Then .... everything suddenly became dark. Her step missed the plank and she fell down on one side. Her hand let go of the rail and she fell into the water below!

Five minutes later, only the banana leaves, which were used to wrap the parsley could be seen floating in the water. Bubbles came up and gradually disappeared. The flow of water carried away the banana leaves and other light objects which came up from under the water later. Some of them floated along and then got stuck in the bushes of tall grass or the java-weeds with pale purple flowers growing on the side of the canal. None of the people who crossed the bridge would ever suspect that below them was the deathbed of a poor old woman!

The people in the neighborhood of Samson Nai, Bangsue will no more hear her voice. The familiar hawking of "Sakoo-sai-moo...mianglao" no more to reach their ears. Those she left behind will feel sad, will miss her or mourn her death only when they begin to miss her helping hand and the good deeds she once rendered them. But their mourning will only soothe the memories.

The Afternoon of a Solar Eclipse

Shinjiro Kurahara

Quietly, quietly, fall the paulownia flowers
in the afternoon of a solar eclipse.

I walk alone on a mountain path,
where glides, like a sorrow,
the shadow of heaven.

Crossing the heart of man,
piercing the thought of man,
it fades away beyond the earth.

The crescent moon of midday
hangs over the paulownia trees.
The thought of far, far distance flows
in man's world this afternoon,
the feeling of unknown solitude today.

I walk alone across the hills and streams;
at the end of exhaustion, there burns
the scarlet of the setting sun.

Poem

Shuntaro Tanikawa

I tried to be a little god.
But during the festivities I looked back, and saw
In the brief intervals between religious myths,
Man's ascent occurring.

Bird

Ishikawa Itsuko

My male macaw escaped —
leaving his mate behind in the cage,
he opened the door himself.

Hurriedly I looked for him
and then —
I spied my green bird chattering away
On the top of a high elm tree.

I bought a net and went after him,
but that bird got away;
there was a green glittering over the roof,
but then it was gone.

That stupid creature!
no matter how far he flies
he can't find food for himself;
separation from his mate
is the same as death,
but frolicking through the trees and clouds
he's a light-hearted bird of the roofs.

Now I wonder where he is . . .
all shriveled, stomach shrunken,
and very full of pride.

The Wives of a Few Bureaucrats

Abdul Gani Hazari

We the wives of a few bureaucrats
Turn our face to you
O lord save us
Devastated in relaxation are we
Wives of a few bureaucrats

O lord our husbands are
Divers in the bottomless sea of files
(They alone know what they gather)
We are destitutes through family planning
Time rolls by crushing us

We the wives of a few bureaucrats
From dawn to dusk
On the verge of some noble thought
And the faded pages of fashion journals
Movie advertisements in dailies
And nude pictures of health and beauty
And the sensation of a nearly achieved greatness

Encroachment of fat in the valley of the waist
The swelling of the belly
The double chin
Panicky at breasts' decline
O lord we
Gasp in the mausoleum of fat
We the wives of a few bureaucrats

Our store is full of provisions
Surplus pocket money in the fold of our pillow
Helen Curtis in glass drawers
Annie Frenchmilk
Astringent
Deodorant
Hand Lotion
Revlon

Christian Dior
And Rubenstein
Obviously middle-aged compensation
From our husbands
For the shortage of warm love

Proud of the salute of orderlies
Our husbands are always in the office
Obstructions to others' promotion
Rejection of applications
And a few dignified signatures

Even on getting back home
Jealous at the friend's lift
Profit and loss of business run under another's name
And telephone
And telephone
And again telephone

The revlon on our lips
The foundation cream on our face
The careful beauty spot on our forehead
Grow dusty
The evening invitation gets old and stale.

And then O lord
Thoughts of the second man
Make us restless for a moment
The old lover is married
Young adolescents' aunt
The subordinates' mother
Granny in the sister's home
And the evening invitation old and stale

On the pages of the British magazine
Maggie's amour
Jacqueline's hymn
Flirtations of Liz Taylor
BB's measurements
Lola's lust
And Marylin's suicide
And suicide
And suicide
Alas the evening invitation

And then O lord
Our body insipid at night
The bloodless moon at the window
The used body
Snoring husband
Sleepless night
And tranquilizer

O lord with no other means left
We turn our face to you
Give us some work
Mirror in vanity bags
Foundation and lipstick
And social service
Savage criticism of Kindergartens
Or the front row seat in ladies' clubs
Or inauguration of the child clinic
By virtue of our husbands' rank

We the wives of a few bureaucrats
O lord
Give us some work any thing at all
That we may throw ourselves
Into its abyss.

Translated by Kabir Chowdhury

The Late Fall

Kim Chong-mun

Dead leaves
Cling
To the tips
Of branches.
In the wind
Branches
Pucker the face
Of the wrinkling, lowering sky.
Is earth then only a skeleton sun
Where springs will run dry forever?
Lives well up in delusions
Of youth
Only to lie under a tombstone waiting
Forever.
Moon,
Eternal moon,
Lamp of memory—
Lovers embrace
Under the moon do they not?
If there is enough time
Will love not move in them, show itself?
Only a posture
Believing despair in happiness
With a prayer out of despair that cannot forego happiness.
Are the vultures flying?
Flesh caught in a spasm,
From eyes of hollow socket
A not yet freed silver arrow of salvation—
Will the dead leaves fall
In the wind rising from black wings?
The dead leaves—
Men, for a moment only,
Together.
Time.
Time.
Time.

Together
With
Spring's
With summer's forms
Man presents himself
On this revolving stage called earth —
Before the black curtain falls
It pleases him to say,
Peace
Farewell.

Translated by S. E. Solberg

Enterprise

Nissim Ezekiel

It started as a pilgrimage,
Exalting minds and making all
The burdens light. The second stage
Explored but did not test the call.
The sun beat down to match our rage.

We stood it very well, I thought,
Observed and put down copious notes
On things the peasants sold and bought.
The way of serpents and of goats,
Three cities where a sage had taught.

But when the differences arose
On how to cross a desert patch,
We lost a friend whose stylish prose
Was quite the best of all our batch.
A shadow falls on us — and grows.

Another phase was reached when we
Were twice attacked and lost our way.
A section claimed its liberty
To leave the group. I tried to pray.
Our leader said he smelt the sea.

We noticed nothing as we went,
A straggling crowd of little hope,
Ignoring what the thunder meant,
Deprived of common needs like soap.
Some were broken, some merely bent.

When finally we reached the place,
We hardly knew why we were there.
The trip had darkened every face
Our deeds were neither great nor rare.
Home is where we have to gather grace.

Poet, Lover, Birdwatcher

Nissim Ezekiel

To force the pace and never to be still
Is not the way of those observing birds
Or women. The best poets wait for words.
The hunt is not an exercise of will
But patient loves relaxing on a hill
To note the movement of a timid wing;
Until the one who knows that she is loved
No longer waits but risks surrendering ...
In this the poet finds his moral proved,
Who never spoke unless his spirit moved.

The slow movement seems, somehow, to say much more.
To watch the rarer birds, you have to go
Along deserted lanes and where the rivers flow
In silence near the source, or by a shore
Remote and thorny, like the heart's dark floor.
And there the women slowly turn around,
Not only flesh and bone but myths of light
With darkness at the core, and sense is found
By poets lost in crooked, restless flight,
The deaf can hear, the blind recover sight.

Mid-Morning for Sheba

Edith L. Tiempo

Her dog yapped among the running shadows;
These, too, my heart, they slant fast and small across the valley,
Shouts scaling the slope, fierce shadow-shouts like the wide billows
Whipping the white clothes she had hung on the line.
Through the sparse grass the tumult of legs brown and skinny
Dazed the eyes, and she wondered, Did I have to climb
The slope in mid-morning? — just to look down and listen?
Look then: trees, grass. Listen: a dog yapping, children...
There was a girl running and running in the sun,
Sweaty sun and roaring green wind and suddenly the thorn
Pulling back her struggling braids, and she saw she was not alone;
A bull ripped the old fence-row, wires tangled on its horn.
Shaking and twisting they both broke away,
Girl and bull tearing through the hot fields, stamping,
Dog and shouting shadows. And it was all day,
All day, and no late mid-morning,
With half the wash on the line and a brisk wind blowing.

Invisible Tree

Ruichi Tamura

On the snow I found prints
and for the first time knew
the world of small life, birds and beasts
in the forest:
squirrel, footprints down an old elm,
across the path . . . . . gone among firs —
no anxiety, hesitation, nowhere
a question;
a fox, cursing straight down the road
through the valley north of my village —
my hunger never drew so straight a line,
never in my mind so smooth, blind, sure
a rhythm;
a bird now, prints clearer than her voice,
claw-marks sharper than her life,
feather-flicks frozen in the sloping snow —
my terror could never tremble to such pattern,
in my mind never such a pagan, sensual,
affirmative beat.

Suddenly: sunset, big on the summit of Asama.
Something not known has built a forest,
pushed open the mouth of the valley,
split the cold air.
Back in my hut
I light the stove
thinking an invisible tree
invisible bird
invisible small things living
rhythm invisible.

Translated by Rikutaro Fukuda

Parting

Chong Han-mo

It can be now
Rather beautiful:
That is a string instrument,
Or a high tone of the wood-wind.

Leaving cracks at my heart
With its tremolo,
A few partings
Had faded away from me—
But sadness still
An irritating relish,
The taste of ice-candy.

Floating on the blue bed
Of the rolling sea,
The flickery white flowers withered
And our parting was over.

Ending
Is a light-hearted rest,
Or something like a quiet prayer.

The rings of moon spreading within lips
That used to be hot;
Recollections, spreading like that.

Light on window.
Sound of whistle.
Sound of breath.
Dew-lapped path.

Sound of rain.
Sound of wind.
White snowy road.

Even heart-break
Of torture could be once
A burning life,

That is,
A dim written word
Wiped out by fallen tears,
Or lingering perfume.

It has become now
A thing like the stars,
Neither yours nor mine,
Glittering, quivering in the wind.

Translated by Ko Won

The Tropic Night

The warm tropic night is never silent,
But full of sounds that linger in the dark:
The call of cicadas never ceases
With shrill cries to shake the thick perfumed air;
While full-throated bullfrogs croak lustily
In quaint serenade by the lotus pond;
Now and again, some little white-winged bird
Quarrels with her mate in their tree-top nest;
The wakeful cock crows loud when he perceives
The false flushing dawn of a waning moon;
And dogs bay at some invisible shape
Stealing softly through the hibiscus hedge —

The harmony of such disharmony
Strangely lulls our sun-scorched human senses,
And seals our tired spirits in sweet slumber
That gently enfolds till the break of day.

The Canal of A Hundred Thousand Sores

The wind sighs in the tall casuarinas
And moans among the clusters of bamboo
By the water's edge, before pursuing
Its gusty way across parched, sun-baked fields,
Leaving behind a few dancing ripples
Which are lapped into waves by a steam tug
Chugging downstream, towing a string of boats
Laden with paddy going to the mills.
Each wave lightly tosses the frail canoes
Full of merchandise, and makes them dance too,
Before shaking the green reeds by the banks,
Whence, when the tired sun sinks low in the west,
Will rise a hundred thousand mosquitoes.
That is why our fathers aptly called this
The Canal of a Hundred Thousand Sores.

An Early-Morning Thought

A dewdrop in the garden of eternity
Is all that we on earth can ever hope to be —
Fallen from heaven, shedding lustre on the ground,
And when the warm sun rises not a trace is found;
Perchance one here or there may fall upon a bloom,
Enhancing its loveliness to the edge of doom.

The Flute

Full many a time on a pitch-black, drizzling night,
I have heard the voice of a flute whose plaintive note
Rose high above the steady patter of the rain
And died away, leaving an echo in my heart,
Which is ever swayed by a long lingering cry
Amid the ceaseless rumble of the wheels of war.

Pieta

James McAuley

A year ago you came
Early into the light.
You lived a day and night,
Then died; no one to blame.

Once only, with one hand,
Your mother in farewell
Touched you. I cannot tell,
I cannot understand

A thing so dark and deep,
So physical a loss:
One touch, and that was all

She had of you to keep.
Clean wounds, but terrible,
Are those made with the Cross.

Chasms and Gold Harvest Crumble

Wai Lim Yip

Chasms and gold harvest crumble together from my loins
Seeds of peartress and almonds are buried one by one, I turn to you
Sleepless and martial Accident!   Your uprising
Monolith following your directions just as
The youth on horseback following the custom, unwarnedly wrests
The bride from the sea and thrives and
Unwarnedly with loamy soil gives the long hot towns wings
And feeds the baked aspirations of his people with rustling of leaves
And with the rhythm of strained bronze muscles the river-raft is driven
And suddenly exploding on high boughs the millenial flower
Opens to the surf spring of children.   When the perpetual drumming
Of hooves rushes into our first acquaintance, the caravans, however,
    depend
On their unhurried speed toward the long sky-linking road, woman
    tea-pickers
Turn from Buddha caves and pass to the slope of tea-forests
When the climate that carved jagged mountains carves war and love
I will lead you to wrangle for a sunset of our ancestors on the
    black steppe
And regain two banks of caroling on the tranquil river

> There's a lil garl
> She roun' like de sun
> She smoot like de water
> She bright like de sky
> She plump like de corn
> There's a lil garl
> She breathe like de orchid
> She warm like de earth

I will lead you to weep, for the legendary color and for rye
And then put on a bit of white worsted to resist all he diseases
Dark and mysterious Accident! Seeds of peartrees and almonds are all
    buried
Chasms and gold harvest fall altogether from my loins and I am
An uprising monolith following your direction. . . .

The Child in a Red Shirt

A. S. Amin

Yesterday the light held long
between pulsing hearts and bleeding men.
How pale the moon in the sky,
clouded by the anxieties of life.

We have already lived long
with blood rushing to our faces,
whiteness as far as our eyes can see.

They turn back halfway,
dark clouds massing,
aspiring like the undan.

The child in a red shirt,
the child in a red shirt.

My Lion City

Masuri S. N.

I was born,
At the fated hour,
Knocking at the door
Of a difficult passage.

I came
To say something new;
My soul
Once touched the heart of turmoil.

Whatever attracts me
Or whatever I attract,
I am fettered at the heart,
I am fixed in my city.

As far back as I remember
I was acquainted with a dim star,
My father so constantly
Praying, imploring hope.

In moments of raging difficulty
My soul goes on saying:
Rise from the debris and ruins of torment.
I remain in my city.

Never in my life
Have I betrayed my integrity,
Escaped from myself
To intercept the pleasure of dreams

Because my dream
Is my life,
Which in my life becomes my dream,
Becomes the blood of my world.

Trees, branches,
The lovely sand, the waves of the ocean,
Never, by my faith,
Have I doubted your love.

Like liquid frozen
Never to melt again,
I know all my love
Is for the earth of the city I have embraced.

Gift

(For my child's birthday)

Usman Awang

My child cannot yet talk,
His heart is as white as the face of the Prophet,
The flower opening in the morning sun.
His smiles and cryings are the words of 'his heart,

Friends come with gifts,
Tokens of good luck, tokens of respect,
In honour of his birthday.

O why do you bring him guns,
Artillery tanks and war planes —
Through only playthings —
As souvenirs of this bright day?

How can you reconcile the truths
Of honour and the staunchest faith
With teaching children how to murder?

Whatever good thing the world possesses,
O, give it to him, he can still smile
With only a broken piece of wood, a pencil.

My child and all our children,
Let not their hearts be injured with weapons!
Let love bloom on their faces and in their hearts
For a peaceful world, a prosperous life!

Direction

A. Samad Said

Until now the dusk was purple,
     cinemascopic,
the whispering wind was the climax of love,
     stereophonic,
     but now they stop
     beneath your brow,

     you who breathe so savagely,
     bruising the heart and the gentle pulse,
     unconscious of the wild throes,

        the frothing sin
        in the abyss of evil,
        wide as space,

     and every step flaming red,
     every eye wildly burning,
     fierce as the storm on the haunted sea,

        slashing,
        tearing,
        under your lips.
Until now the night was black,
the adventuring wind was lonely,
     disharmonic,
     pursuing,
     under your feet.

     To where?

Contributors

ROSEMARY DOBSON studied and taught art for a number of years, then worked in a London publishing house. She now lives in Sydney and is married to a publisher. Her published works include *In a Convex Mirror* (1944); *The Ship of Ice* (1948); *Child with a Cockatoo* (1955).

RODNEY HALL was born in England in 1935. He was brought to Australia at an early age, and with his family, settled at Brisbane. Since leaving school at 16, he has worked at many jobs in many parts of the world. Several of his poems have been published in England and Australia. His first full collection, *Eyewitness,* will be published in London in 1966. He is married and has a daughter.

JOHN HETHERINGTON is on the editorial staff of *The Age,* a Melbourne newspaper. He was a war correspondent in World War II and much of his writing has been of a biographical and documentary nature. He has written biographies of two great Australian soldiers, Sir John Monash and Sir Thomas Blamey, and more recently, a series of profiles of living Australian writers, entitled, *Forty-Two Faces.*

GWEN HARWOOD has been published in Australian literary periodicals; her first volume, *Poems* (1964) was regarded by many critics as significant. She is married to a Reader in Linguistics of the University of Tasmania and lives in Hobart.

JAMES McAULEY is professor of English at the University of Tasmania. He was for many years concerned with New Guinea affairs and lectured in the Australian School of Pacific Administration. In 1956, he was founding editor of *Quadrant,* then a quarterly, but now a bi-monthly which he continues to edit with Donald Horne. He has published four volumes of verse and a volume of criticism.

BURMA

U WIN PE is a poet, short story writer, economist and translator. A graduate of Harvard, he is presently with the Ministry of Planning of the Union Government of Burma.

CEYLON

GUNADASA AMARASEKARA was born on November 12, 1929 in Yatala-matta, Ceylon. He has published three novels, *Karumalekenayo, Yali Uppanu-nemi,* and *Depa Nodado;* several short stories and poems. By profession, he is a dental surgeon. At present he is with the University of Ceylon.

MARTIN WICKRAMASINGHE is Ceylon's leading Sinhalese novelist. He has worked for a time as the editor of a leading Colombo newspaper and has written several books both fiction and non-fiction. He has won international awards in literature, and his books have been translated into several European languages. He is now in his 70's and lives in retirement in a village outside Colombo.

GULABDAS BROKER studied at Porbundor and Bombay, graduating with a degree in literature from Elphinstone College, Bombay. He was active in the Civil Disobedience Movement of 1930-32, and courted jail in 1932 for 16 months. He is the author of more than a dozen books, including 11 collections of short stories, a collection of one-act plays and a full-length play. He has also been awarded several prizes by the Government of Bombay for his plays. He is a member of the Executive Committee of the PEN All-India Centre and joint Honorary Secretary of the Gurajarati Sahitya Parishad (Conference of Gurajarati Writers).

KAMALA DAS' maiden name is Madhavi Kutty. She was born on March 31, 1934 in Kerala. She went to school in Calcutta and started writing stories at the age of 10. She published her first story in a magazine in the same year. At 15, she married Madhavi. Her mother is Belamani Amma, a Malayali poet.

NISSIM EZEKIEL was born on December 6, 1924, in Bombay, India. His selections of poems from 1948 to 1960 are *A Time to Change and Other Poems, The Third,* and *The Unfinished Man.* He is also Book Review editor, associate editor and art critic of *Quest, Imprint* and *The Times of India* respectively. In 1956, he was the head of the English Department of the N. M. College of Arts, Vile Parle, in Bombay. He is the Central Secretary of the PEN All-India Center.

GOPI GAUBA, born in Hyderabad-Sind (now in Pakistan), was educated at Karachi and in Egypt. After graduation from Bombay University, she went to Rabindranath Tagore's University at Santiniketan. Two of her stories appeared in an English magazine when she was 13, but she has taken to writing seriously only recently, and is at present working on a novel on the life of Hyderabad-Sind in the 1930s and 1940s as she knew it. Her forte is the short story and humorous essay. She contributes regularly to Indian newspapers and magazines.

ANNADA SANKAR RAY was born in 1904 at Dhenkanal in Orissa, India. He started writing at 16 by contributing to the periodicals in Bengali and Oriya. Later, he made his mark as the author of *Pathe Prabase,* a serial based on his European travels. *Tarunya* (Youth) was his first book to be published in Bengali in 1928. He has also published an epic novel, *Satyasatya* (Truth and Un-truth), in six volumes, and essays and poems. His short story, "Flight and Pursuit" which was written three years ago in Bengali, was translated into English by his wife, Lila Ray.

SARDAR KHUSHWANT SINGH was born on February 2, 1915, in Hadali, West Pakistan. His fiction includes *The Mark of Vishnu* and *Train to Pakistan.* He has also published several historical works among which are *The Sikhs Today, History of the Sikhs* and *Fall of the Kingdom of the Punjab.* He lectured at Oxford University during the 1960 summer term under the auspices of the Spalding Trust.

S. TAKDIR ALISJAHBANA was born on February 11, 1908. He was director of the Office for the Development and Modernization of the Indonesian Language and is widely known as the father of Bahasa Indonesia. His published works in Indonesian include *Modern Indonesian Grammar, Dictionary of Modern Indonesian Scientific Terminology, Of Tensions in Indonesian Life and Culture* and *Le Developpement de La Langue et Literature Indonesienne.* He is a professor, lecturer, publisher and editor.

CHAIRIL ANWAR was born on July 26, 1922, in Medan, and died on April 28, 1949. He is remembered as the leader of the generation of 1945. His poems are collected in *Kerikil Tadiam dan Jang Terampas dan Jang Putus* (Sharp Gravel and Plundered and Broken) 1949, *Deru Tjampur Debu* (Noise Mixed with Dust) 1949. Despite the fact that he did not have a formal education, Anwar made of his brief life a vocation dedicated to poetry. His poignant sensitivity and subtle inhibitions have staged a revolution in Indonesian literature. He died in a hospital, shortly before reaching 30.

AMIR HAMZAH was born on February 28, 1911 and died in March 1946. He translated the Bhagavad Gita into Indonesian and edited the *Setanggi Timur* (Incense from the East). He also translated poems from Persia, China, India, Japan and Turkey.

ACHDIAT KARTA MIHARDJA was born in 1911 in West Java. He is a senior lecturer at the National University of Australia at Canberra. He occupies an important place in Indonesian letters with his novel, *Atheist* (1949), and through his collection of short stories, *Keretakan dan etegangan,* (1950), and *Kesan dan Kenanagan* (1961).

W. S. RENDRA was born on November 7, 1935 in Solo, Java. Burton Raffel, in *An Anthology of Modern Indonesian Poetry* (University of California Press, 1964) wrote about him: "Rendra's work is unlike anything else I know of an Indonesian: long-limbed, one moment magically descriptive, the next, mystical imagery and open sensibility. He seems to me potentially the beginning of vastly exciting things." Rendra has two collections of poems: *Ballada Orang-orang Tertjinta* (Lovers' Ballads, 1957); and, *Empat Kumpulan Sadjak* (Four Groups of Poems, 1961).

SITOR SITUMORANG was born on October 2, 1924 in Harianboho, Sumatra and was educated in Djakarta. After the Japanese occupation, he worked as a free-lance journalist and literary critic. His interest in drama earned him a grant from the Rockefeller Foundation. He studied at Yale where he published a volume of short stories, *Pertempuran dan Saldju di Paris* (Snow and Fighting in Paris). The latter was influenced by his stay there as correspondent in the Indonesian Embassy. He also published a play, *Djalan Mutiara* (Street of Pearls); a film scenario on the revolution, *Darah dan Doa* (Blood and Prayer), thus initiating a revival in drama.

JOHANNES E. TATENGKENG was born on October 10, 1907, in the Sangihe Islands, North Celebes. He was a primary school teacher, and later occupied various ministerial positions in the state of East Indonesia before the recognition of Indonesian Independence. His early poems are collected in *Rindu Dendam* (Passionate Love), 1934. He became a teacher and later a school administrator. Recently, he headed the Cultural Division of the Province of Celebes.

JAPAN

SATA INEKO tried her hand at different jobs before she became associated with a literary magazine, *Roba* (Donkey). Soon after, she married Kubokawa Tsurukiro, a critic, who later published her short stories, "Kyaramer Kojo Kara" (From a Caramel Factory, 1928) and "Nani o Nasubeki ka" (What's to be done?), 1932, all of which elevated her as Japan's leading woman proletarian writer. Her principal works include *Kurenai* (Crimson), *Kikai no Naka no Seishum* (Youth Surrounded by Machines) and *Karada no Naka o Kaze ga Fuku* (It Blows in the Body).

ISHIKAWA ITSUKO was born on February 18, 1933. Majoring in history, she graduated from Ocho No Mizu Women's College. She lives in Tokyo and has published two volumes of poetry.

SHINJIRO KURAHARA was born in 1899. He studied French literature at Keio University in Tokyo. Four collections of his poetry have been published. He also writes short stories.

HIRABAYASHI TAIKO was born on October 3, 1905. Her many published works include *The Goddess of Children* (Hariti), *Flower of the Desert, I Live,* and *Going My Ways.* She was awarded the Women's Literary Prize in 1948. She is a member of the Japan Centre of International PEN.

RUICHI TAMURA was formerly an editor of a publishing house in Tokyo. He has published two books, *Four Thousand Days and Nights,* and *The World Without Words.* For the latter, he was awarded the Kotaro Takamura Poetry Prize in 1964.

SHUNTARO TANIKAWA was born in Tokyo in 1931, and now lives in Tokyo with his wife and two children. His publications include, *Solitude in Two Million Light Years* (1952), *To the World* (1959), *99 Lampoons* (1964), and *Collected Poems* (1956). He also writes plays the most significant of which are *The Room* (1958), *The Hero of Sorts* (1961), and *The Party* (1964), translated into English by J. Brandon.

NAGAI TATSUO was born in 1904. He is a successful journalist but is better known for his short stories, the form of writing in which he specializes and for which he is outstanding among contemporary Japanese writers. His best works appeared during the close of World War II.

MISHIMA YUKIO was born in 1925. His first novel, *Hanazakari no Mori,* was published in 1944. In 1950, he was still the youngest writer of note in the postwar Japanese literary world. His talent showed not only in the novel, but also in theatrical writing and production. His collection of modern versions of classical *Noh* Plays has been translated by Donald Keene and published in New York under the title, *Five Modern Noh Plays.* His major works, *Kamen no Kokuhaku* (Confessions of a Mask), *Shiosai* (The Sound of Waves), *Kinkakuji* (The Temple of the Golden Pavilion), and short stories, were also translated into English, French and German.

KOREA

HAN MO CHUNG was born in 1923 in Choongnam, Korea. He graduated from the National University in 1959. His published works include *Add to the Chaos* (1957), *Lyric for Blank Place* (1957), and *The Study of Modern Writers in Korea* (1960). He teaches at Dongduk Women's College and the Seoul National University.

CHONG MUN KIM was born on April 22, 1919, in South Pyongan, Korea. His collections of poems are *The Wall* (1950), *Uneasy Saturday* (1953), *Poetic Age* (1955) and *Human Sculpture* (1958). He was awarded the Free Literature Prize in 1959 by the Asia Foundation. At present he teaches at the College of Dankuk.

PAKISTAN

SYED ALI AHSAN was born on March 26, 1922 in Jessore, East Pakistan. He has been published widely. Among his anthologies of poems are, *Anek Akash* (Many Skies), a book of lyrics; *Ekak Sandhaya Basanta* (Spring on a Lonely Evening), a collection of poems. He has written treaties on poetry, a history of modern Bengali literature, *Bengla Sahityer Itibritwa*, and translated *Oedipus Rex* of Sophocles into Bengali, the love poems of Yvan Goll from the French, and the works of Iqubaler Kavita into Bengali. Ahsan has held editorial positions in the *Pakistan Literary Review*, the *Bengali Literary Review*, and the *Bengla Academy Patrika*, a journal in aesthetics and linguistics, and the *Loka Sahitya*, a quarterly journal on Bengali folklore. He is at present director of the Bengali Academy in Dacca, East Pakistan, Secretary of the Pakistan Branch of International PEN, and managing editor of the Pakistan *Observer*.

ABDUL GHANI HAZARI was born in 1925 in Pabna, East Pakistan and was educated in Calcutta University. Hazari is also a literary critic and satirist. His book of poems in Bengali, *Samanya Dhon* (Little Treasure) was published in 1959. His Bengali translation of Apuleius' *Golden Ass* has recently been published by the Bengali Academy. He is at present engaged in translating Freud.

CARLOS A. ANGELES has been included in several poetry anthologies. His first volume, *Stun of Jewels,* won the first prize in the Palanca Memorial Award for Poetry, 1964 and the Heritage Award in the same year. He works in a public relations office of an airline company in Manila and is a member of the board of directors of the Philippine Center of International PEN.

NVM GONZALEZ is the author of several books, notably, the novels — *Winds of April, A Season of Grace* and *The Bamboo Dancers.* He was awarded the Philippine Republican Award in 1954 and the first Philippine Cultural Heritage Award in 1960. He was also the recipient of Rockefeller Foundation Awards. At present he teaches at the University of the Philippines.

NICK JOAQUIN is a short story writer and poet in English. He has been a winner of several short story awards, and a two-year Rockefeller grant to Spain, the United States and Mexico to write a novel. Published a collection of his works, *Nick Joaquin: Prose and Poems,* and his novel, *The Woman Who Had Two Navels.* He has translated works of Jose Rizal, Filipino national hero, from the original Spanish to English. He is at present a staff member and feature writer of the *Philippines Free Press,* a weekly news magazine. He is a member of the Philippine Center of International PEN.

VALDEMAR OLAGUER was born in Manila. He received his Master's degree in Literature at the San Francisco State College. His work has been published abroad in publications such as the *Beloit Poetry Journal,* the *Juggler of Notre Dame,* and *World Writing 17.* In 1965 he won a Palanca Memorial Award for several of his poems.

KERIMA POLOTAN won the 1961 Stonehill Award for the Filipino Novel with her, *The Hand of the Enemy.* She has won four first-prize Palanca Memorial Awards for her short stories and a prize in the *Philippines Free Press* short story contest. She teaches Creative Writing and Literature at the Arellano University in Manila and is now on the staff of the *Philippines Free Press.*

BIENVENIDO SANTOS is a poet and short story writer in English. He was a government *pensionado* to the United States before the outbreak of World War II and studied at Illinois, Columbia and Harvard Universities. He lectured extensively on the Philippines for the Commonwealth government while in exile. He has won major prizes in literature, the most significant of which are the *New York Tribune* Award for short story, and the Palanca Memorial Award. Two collections of his short stories and *The Wounded Stag,* a collection of poems, were published in Manila. His novels, *Villa Magdalena* and *The Volcano* have recently been published. He teaches Creative Writing and English Literature at the University of Nueva Caceres in Naga City (Philippines).

EDITH L. TIEMPO won two Palanca Memorial Awards for her short stories and a *Philippines Free Press* short story prize. Her novel, *A Blade of Fern* is scheduled for publication soon. At present, she teaches at Kalamazoo, Michigan, on an exchange-professor grant.

JOSE GARCIA VILLA was born in Manila in 1906. Expelled from the University of the Philippines for writing "obscene" poetry, he sailed to the United States with the $1,000 he had won in a short story contest. In America he earned raves for his poems from internationally known critics. His poems and prose have been published in several small volumes, among them *Have Come, Am Here, Volume Two, Selected Poems and New,* and *Poems 55 and Selected Stories.* He had been awarded a Guggenheim Fellowship, an American Academy of Arts and Letters award, a Bollinger Fellowship in criticism, and a Shelley Memorial Award for poetry. He lives in New York.

TAIWAN

TSU HSI-NIN is the pen name of Tsu Ching-hai. Tsu, a native of Shantung province, was born in 1927. He has three books, *The Torch of Love, Molten Iron*, and *The Wolf*.

WAI LIM YIP's name sometimes appears in its Mandarin version, Wei-lien Yeh. He received his B.A. and M.A. degrees from the National University of Taiwan and the Taiwan Normal University respectively. Under the joint sponsorship of the Asia Foundation and the Iowa Writers' Workshop, he went to Iowa University for an M.F.A. His poems in English have appeared in several American and Taipei literary journals. He was editor of the *New Current, Modern Literature, The Epoch Poetry Quarterly* and *Modern Editions,* published in Hongkong and Taiwan.

THAILAND

PREM CHAYA is the distinguished poet, journalist and translator who is leading Thailand's contemporary literary movement. He is the dean of Modern Languages at Chulalongkorn University and president of the Thailand PEN Centre. He is better known to international cultural societies as Prince Prem Purachatra.

RIEM ENG's real name is Malai Choopinit. He was born in 1906, was educated at Suan Kularb College. He gave up teaching to become a journalist and writer. He has translated several stories and novels from English into

VIETNAM

PHAN DU was born on May 1, 1915, at Quang Nam province. He has collaborated with many well-known reviews, periodicals and magazines. Among his published short stories and novels are *Bua Com Chay* (A Buddhist Repast, Hanoi, 1942); *Co Gai Xom Ngheo* (A Girl in a Poor Hamlet, 1959); *Uat han len men* (A Rising Choler, 1964); his latest, *Tinh Nguoi* (Humankind), is scheduled for publication soon.